Mathematics Today

Today

A Programmed Course 5A

Mathematics Today

A Programmed Course 5A

K. S. Leung

M. K. Lai

C. P. Lai

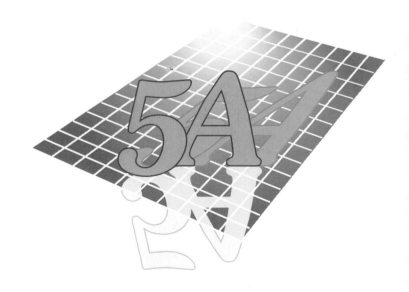

Canotta Publishing Co., Ltd.

Authors

Dr. K. S. Leung 梁貫成   [B.Sc., Cert. Ed., M.Ed., Ph.D.]

Mr. M. K. Lai 黎文傑   [B.Sc., Cert. Ed., M.Phil.]

Mr. C. P. Lai 黎鎮邦   [B.A., Cert. Ed., Adv. Dip. Ed., M. Ed., M. Sc.]

Editorial Advisers

Mr. F. L. Lee 李芳樂   [B.Sc., Dip. Ed., M.A. (Ed.)]

Mr. S. N. Suen 孫淑南   [B.A., Cert. Ed., M.Ed.]

Language Consultant

Dr. J. A. G. McClelland   [B.Sc. (Mathematics), B.Sc. (Physics), Ph.D.]

First Edition* 1997
Reprint 1998 (with minor amendment)
Reprint 1999, 2000, 2001, 2002

Printed by Lammar Offset Printing Ltd.
ISBN 962-19-8032-1

Publisher: **Canotta Publishing Co., Ltd.**
Room B607, 6/F, Block B,
Sea View Estate,
2 Watson Road,
North Point, Hong Kong.
Tel: 2578 0023

❏ **Dr. Frederick Koon-shing LEUNG**（梁貫成）graduated from the University of Hong Kong with a Mathematics degree and taught Mathematics for quite a number of years in several secondary schools. He joined the University of Hong Kong as a teaching consultant in 1982, and was offered a lectureship in Mathematics Education in 1984. Dr. Leung obtained his Certificate in Education from the University of Hong Kong in 1980, majoring in Mathematics, and his Master of Education degree from the same university in 1984. Dr. Leung got his Doctor of Philosophy degree in Mathematics Education from the University of London in 1992. He is currently the Hong Kong Research Co-ordinator for the Third International Mathematics and Science Study. He has been actively involved in various committees of the Hong Kong Education Department and the Hong Kong Examinations Authority. Dr. Leung is now the Dean of the Faculty of Education at the University of Hong Kong.

❏ **Mr. Man-kit LAI**（黎文傑）graduated from the University of Hong Kong and obtained a Bachelor of Science (Honours) degree, majoring in Mathematics. Mr. Lai took up the teaching career right after he graduated. He received the Certificate in Education from the University of Hong Kong several years later after he had been teaching Mathematics in one of the top secondary schools in Kowloon. Being an experienced and enthusiastic Mathematics teacher, Mr. Lai is always concerned with the present Mathematics curriculum in Hong Kong and the needs of Hong Kong students today in learning Mathematics at secondary level. Mr. Lai currently is the Mathematics panel chairman of a very famous Catholic (boys') school on the Hong Kong Island.

❏ **Mr. Chan-pong LAI**（黎鎮邦）is a graduate of the University of Hong Kong where he obtained his Bachelor of Arts degree in Mathematics and his Master degree in Education. He also has a Master degree in Science from the University of Oxford. Mr. Lai had been the panel chairman of Mathematics in a top secondary school in Hong Kong for many years. He is now teaching at university.

SPECIAL THANKS

Thanks to the Editorial Advisers

Special thanks must be given to Mr. F. L. Lee (李芳樂), currently a lecturer of the School of Education(CUHK). Being an experienced and enthusiastic educator, he has contributed tremendously to this senior Form "Mathematics Today" series by enlightening our editors with the latest theories and trends in Mathematics education. In so doing our editors have been able to arrange the content materials in a more systematic and practical way to suit the needs of students and teachers.

We must also thank Mr. S. N. Suen (孫淑南), who has long been known among Mathematics teachers as active and efficient in promoting high quality Mathematics education. On many occasions Mr. Suen has urged Canotta to produce a greater number of high quality Mathematics books. This time he has helped out by sharing with our editors much of his experience in grouping and grading exercise so that the questions in our course books can suit a wide range of students with different abilities. Mr. Suen has also suggested how we should choose our worked examples and prepare the step-by-step solutions so that they can correspond closely with the exercises and what we expect the students can do in their solutions.

Thanks to the Language Consultant

The authors and the editors of this series of senior Form course books wish to specially thank Dr. J.A.G. McClelland for his many precious suggestions for improvements in the manuscripts. Dr. McClelland has scrutinized every detail of each course book of *"Mathematics Today – A Programmed Course"*. He has given many invaluable comments and opinions on the proper use of words and sentence structures. Most important of all, he has offered to put in *additional comments on the description and logical presentation of the mathematical concepts* in the text.

Thanks to Reviewers

Thanks must also be extended to the following experienced and devoted teachers of various schools for their priceless suggestions in the content and the exercises of this new series of Mathematics course books for senior Forms. Their contributions, in terms of time and effort, have surely made "***Mathematics Today – A Programmed Course***" the best secondary Mathematics course book series for senior Forms.

* Mr. H. H. Chau	周漢雄	*[Yen Ching College]*
* Mr. S. W. Chu	朱少榮	*[S. K. H. Tang Shiu Kin Sec. School]*
* Mr. S. W. Kwan	關仕華	*[St. Teresa Sec. School]*
* Mr. P. K. Lee	李寶權	*[S. K. H. Kei Hau Sec. School]*
* Mr. Y. H. Wan	尹鎏鴻	*[H. K. & Kln. Chiu Chow School]*
Miss K. S. Cheng	鄭國琛	*[Christ College]*
Mr. T. W. Fung	馮德華	*[Christian Alliance S. C. Chan Memorial College]*
Mr. C. K. Kwok	郭志堅	*[Buddhist Tai Hung College]*
Miss W. K. Luk	陸惠群	*[L. S. T. Ku Chiu Man Sec. School]*
Mr. P. L. Sham	岑步良	*[Shek Lei Catholic Sec. School]*
Mr. C. K. Wong	黃正坤	*[S. T. F. A. Leung Kau Kui College]*

Note: The group of reviewers marked with ' * ' have kindly supplied the authors with many of their past tests and examination papers for reference. With such reinforcement, the authors have been able to put in richer variety of questions in the books.

Thanks also to Mr. K. L. Choy (蔡高亮), Miss M. F. Ho (何美芬) and other teachers (whose names are not mentioned here) for offering their help in this series of senior Form course books.

PREFACE

"Mathematics Today – A Programmed Course" **Books 1–5 : a new series of secondary level Mathematics course books, which matches closely the latest teaching syllabus as well as the examination syllabus, represents a brand-new concept in the production of course books in today's world. The series is a self-contained comprehensive learning programme which provides students and educators with high quality course books and a <u>rich variety of supporting aids</u>. Every bit of feature and component of this programme is designed to meet the needs of today's educators, and to arouse the interests in study of today's students.**

The Senior Form Course Books

(I) Volume:

The Course Book for the school year of each senior Form[†] is divided into <u>TWO</u> volumes: A and B.

(II) Approach:

A practical approach is the authors' idea in writing the text as well as the exercises of the books. As a result the mathematical concepts presented in the text and the questions asked in the exercises are often related to our everyday lives. To make the books more attractive and more interesting to the readers, we have put in *full-coloured* designs, graphics, photographs and cartoons throughout the books where appropriate.

†*Note: Details of the Course Books for junior Forms (i.e. Bks 1A-3B) and the corresponding supporting materials are listed in the Preface of the junior Form Course Books respectively.*

(III) Structure:

(1) Every chapter begins with a colourful photograph (a Chapter Page). It aims at motivating students to think beforehand about the topic of Mathematics that they are going to learn, and to be curious about how the topic is related to the world around us today.

(2) To learn Mathematics effectively, ample and self-explanatory Worked Examples are essential. In view of this, the Course Book has included plenty of Worked Examples with detailed step-by-step solutions to illustrate clearly the concepts and techniques discussed in the corresponding section.

(3) Adding to this, "*Mathematics Today – A Programmed Course*" has put in a number of Class Discussions, Class Activities and Class Explorers to enhance the discovery and exploration of essential mathematical concepts and theorems in the classroom. Furthermore, the Course Book contains a large number of Class Practices so that students can have enough simple and direct classroom practice on the theories and techniques that they have just learnt from the text.

(4) (i) To meet the needs of students with different abilities, plentiful 'core' Exercises of various types and levels of difficulty corresponding to each section of the chapter are provided. Each exercise is graded into two distinct levels : Level 1 and Level 2. More difficult questions can be found in the Level 2 section of the exercise. The even more difficult questions are each indicated by an asterisk (*).

(ii) Besides the 'core' Exercises, at the end of the whole chapter, there is an additional exercise called the Supplementary Exercise, with questions rich in variety. The Supplementary Exercise consists of 3 parts:

PART I : Further Practice

Questions are grouped according to the corresponding 'core' Exercises. The Further Practice provides an extra chance for students to consolidate the skills learnt in each Exercise of the chapter.

PART II : Miscellaneous

Questions are no longer grouped according to the corresponding 'core' Exercises. These questions may require techniques learnt in all the sections of the chapter and they may even require techniques learnt from previous chapters.

PART III : HKCEE Questions

They are all current HKCEE questions related to the topics learnt in the chapter. It helps students know at an early stage the style and the form of questions they will face in HKCEE. This part includes Section A Questions, Section B Questions and Multiple Choice Questions.

(iii) At the end of some chapters, there are 1 to 2 questions of Application type. In the Application Question, the knowledge learnt in the chapter is applied to solve everyday life problems.

(5) At the end of each of the Course books 4A, 4B and 5A, there are several revision exercises called Preparatory Exercises for HKCEE. These exercises are grouped according to strands: Algebra, Geometry, Trigonometry or Statistics. In these Exercises, questions are set to include all the techniques learnt in the whole book; the formats and styles are in close resemblance with the current HKCEE questions.

Within each strand of the Preparatory Exercise, questions are arranged according to their levels of difficulty in the following way:

A. Short Questions

The questions are similar to the Section A questions in the HKCEE paper and they normally require simple solutions or answers. The short questions are further divided into two groups: Group 1 and Group 2. Group 1 questions are strictly short questions while Group 2 questions can be treated either as short questions or as multiple choice questions. When the Group 2 questions are treated as multiple choice questions, then students can circle the choices given in the multiple choice pack of the accompanying Student Handbook as the corresponding answers.

B. Long Questions

They are conventional questions of structured-type, similar to the Section B questions of the HKCEE paper.

(6) After the Preparatory Exercise, there is an Appendix showing calculator programs that are useful and allowed in the HKCEE.

(7) Other distinctive features include

– Margin columns where Explanatory Notes, Brief Reminders, Recreational Mathematics, etc., are given.

– Important mathematical terms are supplied with Chinese translations and they are grouped under the section called Index at the end of the book. Besides mathematical terms, the meanings of some difficult English words are given with their Chinese translations alongside in the text.

(8) "*Mathematics Today – A Programmed Course 5B*" is specially designed to help students prepare for the HKCE Examination. In response to the introduction of the Tailored / Whole Syllabuses in the 1998 HKCE Examination, the exercises and the examples included in the course book 5B are specially written and graded to suit the latest changes. Details of the features of the 5B course book are given in its Preface.

Senior Form Supporting Materials for Students

For each volume of the Course Book in the senior Form series, there are plentiful supporting aids.

(I) Student Handbook

FREE to Students

For each volume of the "*Mathematics Today* " senior Form Course Books 4A, 4B and 5A, students would get a copy of Student Handbook (free of charge) when they purchase the corresponding Course Books*. These handbooks are meant to be a fast and handy tool for revising essential mathematical concepts, theorems and formulae.

(1) Each chapter of the handbook contains:
  • Revision Notes; key concepts; theorems and formulae.
  • Worked Examples.

(2) At the end of each handbook, students can find:
  • a multiple choice pack.
  • a homework pack.

*__Note:__ There will __NOT__ be any Handbook for the Course Book 5B.

(II) Workbook

Each of the Course Books 4A, 4B and 5A is accompanied by one Workbook, which contains controlled exercises of short questions, long questions and multiple choice questions. Students using the workbooks will be better prepared for all their examinations.

In addition, a Revision Test is put at the back of the Workbook to familiarize senior Form students with the format and style of the latest HKCE Examination.

Senior Form Supporting Materials for Teachers

Besides the rich supporting materials that our senior Form programmes have provided for our students, the authors and the editors of this series of Course Books have also designed a full range of teaching materials to back up our teachers at the teaching front. The supporting materials for teachers include:

- Teacher's Book for Each of the Course Books 4A, 4B and 5A.

FREE to Teachers

FREE to Teachers

- Teacher's Manual for Each Volume of the Course Books

  ("Tailoring Guide" is included in each manual except the Teacher's Manual 5B.)

- Teacher's Edition for Each Volume of the Workbooks.

FREE to Teachers

• Test Bank with CD for Each Form.

In the Preface of each of the above-mentioned supporting materials for teachers, the corresponding features will be listed in detail.

K. S. Leung , M. K. Lai , C. P. Lai

ACKNOWLEDGEMENT

All questions from the Hong Kong Certificate of Education Examination papers are reproduced by permission of the Hong Kong Examinations Authority.

The authors wish to thank the Hong Kong Examinations Authority for permission to use the questions taken from their past examination papers. The following list indicates the places where these HKCEE questions would appear in our Course Books and the year to which the questions belong.

Course Book	Place in the text	Type of HKCEE questions	Year of HKCEE
4A, 4B, 5A	Supplementary Exercise	Short questions (Section A)	*84, 86, 88, 90, 92, 94.*
		Long questions (Section B)	
		Multiple Choice questions	*90, 92, 94.*
5B	Revision Exercise	Short questions (Section A)	*85, 87, 89, 91, 93, 95, 96.*
		Long questions (Section B)	
		Multiple Choice questions	*87, 91, 93, 95, 96.*

CONTENTS

(A) **1**

Arithmetic and Geometric Sequences

(A) **2**

Series: Arithmetic and Geometric Series

(G) **3**

Coordinate Geometry of Circles

(A) **4**

Inequalities in One Unknown

(A) **5**

Inequalities in Two Unknowns and Linear Programming

(A)

6

Approximate Solution of Equations

(S)

7

Probability

(S) **8**

Statistics

MATHEMATICAL SYMBOLS

SYMBOL	MEANING	EXAMPLE
$\equiv$	is identical to	$2x + 10 \equiv 2(x + 5)$
$>$	is greater than	$9 > 5$
$\geqslant$	is greater than or equal to	$x \geqslant 6$
$<$	is less than	$8 < 10$
$\leqslant$	is less than or equal to	$y \leqslant 12$
$\sqrt{a}$	positive square root of $a\,(a > 0)$	$\sqrt{9}$
$\sqrt[n]{a}$	nth root of a	$\sqrt[3]{125}$
∞	infinity	In Quad. I, $\tan x$ increases from 0 to $+\infty$.
$\pm$	plus or minus	± 3
Δ	discriminant	$\Delta = b^2 - 4ac$
$\propto$	varies as	$A \propto r^2$
$/\!/$	is parallel to	AB $/\!/$ CD
$\perp$	is perpendicular to	EF $\perp$ MN
$\triangle$	triangle	$\triangle$ABC
$\cong$	is congruent to	$\triangle$ABC $\cong$ $\triangle$DEF
$\sim$	is similar to	$\triangle$PQR $\sim$ $\triangle$XYZ
$\frown$	arc	$\overparen{AB}$
$\bar{x}$	arithmetic mean	For $3, 3, 6 : \bar{x} = 4$
σ	standard deviation	For $3, 3, 6 : \sigma = \sqrt{2}$

TABLES OF MEASUREMENT

I. UNITS COMMONLY USED IN MATHEMATICS

(A) Metric Units

QUANTITY	UNIT	REMARK
LENGTH （長度）	millimetre　毫米　(mm) centimetre　厘米　(cm) metre　　　米　(m) kilometre　公里　(km)	1 cm　=　10 mm 1 m　=　100 cm 1 km　=　1 000 m
AREA （面積）	square millimetre　平方毫米　(mm^2) square centimetre　平方厘米　(cm^2) square metre　　　　平方米　(m^2) square kilometre　平方公里　(km^2)	$1\ cm^2\ =\ 100\ mm^2$ $1\ m^2\ =\ 10\ 000\ cm^2$ $1\ km^2\ =\ 1\ 000\ 000\ m^2$
VOLUME （體積）	cubic millimetre　立方毫米　(mm^3) cubic centimetre　立方厘米　(cm^3) cubic metre　　　　立方米　(m^3)	$1\ cm^3\ =\ 1\ 000\ mm^3$ $1\ m^3\ =\ 1\ 000\ 000\ cm^3$
CAPACITY （容量）	millilitre　毫升　(mL) litre　　　升　(L)	$1\ mL\ =\ 1\ cm^3$ 1 L　=　1 000 mL
WEIGHT （重量）	milligram　毫克　(mg) gram　　　克　(g) kilogram　公斤　(kg) *tonne　　公噸　(t)	1 g　　=　1 000 mg 1 kg　=　1 000 g 1 tonne = 1 000 kg
SPEED （速率）	metre per second　每秒 ………… 米 (m/s) kilometre per hour　每小時 ……. 公里(km/h)	$1\ km/h = \dfrac{5}{18}\ m/s$
TEMPERATURE （溫度）	degree Celsius　　　攝氏度　(°C) degree Fahrenheit　華氏度　(°F)	$t\ °C = \left(\dfrac{9t}{5} + 32\right)\ °F$ $t\ °F = \dfrac{5(t-32)}{9}\ °C$

(B) Other Units

QUANTITY	UNIT	REMARK
TIME （時間）	second　　秒　(s) minute　分鐘　(min) hour　　小時　(h)	1 min　=　60 s 1 h　　=　60 min
ANGLE （角度）	second　　秒　(″) minute　　分　(′) degree　　度　(°)	1′　=　60″ 1°　=　60′

Note: The recognized symbol for 'tonne' (metric unit) is 't'. But certain people still use the symbol 't' for 'ton' (non-metric unit). To avoid confusion, it is advised to use the whole word instead of the symbol.

II. COMMON NON-METRIC UNITS & THEIR CONVERSIONS

QUANTITY	NON-METRIC UNIT	NON-METRIC → METRIC[†]	METRIC → NON-METRIC[†]
LENGTH (長度)	inch 吋 (in) foot 呎 (ft) yard 碼 (yd) mile 哩	1 in = 2.54 cm 1 ft = 30.5 cm 1 yd = 0.914 m 1 mile = 1.61 km	1 cm = 0.394 in 1 m = 3.28 ft 1 m = 1.09 yd 1 km = 0.621 mile
AREA (面積)	square foot 平方呎 (ft^2) square mile 平方哩 acre 英畝	1 ft^2 = 929 cm^2 1 square mile = 2.59 km^2 1 acre = 4 050 m^2	1 m^2 = 10.8 ft^2 1 km^2 = 0.387 square mile 1 km^2 = 247 acres
VOLUME (體積)	cubic foot 立方呎 (ft^3)	1 ft^3 = 0.028 3 m^3	1 m^3 = 35.3 ft^3
CAPACITY (容量)	gallon UK 英制加侖 (gal. UK) gallon US 美制加侖 (gal. US)	1 gal. UK = 4.55 L 1 gal. US = 3.79 L	1 L = 0.220 gal. UK 1 L = 0.264 gal. US
WEIGHT (重量)	ounce 安士 (oz) pound 磅 (lb) ton 噸 tael 兩 catty 斤	1 oz = 28.3 g 1 lb = 454 g 1 ton = 1.02 tonne 1 tael = 37.8 g 1 catty = 0.605 kg	1 g = 0.035 3 oz 1 kg = 2.20 lb 1 tonne = 0.984 ton 1 g = 0.026 5 tael 1 kg = 1.65 catties
SPEED (速率)	mile per hour 每小時 ⋯⋯ 哩 (mph)	1 mph = 1.61 km/h	1 km/h = 0.621 mph

[†]*Note: All conversions are approximations only. They are rounded to 3 significant figures.*

In some countries, the harvest of crops increases by a *'fixed amount'* each year. Food scientists in these countries claim that their annual food supplies in consecutive years form an *'arithmetic'* sequence.

In the same countries, on the other hand, the human population increases by a *'fixed ratio'* each year. Environmentalists claim that in these countries, their annual populations in consecutive years form a *'geometric'* sequence.

The concepts of *'arithmetic sequence and geometric sequence'* will be discussed in this chapter.

CHAPTER 1

Arithmetic and Geometric Sequences

CHAPTER

1.1 Sequences

The owner of a music shop records the number of compact discs (abbreviated as CDs) sold each day in a certain week. He obtains a list of numbers like this:

89, 27, 64, 53, 53, 87, 120.

We say that this list of numbers forms a **sequence***. In general, a sequence is a list of numbers following one another. Each number in a sequence is called a **term*** of the sequence. In this example, there is no pattern in the sequence of numbers, but, for other sequences, the numbers in the sequence may form a pattern.

Below are some examples:

(i) 1, 3, 5, 7, ⋯

The terms in sequence **(i)** are odd numbers and each term after the first is two more than the preceding term. Thus we can easily continue the sequence with the numbers 9, 11, 13, etc.

◀ *The dots '⋯' indicate that the terms in the sequence continue, i.e. there are more terms in the sequence.*

(ii) $\frac{1}{2}$, $\frac{1}{4}$, $\frac{1}{8}$, $\frac{1}{16}$, ⋯

Each term after the first in sequence **(ii)** is formed by multiplying the preceding term by $\frac{1}{2}$. Thus we can easily continue the sequence with the numbers $\frac{1}{32}$, $\frac{1}{64}$, $\frac{1}{128}$, etc.

(iii) 1, 4, 9, 16, ⋯

For this sequence, refer to the figure below. In each of the figures, the dots form the shape of a square. The number of dots in each figure forms a term of the given sequence.

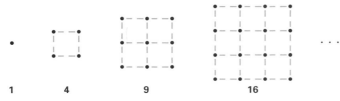

What do you think the next two figures should be and what are the numbers of dots in those figures?

sequence 序列
term 項

The terms of a sequence are usually denoted by the symbols:

$$T(1),\ T(2),\ T(3),\ \cdots,\ T(n),\ \cdots$$

where $T(1)$ is the first term;

           $T(2)$ is the second term;

           $T(3)$ is the third term;

          $\vdots$

          $T(n)$ is the nth term, also called the **general term***.

Note :   Alternatively, we may also denote $T(1),\ T(2),\ T(3),\ \cdots,$ $T(n)$ by the symbols $T_1,\ T_2,\ T_3,\ \cdots,\ T_n$ respectively.

FINDING THE GENERAL TERM

Given a sequence which follows a simple pattern, it is usually possible to work out a formula for the nth term (the general term) by observing the relationship among the first few terms and their positions in the sequence.

Example 1   Determine the general term $T(n)$ for the three sequences on P. 1.

     (a)   1, 3, 5, 7, $\cdots$ **(b)** $\dfrac{1}{2},\ \dfrac{1}{4},\ \dfrac{1}{8},\ \dfrac{1}{16},\ \cdots$

     (c)   1, 4, 9, 16, $\cdots$

Solution   **(a)**   Observing the given terms:

$$T(1) = 1 = 2(1) - 1$$

$$T(2) = 3 = 2(2) - 1$$

$$T(3) = 5 = 2(3) - 1$$

$$T(4) = 7 = 2(4) - 1$$

$$\therefore \quad T(n) = \underline{\underline{2n - 1}}$$

     (b)   Observing the given terms:

$$T(1) = \frac{1}{2} = \frac{1}{2^{(1)}}$$

$$T(2) = \frac{1}{4} = \frac{1}{2^{(2)}}$$

$$T(3) = \frac{1}{8} = \frac{1}{2^{(3)}}$$

$$T(4) = \frac{1}{16} = \frac{1}{2^{(4)}}$$

$$\therefore \quad T(n) = \underline{\underline{\frac{1}{2^{n}}}}$$

general term 通項

(c) Observing the given terms:

$$T(1) = 1 = (1)^2$$

$$T(2) = 4 = (2)^2$$

$$T(3) = 9 = (3)^2$$

$$T(4) = 16 = (4)^2$$

$$\therefore \quad T(n) = \underline{\underline{n^2}}$$

◀ *Note:*
In these examples, the general terms are found under the assumption that the simple pattern which the terms in the sequence follows is consistent and so we can 'predict' what the nth term is.

FINDING THE TERMS OF A SEQUENCE

Given the formula or the expression for the general term of a sequence, we can find the value of any term in the sequence. In **Example 1(a)**, since $T(n) = 2n - 1$, we can find the value of the fifth term by putting n equal to 5 and get $T(5) = 2(5) - 1 = 9$.

Similarly, $T(6) = 2(6) - 1 = 11$,

$$T(7) = 2(7) - 1 = 13,$$

$$T(8) = 2(8) - 1 = 15, \text{ etc.}$$

Example 2 In each of the following, the general term $T(n)$ of a sequence is given. Write down the first four terms of each sequence.

(a) $T(n) = \dfrac{n(n+1)}{2}$

(b) $T(n) = \dfrac{1}{2^{n-1}}$

Solution   **(a)** Since the general term $T(n)$ of the sequence is $\dfrac{n(n+1)}{2}$, we have

the 1st term, $T(1) = \dfrac{1(1+1)}{2} = 1$;

◀ *Put $n = 1$.*

the 2nd term, $T(2) = \dfrac{2(2+1)}{2} = 3$;

◀ *Put $n = 2$.*

the 3rd term, $T(3) = \dfrac{3(3+1)}{2} = 6$;

◀ *Put $n = 3$.*

the 4th term, $T(4) = \dfrac{4(4+1)}{2} = 10$.

◀ *Put $n = 4$.*

Thus the first four terms of the sequence are 1, 3, 6 and 10.

(b) Since the general term $T(n)$ of the sequence is $\dfrac{1}{2^{n-1}}$, we have

the 1st term, $T(1) = \dfrac{1}{2^{(1)-1}} = \dfrac{1}{2^0} = 1$;   ◄ *Recall that* $2^0 = 1$.

the 2nd term, $T(2) = \dfrac{1}{2^{(2)-1}} = \dfrac{1}{2^1} = \dfrac{1}{2}$;

the 3rd term, $T(3) = \dfrac{1}{2^{(3)-1}} = \dfrac{1}{2^2} = \dfrac{1}{4}$;

the 4th term, $T(4) = \dfrac{1}{2^{(4)-1}} = \dfrac{1}{2^3} = \dfrac{1}{8}$.

Thus the first four terms of the sequence are 1, $\dfrac{1}{2}$, $\dfrac{1}{4}$ and $\dfrac{1}{8}$.

Example 3   Find $T(1)$, $T(2)$, $T(10)$ and $T(20)$ of the sequence whose general term $T(n)$ is

(a) $(n-2)(n+3)$,

(b) $4(2)^{n-1}$.

Solution   **(a)** Since $T(n) = (n-2)(n+3)$,

$$T(1) = (1-2)(1+3) = \underline{\underline{-4}}$$

$$T(2) = (2-2)(2+3) = \underline{\underline{0}}$$

$$T(10) = (10-2)(10+3) = \underline{\underline{104}}$$

$$T(20) = (20-2)(20+3) = \underline{\underline{414}}$$

(b) Since $T(n) = 4(2)^{n-1}$,

$$T(1) = 4(2)^{1-1} = 4(2)^0 = \underline{\underline{4}}$$

$$T(2) = 4(2)^{2-1} = 4(2)^1 = \underline{\underline{8}}$$

$$T(10) = 4(2)^{10-1} = 4(2)^9 = \underline{\underline{2\,048}}$$

$$T(20) = 4(2)^{20-1} = 4(2)^{19} = \underline{\underline{2^{21}}}$$

◄ $\begin{aligned} 4(2)^{19} &= 2^2 \cdot 2^{19} \\ &= 2^{2+19} \\ &= 2^{21} \end{aligned}$

Note : In some sequences, the terms may get very large or very small quickly. The last answer 2^{21} to part **(b)** above is quite acceptable as it is. So be prepared to leave answers in index notation if necessary.

Example 4 In a lecture room, it is known that the number of seats in the nth row is given by $T(n)$, where $T(n) = 8 + 2n$.

(a) Find the number of seats in the 7th row. 22

(b) If there are 28 seats in the last row in the room, how many rows are there in the lecture room altogether? 10

(c) Is it correct to say that in the lecture room each subsequent row has two more seats than the row immediately in front of it? yes.

Solution **(a)** When $n = 7$, $T(7) = 8 + 2(7)$ $\qquad$ ◄ $T(n) = 8 + 2n$
$$= 22$$

∴ There are 22 seats in the 7th row.

(b) $\qquad T(n) = 28$
i.e. $\quad 8 + 2n = 28$
$$2n = 20$$
$$n = 10$$

∴ There are 10 rows in the lecture room altogether.

(c) For the kth row, i.e. any row, $T(k) = 8 + 2k$.

For the $(k-1)$th row, i.e. the row immediately in front of the kth row,
$$T(k-1) = 8 + 2(k-1)$$
$$= 6 + 2k$$
$$T(k) - T(k-1) = 8 + 2k - (6 + 2k)$$
$$= 2$$

In fact,
$T(1) = 8 + 2(1) = 10$
$T(2) = 8 + 2(2) = 12$
$T(3) = 8 + 2(3) = 14$
$\qquad \vdots \qquad\qquad \vdots$
$T(10) = 8 + 2(10) = 28$

∴ It is correct to say that in the lecture room, each subsequent row has two more seats than the row immediately in front of it.

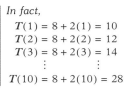

EXERCISE 1A

(*Level 1*)

1. Write down the next two terms for each of the following sequences:

(a) 2, 5, 8, 11, ⋯ $\qquad$ **(b)** 3, 6, 12, 24, ⋯ $\qquad$ **(c)** 1, −1, 1, −1, ⋯

2. In each of the following, the general term $T(n)$ of a sequence is given. Write down the first four terms of each sequence.

(a) $T(n) = 2n + 1$ $\qquad$ **(b)** $T(n) = 3^n$ $\qquad$ **(c)** $T(n) = \dfrac{n(n+3)}{2}$

3. In each of the following, the general term $T(n)$ of a sequence is given. Find for each sequence
   (i) $T(1)$, **(ii)** $T(5)$, **(iii)** $T(20)$.

   (a) $T(n) = 2n - 3$

   (b) $T(n) = \dfrac{3n + 1}{3n - 1}$

   (c) $T(n) = n^2 - 2$

4. Determine the general term $T(n)$ for each of the following sequences:

   (a) 2, 3, 4, 5, $\cdots$

   (b) 3, 6, 9, 12, $\cdots$

   (c) $\dfrac{1}{3}, \dfrac{1}{9}, \dfrac{1}{27}, \dfrac{1}{81}, \cdots$

   (d) 1, 8, 27, 64, $\cdots$

5. Starting from the 19th century, the years in which the nth Olympic Games are held form a sequence with the general term $T(n)$, where $T(n) = 1892 + 4n$. Will the Olympic Games be held in the year 2004?

(Level 2)

6. Write down the next three terms for each of the following sequences:

   0,4,05

   (a) 0, 1, 0, 2, 0, 3, $\cdots$

   (b) 1, 2, 6, 24, 120, 720, $\cdots$

   (c) 0, 1, 5, 14, $\cdots$

7. In each of the following, the general term $T(n)$ of a sequence is given. Write down the first five terms of each sequence.

   (a) $T(n) = \dfrac{2^n}{512}$

   (b) $T(n) =$ the nth prime number

   (c) $T(n) =$ the remainder obtained when 50 is divided by n

8. Determine the general term $T(n)$ for each of the following sequences:

   (a) 11, 101, 1 001, $\cdots$
   $10^n + 1$

   (b) $\dfrac{1}{3}, \dfrac{1}{4}, \dfrac{3}{16}, \dfrac{9}{64}, \cdots$

9. Suppose the general term $T(n)$ of the sequence 1, 3, 7, 13, $\cdots$ is given by $T(n) = an^2 + bn + 1$, where a and b are constants.

   (a) Find a and b.

   (b) Hence find the fifth term of the sequence.

$T(1) = a(1)^2 + b(1) + 1$

$\therefore a = 1$ and $b = -1$

$T(2) = a(2)^2 + b(2) + 1 = 3$

$a + b + 1 = 1 \qquad 4a + 2b = 2$

$a + b = 0 \qquad 4(-b) + 2b = 2$

$\qquad\qquad -4b + 2b = 2$

$\qquad\qquad -2b = 2$

$\qquad\qquad b = -1$

$\qquad\qquad \therefore a = 1$

10. The height of a helicopter above sea-level n seconds after it has taken off from a mountain peak is $T(n)$ metres, where $T(n) = 265 + 5n$.

   (a) Find the height of the helicopter above sea-level 10 seconds after it has taken off.

   (b) How long will it take for the helicopter to climb from a height of 300 m to the height found in **(a)**?

1.2 Arithmetic Sequences

A. *Arithmetic Sequences*

Consider the following sequence:

   2, 5, 8, 11, 14, 17.

In this sequence, we notice that the *difference* between any two adjacent terms is a *constant*.

i.e. $17 - 14 = 14 - 11 = 11 - 8 = 8 - 5 = 5 - 2 (= 3)$

The constant 3 is called the common difference* of the sequence and the sequence itself is called an arithmetic sequence*.

In general,

◀ $T(6) - T(5)$
$= T(5) - T(4)$
$= T(4) - T(3)$
$= T(3) - T(2)$
$= T(2) - T(1)$
$= 3$

> **an arithmetic sequence is a sequence having a common difference between successive terms.**

Let us study a few more examples of arithmetic sequences.

e.g. **(i)** $9, 4, -1, -6, -11, -16, -21$.

   The *common difference*
   $= -21 - (-16) = -16 - (-11) = -11 - (-6) = -6 - (-1)$
   $= -1 - 4 = 4 - 9 = -5$

(ii) $a, a + d, a + 2d, a + 3d$.

   The *common difference*
   $= (a + 3d) - (a + 2d) = (a + 2d) - (a + d) = (a + d) - a$
   $= d$

Note : An arithmetic sequence is used to be called an 'Arithmetic Progression', abbreviated to 'A.P.'.

┌ *Note:*
If we add an extra term -22 to this sequence, then the new sequence $9, 4, -1, -6, -11, -16, -21, -22$ is ◀
NOT an arithmetic sequence. This is because the difference between the last two terms of the new sequence is $-1 (\neq -5)$ and so there is not a <u>common</u> difference in the new sequence.

◀ *If we examine* Example 4 *on P. 5, we shall notice that the number of seats in the rows forms an arithmetic sequence.*

└ *The term 'Arithmetic Progression' can be found in HKCE Examination questions up to 1996.*

───────────────

common difference 公差
arithmetic sequence 等差數列

For an arithmetic sequence, once we know the 1st term and the common difference, we can get

the 2nd term by adding $1 \times$ common difference to the 1st term;

the 3rd term by adding $2 \times$ common difference to the 1st term;

the 4th term by adding $3 \times$ common difference to the 1st term;

$\vdots$

the nth term by adding $(n-1) \times$ common difference to the 1st term.

Thus, for an arithmetic sequence,

if the 1st term is a and the common difference is d,

then $T(1) = a$

$T(2) = a + d$

$T(3) = a + 2d$

$T(4) = a + 3d$

$\vdots$

$T(n) = a + (n-1)d.$

Hence, for an arithmetic sequence with 1st term a and common difference d, the general term, $T(n)$, is given by

$$T(n) = a + (n-1)d, \quad \text{where } n \text{ is a positive integer.} \quad \ldots \ldots (1)$$

CLASS PRACTICE

1. For each of the following sequences, if it is an arithmetic sequence, put a tick '$\checkmark$' in the Yes box: 'Yes ☐'; otherwise put a tick '$\checkmark$' in the No box: 'No ☐'.

	Yes	No			Yes	No
(a) 1, 2, 3, 4, 5	✓	☐	**(b)** 1, 4, 9, 16, 25		☐	✓
(c) 3, 9, 27, 81, 243	☐	✓	**(d)** 4, 1, −2, −5, −8		✓	☐

2. The 1st term of an arithmetic sequence is 3 and the common difference is 7. Write down the first 5 terms of the sequence.

    Solution $T(1) = 3$

    $T(2) = 3 + (\ 7\ ) = \underline{16}$

    $T(3) = 3 + (\ 2\,(7)\ ) = \underline{17}$

    $T(4) = 3 + (\ 3\,(7)\ ) = 24$

    $T(5) = 3 + (\ 4\,(7)\ ) = 31$

Example 5 Given an arithmetic sequence $1, 7, 13, 19, \cdots$, find

(a) the general term $T(n)$, (b) $T(7)$ and $T(21)$.

◄ *Recall:*
The dots '$\cdots$' indicate that the terms in the sequence continue, i.e. there are more terms in the given arithmetic sequence.

Solution Here the first term $a = 1$ and the common difference $d = 7 - 1 = 6$.

(a) The general term $T(n) = a + (n-1)d$
$$= 1 + (n-1)(6)$$
$$= 6n - 5$$

◄ *Use formula* (1) *and substitute* $a = 1$, $d = 6$ *into it.*

(b) From (a), $T(n) = 6n - 5$
$$\therefore \quad T(7) = 6(7) - 5$$
$$= 37$$

$$T(21) = 6(21) - 5$$
$$= 121$$

If we can find the first term and the common difference of an arithmetic sequence, then we can make use of formula (1) on P. 8 to find the general term.

◄ *Formula* (1):
$T(n) = a + (n-1)d$, *where n is a positive integer.*

Example 6 In an arithmetic sequence, $T(7) = 6$ and $T(21) = -22$. Find

(a) the first term and the common difference,

(b) the general term $T(n)$,

(c) the value of k when $T(k) = -82$.

Solution (a) Let the first term $T(1)$ be a and the common difference be d.

Then $T(7) = a + 6d = 6$ .... (i)
$T(21) = a + 20d = -22$ .... (ii)

Solving (i) and (ii), we have
$$a = 18, \ d = -2.$$

$\therefore$ The first term is 18 and the common difference is -2.

(b) $T(n) = a + (n-1)d$
$$= 18 + (n-1)(-2)$$
$$= 20 - 2n$$

◄ $a = 18$, $d = -2$

(c) $T(k) = -82$
i.e. $20 - 2k = -82$
$$-2k = -102$$
$$k = 51$$

◄ $T(n) = 20 - 2n$

EXERCISE 1B

(*Level 1*)

1. For each of the following arithmetic sequences, find
   (i) the common difference (d),
   (ii) the general term $T(n)$.

   (a) 6, 9, 12, 15, $\cdots$
   (b) -4, 0, 4, 8, 12, $\cdots$
   (c) 20, 5, $-10, -25, \cdots$

2. Given the general term $T(n)$ of an arithmetic sequence, find
   (i) the first term,   (ii) the common difference.

   (a) $T(n) = 2n + 3$
   (b) $T(n) = 4 - 7n$
   (c) $T(n) = \frac{1}{2}(n - 1)$

3. In each of the following, the first term $T(1)$ and the common difference (d) of an arithmetic sequence are given. Find
   (i) the general term,   (ii) the tenth term.

   (a) $T(1) = 2, d = 2$
   (b) $T(1) = -7, d = 3$
   (c) $T(1) = 3, d = -\frac{1}{2}$

4. The common difference of an arithmetic sequence is 3. The tenth term is 23. Find the first term.

5. Given an arithmetic sequence 4, 8, 12, 16, $\cdots$. If the nth term of the arithmetic sequence is 380, find the value of n.

6. Find the number of terms in each of the two arithmetic sequences below:
   (a) 5, 12, 19, 26, $\cdots$, 180
   (b) 91, 82, 73, $\cdots$, 1

7. Given an arithmetic sequence 7, 12, 17, 22, 27, 32.

   (a) If 10 is subtracted from each term of the sequence, is the new sequence still an arithmetic sequence?
   (b) If each term of the sequence is multiplied by $\frac{1}{10}$, is the new sequence still an arithmetic sequence?
   Explain your answers.

8. A computer is sold at $12 000 in the 1st year. If its selling price decreases by $1 100 in each subsequent year, find the selling price of the computer

   (a) in the 2nd year,

   (b) in the nth year.
   (*Give the answer in terms of n.*)

(Level 2)

9. For each of the following arithmetic sequences, find
   (i) the common difference (d),
   (ii) the general term $T(n)$.

   $[x + 7n - 4]$
   $x + 3 + 7n - 7$

   (a) $x + 3$, $x + 10$, $x + 17$, $x + 24$, $\cdots$ i) $d = 7$ ii) $T(n) = a + (n-1)d$ $T(n) = x + 3 + (n-1)7$

   (b) $a + b$, $2a + 3b$, $3a + 5b$, $4a + 7b$, $\cdots$ i) $a + 2b$ ii) $T(n) = a + b + (n-1)(a + 2b)$
   $= a + b + (an + 2bn - a - 2b)$
   $= a + b + an + 2bn - a - 2b)$
   $= an + 2bn - b$

10. Find the number of terms in the arithmetic sequence
    $\frac{1}{8}$, $\frac{5}{8}$, $1\frac{1}{8}$, $\cdots$, $3\frac{5}{8}$. $T(n) = a + (n-1)d$
    \# of terms $= 8$ $T(n) = \frac{1}{8} + (n-1)\frac{1}{2}$ $T(n) = \frac{1}{8} + \frac{1}{2}n - \frac{1}{2}$ $T(n) = \frac{1}{2}n - \frac{3}{8} = 3\frac{5}{8}$
    $\frac{1}{2}n = 4$
    $n = 8$

11. The 40th term of an arithmetic sequence is equal to the sum of the 20th term and the 21st term. If the common difference is -10, find $T(40) = a + (39d) = T(20) + T(21)$ $a + 19d$
    $a + 20d$

    (a) the first term, $a + 39d = a + 19d + a + 20d$ $\therefore a = 0$

    (b) the 10th term. $a + 390 = a - 190 + a - 200$
    $T(10) = a + 9d$ $a = 0 - 90$
    $= a - 90$ $\therefore T(10) = -90$

12. The nth term of an arithmetic sequence is given by $T(n) = 4n - 79$. If the first positive term in the sequence is $T(k)$, find $T(1) = 4(1) - 79$ $T(2) = 4(2) - 79$ $4k - 79 > 0$ $\therefore k = 20$
    $T(1) = -75$ $T(2) = -71$ $4k > 79$
    (a) the value of k, $\therefore a = -75$ $d = 4$ $\therefore k > 19.75$

    (b) the value of $T(k)$.

13. In a test consisting of 12 questions, each question after the first one is worth 2 marks more than the preceding question. If the fifth question is worth 20 marks, how many marks is the last question worth?

14. Dr. Knowall discovered a new comet in 1740. From its *orbit* 軌道 , he calculated that the comet would be visible again from Earth in 1823, 1906, 1989 and so on.

    (a) In which year will the comet be expected to appear again?

    (b) Would you expect the comet to appear in 2500? Why?

*15. The figure shows three squares, P, Q and R. AB, BC and CD are the sides of P, Q and R respectively. The lengths of AB, BC and CD form three consecutive terms of an arithmetic sequence. If ABCD is a straight line of length 21 cm and the total area of the three squares is 179 cm²,

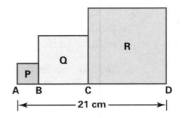

(a) find the length of BC,

(b) find the difference in lengths between AB and BC,

(c) hence find the lengths of AB and CD.

B. Arithmetic Mean

If a, b and c are any three consecutive terms of an arithmetic sequence, the middle term b is called the **arithmetic mean*** of a and c.

Since $\qquad c - b = b - a,$ ◀ *If $c - b = d$, then $b - a = d$.*

then $\qquad 2b = a + c.$

$\therefore$ $\qquad \boxed{b = \dfrac{a+c}{2}}$ . . . . (2)

e.g. Consider the following three terms of an arithmetic sequence: 17, 21, 25.

$$21 = \frac{17 + 25}{2}$$

◀ *Since $25 - 21 = 21 - 17 = 4$, it is a sequence with a common difference 4 and we say it is an arithmetic sequence.*

$\therefore$ 21 is the arithmetic mean of 17 and 25.

Between two terms of an arithmetic sequence, we can have <u>more than one</u> arithmetic mean. In fact, all the intermediate terms between any two specified terms of an arithmetic sequence are the arithmetic means between these two terms.

e.g. Consider the following arithmetic sequence:

$\qquad -4, \ -2, \ 0, \ 2, \ 4, \ 6.$

-2 is the arithmetic mean between -4 and 0;

-2 and 0 are the arithmetic means between -4 and 2;

-2, 0 and 2 are the arithmetic means between -4 and 4;

-2, 0, 2 and 4 are the arithmetic means between -4 and 6.

: mean 等差中項

Hence, if $T(1)$, $T(2)$, $T(3)$, $T(4)$, $T(5)$, $\cdots$, $T(n)$, $T(n+1)$ are the terms of an arithmetic sequence,

then $T(2)$ and $T(3)$ are <u>two</u> arithmetic means between $T(1)$ and $T(4)$;

$T(2)$, $T(3)$ and $T(4)$ are <u>three</u> arithmetic means between $T(1)$ and $T(5)$;

$T(2)$, $T(3)$, $\cdots$, $T(n)$ are $n-1$ arithmetic means between $T(1)$ and $T(n+1)$.

Example 7 Given two numbers 11 and 29.

     (a) Insert 3 arithmetic means between them.

     (b) Insert 8 arithmetic means between them.

Solution **(a)** Let d be the common difference of the arithmetic sequence to be formed.

Then the 5 terms of the arithmetic sequence are:
11, $11+d$, $11+2d$, $11+3d$, 29.

But the 5th term, 29, is also given by $11+4d$.

i.e. $29 = 11 + 4d$

$\therefore$ $4d = 29 - 11$

$= 18$

$d = 4.5$

$\therefore$ <u>The 3 required arithmetic means are 15.5, 20</u>
<u>and 24.5.</u>

$\begin{aligned} 11+d &= 11+4.5 = 15.5; \\ 11+2d &= 11+9 = 20; \\ 11+3d &= 11+13.5 = 24.5. \end{aligned}$

(b) Let d_1 be the common difference of the arithmetic sequence formed.

◀ *We use d_1 here because it is different from the common difference d in* **(a)**.

Then the 10 terms of the arithmetic sequence are:
11, $11+d_1$, $11+2d_1$, $11+3d_1$, $11+4d_1$, $11+5d_1$, $11+6d_1$, $11+7d_1$, $11+8d_1$, 29.

But the 10th term, 29, is also given by $11+9d_1$.

i.e. $29 = 11 + 9d_1$

$\therefore$ $9d_1 = 29 - 11$

$= 18$

$d_1 = 2$

$\therefore$ <u>The 8 required arithmetic means are 13, 15,</u>
<u>17, 19, 21, 23, 25 and 27.</u>

$\begin{aligned} 11+d_1 &= 11+2 = 13; \\ 11+2d_1 &= 11+4 = 15; \\ 11+3d_1 &= 11+6 = 17; \\ 11+4d_1 &= 11+8 = 19; \\ 11+5d_1 &= 11+10 = 21; \\ 11+6d_1 &= 11+12 = 23; \\ 11+7d_1 &= 11+14 = 25; \\ 11+8d_1 &= 11+16 = 27. \end{aligned}$

From **Example 7** above, we see that when given any two numbers, we can always insert any number of arithmetic means between them.

E X E R C I S E   1C

(*Level 1*)

1. Find the arithmetic mean for each pair of numbers below:

   (a) 2 and 8

   (b) -5 and 0

   (c) -12 and -6

2. Find x if the arithmetic mean of 18 and x is 24.

3. Insert three arithmetic means between 5 and 29.

4. If -18, p, q, r, s, 2 is an arithmetic sequence, find the values of p, q, r and s.

(*Level 2*)

5. If the arithmetic mean of $5x - 7$ and $3x - 11$ is x, find the value of x.

6. **(a)** Insert three arithmetic means between 1 and n.
       (*Give the answers in terms of n.*)

   (b) Hence find the values of a, b and c if 1, a, b, c, 109 is an arithmetic sequence.

7. **(a)** Show that the arithmetic mean of $x - a$ and $x + a$ is always x.

   (b) Hence find the arithmetic mean of $20^2 - 16^2$ and $20^2 + 16^2$.

8. If $\log 4$, a, b, $\log 16$ are in arithmetic sequence, find a and b.

9. Mr. Chan's monthly salary rises by $\$d$ each year from $\$11\,400$ in 1990 to $\$15\,900$ in 1996.

   (a) Find the value of d.

   (b) What was his monthly salary for each year between 1990 and 1996?

1.3   Geometric Sequences

A. Geometric Sequences

Consider the following sequence:

   1, 3, 9, 27, 81, 243.

This is <u>not</u> an arithmetic sequence since this sequence does not have a common difference. But we notice that the *ratio* of a term, after the first, to its preceding term is a *constant*.

◀ $3 - 1 \neq 9 - 3 \neq 27 - 9$, etc.

i.e. $\dfrac{3}{1} = \dfrac{9}{3} = \dfrac{27}{9} = \dfrac{81}{27} = \dfrac{243}{81} \; (= 3)$.

◀ $\dfrac{T(2)}{T(1)} = \dfrac{T(3)}{T(2)} = \dfrac{T(4)}{T(3)}$
$= \dfrac{T(5)}{T(4)} = \dfrac{T(6)}{T(5)}$
$= 3$

The constant 3 is called the **common ratio*** and the sequence itself is called a **geometric sequence***.

In general,

> **a geometric sequence is a sequence having a common ratio between successive terms.**

Let us study a few more examples of geometric sequences.

e.g. **(i)** $1, \; -\dfrac{1}{2}, \; \dfrac{1}{4}, \; -\dfrac{1}{8}, \; \dfrac{1}{16}, \; -\dfrac{1}{32}$.

The *common ratio*

$= \dfrac{-\frac{1}{2}}{1} = \dfrac{\frac{1}{4}}{-\frac{1}{2}} = \dfrac{-\frac{1}{8}}{\frac{1}{4}} = \dfrac{\frac{1}{16}}{-\frac{1}{8}} = \dfrac{-\frac{1}{32}}{\frac{1}{16}} = -\dfrac{1}{2}$

◀ *Note:*
If we add an extra term $-\frac{1}{64}$ to this sequence, then the new sequence $1, -\frac{1}{2}, \frac{1}{4},$ $-\frac{1}{8}, \frac{1}{16}, -\frac{1}{32}, -\frac{1}{64}$ is <u>NOT</u> a geometric sequence. This is because the ratio of the last two terms of the new sequence is $\frac{1}{2}\left(\neq -\frac{1}{2}\right)$ and so there is not a <u>common</u> ratio in the new sequence.

(ii) $a, \; ar, \; ar^2, \; ar^3, \; ar^4, \; ar^5$ where $a \neq 0$ and $r \neq 0$.

The *common ratio*

$= \dfrac{ar}{a} = \dfrac{ar^2}{ar} = \dfrac{ar^3}{ar^2} = \dfrac{ar^4}{ar^3} = \dfrac{ar^5}{ar^4} = r$

Note : A geometric sequence is used to be called a 'Geometric Progression', abbreviated to 'G.P.'.

◀ *The term 'Geometric Progression' can be found in HKCE Examination questions up to 1996.*

---

common ratio 公比
geometric sequence 等比數列

It is obvious that for a geometric sequence, once we know the 1st term and the common ratio, we can get

the 2nd term by multiplying the 1st term by the *common ratio*;

the 3rd term by multiplying the 1st term by the *square of the common ratio*;

the 4th term by multiplying the 1st term by the *cube of the common ratio*;

$\vdots$

the nth term by multiplying the 1st term by the $(n-1)th$ *power of the common ratio*.

Thus, for a geometric sequence,

if the 1st term $= a$ and the common ratio $= r$,

then $T(1) = a$
$T(2) = ar$
$T(3) = ar^2$
$T(4) = ar^3$
$\vdots$
$T(n) = ar^{n-1}$.

Hence, the general term, $T(n)$, of a geometric sequence with the 1st term a and the common ratio r is given by

$$T(n) = ar^{n-1}, \quad \text{where } n \text{ is a positive integer.} \quad \ldots \ldots (3)$$

CLASS PRACTICE

1. For each of the following sequences, if it is a geometric sequence, put a tick '$\checkmark$' in the Yes box: 'Yes ☐'; otherwise put a tick '$\checkmark$' in the No box: 'No ☐'.

	Yes	No
(a) 1, 2, 4, 8, 16	✓	☐
(b) 1, 4, 9, 16, 25	☐	✓
(c) $2, -1, \frac{1}{2}, \frac{1}{4}, -\frac{1}{8}$	✓	☐
(d) $3, -1, -\frac{1}{3}, \frac{1}{9}, \frac{1}{27}$	☐	✓

2. The 1st term of a geometric sequence is 2 and the common ratio is -3. Write down the first 5 terms of the sequence.

Solution $T(1) = 2$

$$T(2) = 2(\quad-3\quad) = \underline{-6}$$

$$T(3) = 2(\quad-3\quad)^2 = \underline{18}$$

$$T(4) = \underline{2(-3)^3} = \underline{54}$$

$$T(5) = \underline{2(-3)^4} = \underline{162}$$

Example 8 Given a geometric sequence $4, -12, 36, -108, \cdots,$ find **(a)** the general term $T(n)$,
 (b) the terms $T(6)$ and $T(9)$.

◀ *Recall:*
The dots '$\cdots$' indicate that there are more terms in the given geometric sequence, but we are not going to list all of them here.

Solution   Here the first term $a = 4$,

and the common ratio $r = \dfrac{-12}{4} = -3$.

(a) The general term $T(n) = ar^{n-1}$

$$= \underline{4(-3)^{n-1}}$$

◀ *Use formula* **(3)** *and substitute $a = 4$, $r = -3$ into it.*

(b) $T(n) = 4(-3)^{n-1}$

$\therefore\ T(6) = 4(-3)^{6-1}$

$$= 4(-3)^5$$

$$= \underline{\underline{-972}}$$

◀ 🖩
$4\boxed{\times}3\boxed{+/-}\boxed{x^y}5\boxed{=}$
$[-972.]$

$T(9) = 4(-3)^{9-1}$

$$= 4(-3)^8$$

$$= \underline{\underline{26\ 244}}$$

◀ 🖩
$4\boxed{\times}3\boxed{+/-}\boxed{x^y}8\boxed{=}$
$[26244.]$

Note : For some models of calculators, the key $\boxed{x^y}$ will function only when the base x is positive.

In **Example 8(b)** above,

$\because\ (-1)^n = \begin{cases} +1 \text{ when } n \text{ is even} \\ -1 \text{ when } n \text{ is odd} \end{cases}$

$\therefore\ 4(-3)^5 = 4(-1 \times 3)^5$

$$= 4(-1)^5(3)^5$$

$$= -4(3)^5$$

Using these calculators, we find the value of $-4(3)^5$ instead.
The keying sequence is:

$4\boxed{+/-}\boxed{\times}3\boxed{x^y}5\boxed{=}$
$[-972.]$

If we can find the first term and the common ratio of a geometric sequence, then we can make use of formula **(3)** on P. 16 to find the general term.

◀ *Formula* **(3)**:
$$T(n) = ar^{n-1}, \text{ where } n \text{ is a positive integer.}$$

Example 9   In a geometric sequence, if all the terms are positive, $T(3) = 16$ and $T(9) = \dfrac{1}{4}$, find

(a) the common ratio,

(b) the first term,

(c) the general term $T(n)$,

(d) $T(11) - T(5)$.

(*Give the answers in decimals if necessary.*)

Solution   **(a)** Let the first term be a and the common ratio be r.

Then $T(3) = ar^2 = 16$ .... **(i)**

$T(9) = ar^8 = \dfrac{1}{4}$ .... **(ii)**

Dividing **(ii)** by **(i)**, we have

$$\frac{ar^8}{ar^2} = \frac{\frac{1}{4}}{16}$$

$$\therefore \quad r^6 = \frac{1}{64}$$

$$r = 0.5 \quad or \quad -0.5 \,(\text{rejected})$$

$\therefore$ The common ratio is 0.5.

$1\ \boxed{a\,^b\!/_c}\ 64\ \boxed{x^{1/y}}\ 6\ \boxed{=}$
[0.5]

Alternatively, for calculators without the $\boxed{a\,^b\!/_c}$ *key, use the following keying sequence:*

◀ $64\ \boxed{1/x}\ \boxed{x^{1/y}}\ 6\ \boxed{=}$

◀ $r = -0.5$ *is rejected because when the common ratio is negative, some of the terms in the geometric sequence must be negative.*

(b) Substituting $r = 0.5$ into **(i)**, we have

$$a\,(0.5)^2 = 16$$
$$0.25a = 16$$
$$a = 64$$

$\therefore$ The first term is 64.

(c) $T(n) = ar^{n-1}$

$$= 64(0.5)^{n-1}$$

(d) $T(11) = 64(0.5)^{11-1}$

$$= 0.062\,5$$

$T(5) = 64(0.5)^{5-1}$

$$= 4$$

$\therefore$ $T(11) - T(5) = 0.062\,5 - 4$

$$= -3.937\,5$$

$64\ \boxed{\times}\ 0.5\ \boxed{x^y}\ 10\ \boxed{=}$
[0.0625]

$64\ \boxed{\times}\ 0.5\ \boxed{x^y}\ 4\ \boxed{=}$
[4.]

Note : If it is not specified in the question that all the terms in the geometric sequence are positive, then we cannot reject $r = -0.5$ as an answer. As a result, the general term is either $T(n) = 64(0.5)^{n-1}$ or $T(n) = 64(-0.5)^{n-1}$ and there are two possible sequences:

(i) $64, 32, 16, 8, 4, \cdots$ (for $r = 0.5$);

(ii) $64, -32, 16, -8, 4, \cdots$ (for $r = -0.5$).

E X E R C I S E 1D

(Level 1)

1. Determine the common ratio (r) and the general term $T(n)$ for each of the following geometric sequences.

   (a) $2, 4, 8, \cdots$

   (b) $2, -10, 50, \cdots$

   (c) $-4, -12, -36, \cdots$

2. In each of the following, the first term $T(1)$ and the common ratio (r) of a geometric sequence are given. Find

   (i) the general term, **(ii)** the fifth term.

   (a) $T(1) = 1, r = 4$

   (b) $T(1) = 2, r = -2$

   (c) $T(1) = -4, r = \dfrac{1}{4}$

3. Given the general term $T(n)$ of a geometric sequence, find

   (i) the first term, **(ii)** the common ratio.

   (a) $T(n) = 4(5)^{n-1}$

   (b) $T(n) = 3(2)^{n}$

   (c) $T(n) = 3^{2n}$

   (d) $T(n) = 2^{-n}$

4. Find the first term of a geometric sequence if both the fifth term and the common ratio are 3.

5. Find the number of terms in each of the following geometric sequences:

   (a) $5, 15, 45, \cdots, 5 \times 3^{20}$

   (b) $2, 6, 18, \cdots, 486$

6. Given two geometric sequences:

$2, 4, \cdots, 64$ and $1, 3, \cdots, 243$

(a) If each term (i.e. 1st, 2nd, 3rd, etc.) of the first sequence is added to the corresponding term (i.e. 1st, 2nd, 3rd, etc.) of the second sequence, is the new sequence so formed still a geometric sequence?

(b) If each term (i.e. 1st, 2nd, 3rd, etc.) of the first sequence is multiplied by the corresponding term (i.e. 1st, 2nd, 3rd, etc.) of the second sequence, is the new sequence so formed still a geometric sequence?

Explain your answers.

(*Level 2*)

7. Find the common ratio (r) and the general term $T(n)$ for the geometric sequence

$7, 2\frac{1}{3}, \frac{7}{9}, \cdots.$ $r = \frac{1}{3}$ $T(n) = ar^{(n-1)}$ $T(n) = 7(\frac{1}{3})^{(n-1)}$

8. The third term of a geometric sequence is 3 and the sixth term is -81. Find

(a) the common ratio,   **(b)** the first term,   **(c)** the eighth term.

9. The sum of the first and the third terms of a geometric sequence is equal to twice the sum of the second and the fourth terms. Find the common ratio of this sequence.

10. Given a geometric sequence $\frac{1}{8}, \frac{1}{4}, \frac{1}{2}, \cdots.$ $T(n) = \frac{1}{8}(2)^{(n-1)}$

Its kth term is denoted by $T(k)$. Find the value of k if $T(k) = \frac{1}{8}(2)^{(k-1)} = 64$

(a) $T(k) = 64$,   **(b)** $T(k)$ is just greater than 4 000. $2^{k-1} = 512$

$\frac{1}{8}(2)^{k-1} > 4000$ $k-1 = 315$ $\therefore k = 16$ $2^{k-1} = 2^9$

$\frac{1}{8}(2)^{k-1} > 4000$ $\frac{32000}{8}$ $k-1 = 9$

$\therefore k = 10$

11. A biological experiment starts at noon on 1st January with 300 bacteria. If the number of bacteria triples every 3 hours and there are N bacteria present at noon on 2nd January,

(a) find the value of N,

(b) at what time are there $\frac{N}{3}$ bacteria present?

12. Mario buys a stamp from a stamp dealer who tells him that the stamp is worth $200 now, but it will increase by 4% in value every month.

(a) Find the value of the stamp after 1 year.
(*Give the answer correct to 3 significant figures.*)

(b) Mario decides to sell the stamp when its value just exceeds $1 000. After how many months from now will Mario sell the stamp?

*13. Alan and Philip work in a company, each with a starting salary of $10 000 and $8 000 per month respectively. If Alan and Philip have regular annual salary increments of 10% and 13% respectively, find

(a) their monthly salaries at the nth year,

(b) the minimum number of years of service required so that the monthly salary of Philip exceeds that of Alan,

(c) the number of years of service required so that the monthly salary of Philip is at least twice that of Alan.

B. *Geometric Mean*

If x, y and z are any three consecutive terms of a geometric sequence, the middle term y is called the **geometric mean*** of x and z.

◀ *Note that x and z must be of the same sign.*

Since $$\frac{z}{y} = \frac{y}{x},$$

then $$y^2 = xz$$

∴ $$\boxed{y = \pm\sqrt{xz}} \quad \dots\dots\dots (4)$$

┌ *Since $\frac{-10}{2} = \frac{50}{-10} = -5$, it is a sequence with a common ratio -5 and we say it is a geometric sequence.*

e.g. Consider the following three terms of a geometric sequence:
$$2, -10, 50.$$
$$-10 = -\sqrt{2 \times 50}$$

◀ $-\sqrt{2 \times 50} = -\sqrt{100} = -10$

∴ -10 is a geometric mean of 2 and 50.

Like the case for an arithmetic sequence, we can have <u>more than one</u> geometric mean between two terms of a geometric sequence. Again all the intermediate terms between any two specified terms of a geometric sequence are the geometric means between the two terms.

e.g. Consider the following geometric sequence:
$$-\frac{1}{3}, \ 1, \ -3, \ 9, \ -27, \ 81.$$

◀ *Question:*
What is the common ratio of this geometric sequence?

1 is the geometric mean between $-\frac{1}{3}$ and -3;

1 and -3 are the geometric means between $-\frac{1}{3}$ and 9;

1, -3 and 9 are the geometric means between $-\frac{1}{3}$ and -27;

1, -3, 9 and -27 are the geometric means between $-\frac{1}{3}$ and 81.

geometric mean 等比中項

Hence, if $T(1)$, $T(2)$, $T(3)$, $T(4)$, $T(5)$, $\cdots$, $T(n)$, $T(n+1)$ are the terms of a geometric sequence,

then $T(2)$ and $T(3)$ are <u>two</u> geometric means between $T(1)$ and $T(4)$;

$T(2)$, $T(3)$ and $T(4)$ are <u>three</u> geometric means between $T(1)$ and $T(5)$;

$T(2)$, $T(3)$, $\cdots$, $T(n)$ are <u>$n-1$</u> geometric means between $T(1)$ and $T(n+1)$.

Example 10 **(a)** In each of the following, find the geometric mean of the two given numbers.

(i) $\frac{3}{4}$ and 12

(ii) -3 and 27

(b) Insert 3 positive geometric means between $\frac{3}{4}$ and 12.

Solution   **(a) (i)** Let the geometric mean be x.

Then $\dfrac{12}{x} = \dfrac{x}{\frac{3}{4}}$

$\therefore \qquad x^2 = 12 \times \dfrac{3}{4}$

$\qquad\qquad = 9$

$\qquad x = \pm 3$

$\therefore$ The geometric mean of $\frac{3}{4}$ and 12 is either 3 *or* -3.

(ii) Let the geometric mean be y.

Then $\dfrac{27}{y} = \dfrac{y}{-3}$

$\therefore \qquad y^2 = -81 \ldots\ldots\ldots$ **(i)**

$\because$ Equation **(i)** has no real roots,

$\therefore$ The geometric mean of -3 and 27 does not exist.

Note : In general, if two numbers a and b are of the same sign (i.e. either both are positive or both are negative), then either $+\sqrt{ab}$ or $-\sqrt{ab}$ can be inserted as a geometric mean. If a and b are of different signs, then <u>no</u> single geometric mean can be inserted between them.

(b) Let the common ratio be r.

Then the five numbers that form the geometric sequence are:

$$\frac{3}{4}, \; \frac{3}{4}r, \; \frac{3}{4}r^2, \; \frac{3}{4}r^3, \; 12.$$

But the 5th term, 12, is also given by $\frac{3}{4}r^4$.

i.e. $12 = \frac{3}{4}r^4$

$\therefore \quad 3r^4 = 48$

$r^4 = 16$

$r = 2 \quad or \quad -2 \; (rejected)$

$\therefore$ The 3 required geometric means are $\frac{3}{2}$, 3 and $\underline{6.}$

◀ *When $r = -2$, the three geometric means are $\frac{3}{-2}$, 3 and -6. Since two of the geometric means so obtained are negative, we reject $r = -2$ as the common ratio.*

EXERCISE 1E

(*Level 1*)

1. Find the positive geometric mean between 7 and 63.

2. Find the negative geometric mean between $\frac{1}{25}$ and $\frac{1}{441}$.

3. Insert two geometric means between 3 and 24.

4. Insert three positive geometric means between 12 and 972.

(*Level 2*)

5. Insert five geometric means between 7 and 5 103.

6. Insert three geometric means between 96 and $\frac{3}{8}$.

7. If the geometric mean of two numbers $k + 9$ and $6 - k$ is $2k$,

   (a) find the values of k,

   (b) what are the two numbers when k is negative?

8. **(a)** Insert, in terms of x, two geometric means between $\frac{3}{x^2}$ and $\frac{x}{9}$.

   (b) If the positive geometric mean between the two geometric means obtained in **(a)** is $\frac{\sqrt{3}}{2}$, what is the value of x?

9. Three positive numbers form a geometric sequence. If the geometric mean of the first two numbers is 6 and the geometric mean of the last two numbers is 24,

   (a) find the common ratio,

   (b) hence find the three numbers.

10. It is noted that from the year 1993 to 1996, the population of a certain housing estate in each subsequent year forms the consecutive terms of a geometric sequence. The two geometric means between the population in 1993 and the population in 1996 are 6 000 and 7 200.

    (a) Find the common ratio of the geometric sequence.

    (b) Hence find the population of the housing estate
       (i) in 1993,
       (ii) in 1996.

    (c) Assuming the rate of increase in population each year remains unchanged, estimate the population of the housing estate in the year 2000 correct to 3 significant figures.

SUPPLEMENTARY
EXERCISE 1

PART I | *Further Practice*

(Ex. 1A)

1. In each of the following, the general term $T(n)$ of a sequence is given. Write down the first four terms of the sequence.

   (a) $T(n) = 1 - 2n$ **(b)** $T(n) = (-1)^n$

   (c) $T(n) = \cos n\pi$ **(d)** $T(n) = n^n$

2. Write down the general term $T(n)$ for each of the following:

   (a) $1, \dfrac{1}{3}, \dfrac{1}{5}, \dfrac{1}{7}, \cdots$ **(b)** $0.1, 0.01, 0.001, 0.000\ 1, \cdots$

   (c) $10, 200, 3\ 000, 40\ 000, \cdots$ **(d)** $\sin\dfrac{\pi}{3}, \sin\dfrac{2\pi}{4}, \sin\dfrac{3\pi}{5}, \sin\dfrac{4\pi}{6}, \cdots$

3. The general term $T(n)$ of a sequence is given by $T(n) = 10 - 2n$.

   (a) How many terms of the sequence are positive?

   (b) Show that each term of the sequence must be an even number.

   (c) Is 654 321 a term of the sequence? Why?

*4. Given that the general term $T(n)$ of a sequence is $n^2 - 1$.

    (a) **(i)** Derive an expression in n to denote $T(n+1)$.

        (ii) Hence, find the result in n when $T(n)$ is subtracted from $T(n+1)$.

    (b) Using the results of **(a)**, find the value of each of the following.

        (i) $T(5) - T(4)$

        (ii) $T(1\,704) - T(1\,703)$

        (iii) $T(998) - T(999)$

(Ex. 1B)

5. In each of the following, two terms of an arithmetic sequence are given. Find the first term and the common difference of the arithmetic sequence.

    (a) $T(4) = 4$, $T(17) = 368$

    (b) $T(2) = -6$, $T(10) = -22$

6. The 9th term and the 12th term of an arithmetic sequence are $9a + 7b$ and $12a + 10b$ respectively. Find, in terms of a and b,

    (a) the first term,

    (b) the common difference.

7. **(a)** Show that each of the two terms $f(n)$ and $g(n)$ given below is the general term of an arithmetic sequence:

$$f(n) = 2n - 3 \quad \text{and} \quad g(n) = n - 2$$

    (b) If $f(n)$ is subtracted from $g(n)$, is the new term still the general term of a new arithmetic sequence?
Explain your answer.

8. In a right-angled triangle, the lengths of its sides form an arithmetic sequence. Let the middle term of this sequence be a cm.

    (a) Find the common difference in terms of a.

    (b) If the hypotenuse of the triangle is 15 cm, find the lengths of the other two sides of the triangle.

9. Given an arithmetic sequence 50, 47, 44, $\cdots$.

    (a) If the nth term of the arithmetic sequence is 14, find the value of n.

    (b) Find the smallest positive term in the arithmetic sequence.

    (c) Find the value of the first negative term in the arithmetic sequence.

*10. Given that x^2, y^2, z^2 form three consecutive terms of an arithmetic sequence.

    (a) If $x+y$, $x+z$ and $y+z$ are all non-zero, show that $\dfrac{1}{x+y}$, $\dfrac{1}{x+z}$, $\dfrac{1}{y+z}$ form three consecutive terms of an arithmetic sequence.

    (b) Show that 25, $84\frac{1}{2}$, 144 form three consecutive terms of an arithmetic sequence.

    (c) Using the results of **(a)** and **(b)**, show that $\dfrac{\sqrt{2}}{13+5\sqrt{2}}$, $\dfrac{1}{17}$, $\dfrac{\sqrt{2}}{13+12\sqrt{2}}$ form three consecutive terms of an arithmetic sequence.

(Ex. 1C)

11. Insert an arithmetic mean between

    (a) -11 and 23,   **(b)** $-\dfrac{1}{8}$ and $-\dfrac{1}{2}$.

12. Insert three arithmetic means between $\sqrt{27}$ and $\sqrt{147}$.

13. **(a)** If x, a, b and y is an arithmetic sequence, express a and b in terms of x and y.

    (b) Hence insert two arithmetic means between $-\sqrt{3}$ and $\sqrt{3}$.

*14. Suppose n arithmetic means are inserted between two non-zero numbers a and b to form an arithmetic sequence.

    (a) Find the common difference of the arithmetic sequence in terms of a, b and n.

    (b) Show that the nth arithmetic mean is equal to $\dfrac{a+nb}{n+1}$.

    (c) Using the result of **(b)**, find the 10th arithmetic mean when 10 arithmetic means are inserted between 25 and 575.

(Ex. 1D)

15. In each of the following, the first three terms and the last term of a geometric sequence are given, find
    (i) the common ratio r,
    (ii) the general term $T(n)$,
    (iii) the number of terms in the geometric sequence.

    (a) $16\,807$, $2\,401$, 343, $\cdots$, $\dfrac{1}{49}$

    (b) 3, $\sqrt{27}$, 9, $\cdots$, 27

16. The fifth term of a geometric sequence is 96 and the common ratio of the sequence is 2. If each term of the sequence is divided by 4,

    (a) find the general term of the new sequence,

    (b) hence, show that the new sequence is also a geometric sequence.

17. **(a)** Find the value(s) of x so that $2x - 5$, $x - 4$ and $10 - 3x$ form three consecutive terms of a geometric sequence.

    (b) Hence write down the three terms of the sequence if they are all integers.

18. The sum of the first two terms of a geometric sequence is $2\frac{1}{2}$ and the third term of the geometric sequence is $2\frac{1}{4}$. If a is the first term and r is the common ratio of the sequence,

    (a) show that

    (i) $a = \dfrac{5}{2(1 + r)}$,   **(ii)** $10r^2 - 9r - 9 = 0$;

    (b) hence find all possible values of a and r.

19. The values of car A and car B depreciate each year by 10% and 20% respectively. If the value of car A is \$120 000 and that of car B is \$230 000 when they are 1 year old, find

    (a) the values of car A and car B in terms of n when they are n years old,

    (b) the minimum value of n for which car A is worth more than car B.

(Ex. 1E)

20. Insert three positive geometric means between $\dfrac{4}{125}$ and $\dfrac{5}{16}$.

21. Find the negative geometric mean between

    (a) $\sqrt{3}$ and $\sqrt{27}$,   **(b)** $(\sqrt{10} - 3)$ and $(\sqrt{10} + 3)$.

22. Two geometric means are inserted between $\left(\dfrac{a + b}{a - b}\right)^2$ and $\dfrac{a - b}{a + b}$.

    (a) What is the common ratio of the geometric sequence formed?
    (*Give the answer in terms of a and b.*)

    (b) Show that one of the geometric means inserted does not depend on the values of a and b.

    (c) Write down the geometric sequence formed when $a = \dfrac{5}{2}$, $b = \dfrac{1}{2}$.

PART II | *Miscellaneous*

23. The population of a city n years after 1990 is denoted by $T(n)$, where $T(n) = 10(1.04)^n$ million and n is a positive integer.

    (a) Find, correct to the nearest thousand,
    - **(i)** the population of the city in 2000;
    - **(ii)** the increase in the population of the city from 1998 to 1999.

    (b) What is the overall percentage increase in the population of the city from 1998 to 2000?

24. The third term of an arithmetic sequence is 11 and the ninth term is 35. Find

    (a) the common difference,

    (b) the first term,

    (c) the 12th term.

25. Show that the arithmetic mean of $2x^2 + 2y^2$ and $-4xy$ is $(x-y)^2$.

26. The sum of the second and the third terms of a geometric sequence is 24. The sixth term of this sequence is eight times the third term. Find

    (a) the first term,

    (b) the seventh term.

27. John saves money each week for 10 weeks such that the sum saved decreases each week by the same amount. In the sixth week, he saves $95 and in the tenth week, he saves $75.

    (a) By how much does the sum he saves decrease each week?

    (b) Find the sum he saves for each week between the sixth and the tenth weeks.

    (c) How much does he save in the first week?

28. **(a)** Show that a, b, c are in geometric sequence if $\dfrac{1}{b-a}$, $\dfrac{1}{2b}$, $\dfrac{1}{b-c}$ are in arithmetic sequence.

    (b) Hence find the values of b if $\dfrac{1}{b-6}$, $\dfrac{1}{2b}$, $\dfrac{1}{b-24}$ are in arithmetic sequence.

29. If $\log(2a-2)$ is the arithmetic mean of $\log(2a+1)$ and $\log a$,

    (a) show that $2a^2 - 9a + 4 = 0$,

    (b) find all the possible value(s) of a.

*30. In the figure, ABCD is a square of side $3a$ cm. The points A_1, B_1, C_1, D_1 divide the sides AB, BC, CD, DA respectively in the ratio $1 : 2$ and the points are joined to form another square $A_1B_1C_1D_1$. This process continues so that squares $A_2B_2C_2D_2$, $A_3B_3C_3D_3$, $\cdots$ are constructed in a similar way.

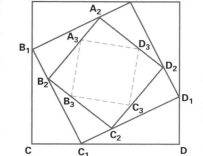

(a) Find, in terms of a, the lengths of the sides
    (i) A_1B_1,
    (ii) A_2B_2,
    (iii) A_3B_3.
    (*Give the answers in surd form if necessary.*)

(b) Hence find the area of the square $A_nB_nC_nD_n$ in terms of a and n.

(c) If $CD = 6$ cm, what is the area of the square $A_{10}B_{10}C_{10}D_{10}$ correct to 2 significant figures?

PART III | HKCEE Questions

[Note that the terms 'arithmetic progression' (abbreviated as 'A. P.') and 'geometric progression' (abbreviated as 'G. P.') mean the same thing as 'arithmetic sequence' and 'geometric sequence' respectively. From 1997 onwards, the term 'sequence' will be used instead of 'progression' in the HKCE Examinations.]

(MC Questions)

31. Let a, x_1, x_2, b and a, y_1, y_2, y_3, b be two arithmetic progressions. $\dfrac{x_2 - x_1}{y_3 - y_2} =$

  A. $\dfrac{3}{4}$

  B. $\dfrac{4}{3}$

  C. 1

  D. $\dfrac{4}{5}$

  E. $\dfrac{5}{4}$ [HKCEE 90]

32. If the quadratic equation $ax^2 - 2bx + c = 0$ has two equal roots, which of the following is/are true?

  I. a, b, c form an arithmetic progression.
  II. a, b, c form a geometric progression.
  III. Both roots are $\dfrac{b}{a}$.

  A. I only
  B. II only
  C. III only
  D. I and II only
  E. II and III only   [HKCEE 92]

33. Find the $(2n)$th term of the G.P. $-\dfrac{1}{2}, 1, -2, 4, \cdots$.

  A. 2^{2n}
  B. -2^{2n}
  C. -2^{2n-3}
  D. 2^{2n-2}
  E. -2^{2n-2} [HKCEE 92]

Legend has it that, when the king of Persia learnt about the game of chess, he was so fond of the game that he insisted the inventor of this game must be awarded. The inventor was brought forth and he said that a satisfactory reward would be one grain of wheat on the first square, two on the second square, four on the third square, eight on the fourth square and so on in geometric sequence, for all sixty-four squares on the game board. Can you imagine how many grains of wheat will the inventor's reward be altogether ? The answer is $2^{64} - 1$ or 18 446 744 073 709 551 615.

In this chapter, we shall learn the method to find the sum of the terms in a geometric sequence.

CHAPTER

2

Series: Arithmetic and Geometric Series

2.1 Series

In Chapter 1 (Section 1.1 on P. 1), in order to illustrate the concept of sequence, we listed the number of CDs sold each day in a certain week at a CD shop. The number of CDs sold is shown below again:

89, 27, 64, 53, 53, 87, 120

a sequence

Suppose we want to find out the total number of CDs sold in that week. We need to add up all the 7 terms in the sequence,

i.e. $89 + 27 + 64 + 53 + 53 + 87 + 120$.

The sum is 493.

The expression $89 + 27 + 64 + 53 + 53 + 87 + 120$ is NOT a sequence. It is an indicated sum of the terms of a sequence and is called a series*. Each of the numbers 89, 27, 64, $\cdots$, 120 in the series is called a term of the series, and the sum *493* is called *the sum of the series*.

In general, for a sequence with n terms: $T(1)$, $T(2)$, $T(3)$, $\cdots$, $T(n)$, the corresponding series is

$T(1) + T(2) + T(3) + \cdots + T(n)$.

The sum to n terms of a series is often denoted by the symbol $S(n)$, ◀ *n must be a positive integer.*

i.e. $S(n) = T(1) + T(2) + T(3) + \cdots + T(n)$. ◀ *In the example about the sales of CDs, $S(7) = 493$.*

CLASS PRACTICE

For each of the following sequences,
(a) write down the corresponding series,
(b) evaluate the sum of the series.

1. 2, 5, 8, 11, 14, 17, 20

    (a) The series: _____

    (b) Sum of the series = _____

---

series 級數

2. 1, 4, 9, 16, 25, 36

   (a) The series: _____

   (b) Sum of the series = _____

◀ *Question:*
Is this an arithmetic sequence or a geometric sequence?

3. 1, 2, 4, 8, 16, 32

   (a) The series: _____

   (b) Sum of the series = _____

Note:
Throughout this series of textbooks, the phrase 'sum of the series' is used consistently. Other books may use the phrase 'sum of the sequence' to express the same meaning.

2.2   Arithmetic Series

Consider the series:

$$a + (a + d) + (a + 2d) + (a + 3d) + \cdots$$

whose terms form an arithmetic sequence with $T(1) = a$ and the common difference $= d$.

◀ *The corresponding arithmetic sequence is a, $a + d$, $a + 2d$, $a + 3d$, $\cdots$.*

Such a series is called an **arithmetic series***.

◀ *Alternatively, we can simply say that the indicated sum of an arithmetic sequence is an arithmetic series.*

If $S(n)$ denotes the sum to n terms of the series and ℓ denotes the last term (i.e. the nth term),

then $\ell = a + (n - 1)d$ ....(i)

◀ $\ell = T(n)$

and $S(n) = a + (a + d) + (a + 2d) + \cdots + (\ell - d) + \ell$ ......(ii)

Writing the series in **(ii)** in reverse order, we have

$$S(n) = \ell + (\ell - d) + (\ell - 2d) + \cdots + (a + d) + a \quad \ldots\ldots(iii)$$

Adding **(iii)** to **(ii)**,

$$\begin{aligned}
S(n) &= a \quad\;\; + (a + d) + (a + 2d) + \cdots + (\ell - d) + \quad \ell \\
+ \;\; S(n) &= \ell \quad\;\; + (\ell - d) + (\ell - 2d) + \cdots + (a + d) + \quad a \\
\hline
2S(n) &= (a + \ell) + (a + \ell) + (a + \ell) + \cdots + (a + \ell) + (a + \ell) \\
&= n(a + \ell)
\end{aligned}$$

◀ *There are n number of $(a + \ell)$.*

$$\therefore \qquad \boxed{S(n) = \frac{n}{2}(a + \ell)} \quad \ldots\ldots\ldots(1)$$

◀ *i.e.* $S(n) = \frac{n}{2}[T(1) + T(n)]$

Since $\ell = a + (n - 1)d$,

◀ *From* **(i)** *above.*

$$a + \ell = 2a + (n - 1)d \quad \ldots\ldots\ldots(*)$$

◀ *Add a to both sides.*

---

arithmetic series 等差級數

Substituting (∗) into (1),

$$\boxed{S(n) = \frac{n}{2}[2a + (n-1)d\,]} \quad \ldots\ldots\ldots(2)$$

Note : To find the sum of an arithmetic series with n terms, it is more convenient to use

(i) formula **(1)** on P. 32 if the first term a and the last term ℓ are given;

(ii) formula **(2)** above if the first term a and the common difference d are given.

Example 1 **(a)** Sum the following arithmetic series to 20 terms:

$$\frac{1}{6} + \frac{1}{3} + \frac{1}{2} + \frac{2}{3} + \cdots .$$

(b) If the sum to m terms of the arithmetic series in **(a)** is $\dfrac{155}{2}$, find the value of m.

Solution Let d be the common difference of the corresponding arithmetic sequence.

$$T(1) = \frac{1}{6}, \quad T(2) = \frac{1}{3} \text{ and } d = T(2) - T(1)$$

$$\therefore \quad d = \frac{1}{3} - \frac{1}{6} = \frac{1}{6}$$

According to formula **(2)**,

$$S(n) = \frac{n}{2}[2a + (n-1)d\,].$$

(a) When $a = T(1) = \dfrac{1}{6}$ and $n = 20$,

$$S(20) = \frac{20}{2}\left[2\left(\frac{1}{6}\right) + (20 - 1)\left(\frac{1}{6}\right)\right]$$

$$= 10\left[\frac{21}{6}\right]$$

$$= \underline{\underline{35}}$$

(b) Here $a = T(1) = \dfrac{1}{6}$, $d = \dfrac{1}{6}$ and $S(m) = \dfrac{155}{2}$.

i.e. $$\frac{155}{2} = \frac{m}{2}\left[2\left(\frac{1}{6}\right) + (m - 1)\left(\frac{1}{6}\right)\right]$$

$\therefore$ $$155 = m\left[\frac{1}{3} + (m - 1)\left(\frac{1}{6}\right)\right]$$

i.e. $$930 = m[2 + m - 1] \qquad \blacktriangleleft \textit{Multiply by 6.}$$

$$m^2 - m + 2m = 930$$

$$m^2 + m - 930 = 0$$

$$(m - 30)(m + 31) = 0$$

$\therefore$ $$m = \underline{\underline{30}} \quad or \quad -31 \; (rejected)$$

$\blacktriangleleft$ *$m = -31$ is rejected because there is no such thing as negative number of terms.*

Example 2 For an arithmetic sequence, if the 1st term is 4 and the 20th term is 61, find

(a) the sum of the corresponding arithmetic series to 20 terms,

(b) the sum to 30 terms of the corresponding arithmetic series,

(c) the value of m if the mth term of the sequence is 91 and the sum to m terms of the series is 1 425.

Solution (a) The corresponding arithmetic series has 20 terms, i.e. $n = 20$,

the first term $a = T(1) = 4$,

the last term $\ell = T(20) = 61$.

According to formula **(1)**,

$$S(n) = \frac{n}{2}(a + \ell).$$

$$\therefore \ S(20) = \frac{20}{2}(4 + 61)$$

$$= \underline{\underline{650}}$$

(b) $a = 4$, $n = 20$ and $T(20) = 61$.

Let the common difference be d.

We have $T(20) = 4 + (20 - 1)d$ ◄ $T(n) = a + (n-1)d$

i.e. $61 = 4 + 19d$

$$19d = 57$$

$$d = 3$$

$a = 4$, $n = 30$ and $d = 3$.

According to formula **(2)**,

$$S(n) = \frac{n}{2}[2a + (n-1)d].$$

$$\therefore \ S(30) = \frac{30}{2}[2(4) + (30 - 1)(3)]$$

$$= \underline{\underline{1\ 425}}$$

(c) Here $T(1) = 4$, $T(m) = 91$ and $S(m) = 1\ 425$.

$$\therefore \ 1\ 425 = \frac{m}{2}(4 + 91)$$ ◄ *Formula* **(1)**:

$$m = \frac{2 \times 1\ 425}{95}$$ $$S(n) = \frac{n}{2}(a + \ell)$$

$$= \underline{\underline{30}}$$

EXERCISE **2A**

(Level 1)

1. Find the sum of the following arithmetic series.

   (a) $2 + 6 + 10 + \cdots$ to 30 terms

   (b) $88 + 82 + 76 + \cdots$ to 15 terms

   (c) $-90 - 80 - 70 - \cdots$ to 20 terms

2. There are 15 terms in each of the following arithmetic series. Find the sum of each series.

   (a) $2 + \cdots + 44$ **(b)** $10 + \cdots - \dfrac{1}{2}$

3. For the arithmetic series $7 + 15 + \cdots + 159$, find

   (a) the number of terms, **(b)** the sum of the series.

4. The first term of an arithmetic sequence is 124, the last term is 111 and the sum of the corresponding arithmetic series is 4 700. Find

   (a) the number of terms, **(b)** the common difference.

5. The manager of a supermarket wants to display canned soft drinks in a triangular pattern with 15 cans on the bottom row, 14 cans on the next row, 13 cans on the third row, and so on, with a single can on the top. How many cans of soft drink are required for this display?

(Level 2)

6. For the arithmetic series $\dfrac{1}{6} + \dfrac{1}{3} + \dfrac{1}{2} + \cdots + \dfrac{5}{3}$, find

   (a) the number of terms, **(b)** the sum of the series.

7. Find the number of terms in each of the following arithmetic series with the given sums.

   (a) $15 + 9 + 3 + \cdots = -81$ **(b)** $30 + 27 + 24 + \cdots = 147$

8. The sum of the third and the fourth terms in an arithmetic sequence is -1 and the sum of the first 15 terms is 195. Find

   (a) the first term of the sequence,

   (b) the common difference of the sequence.

9. **(a)** Find, in terms of n, the sum of each of the following arithmetic series.

   (i) $2 + 5 + 8 + \cdots + (3n - 1)$ **(ii)** $47 + 45 + 43 + \cdots + (49 - 2n)$

   (b) If the sums obtained in **(a)(i)** and **(a)(ii)** are equal, find the value of n.

10. Given an arithmetic sequence 15, $13\frac{1}{2}$, 12, $\cdots$.

    (a) Find, in terms of n, the nth term of the given sequence.

    (b) Find the number of positive terms in the sequence.

    (c) What is the sum of all the positive terms of the arithmetic series $15 + 13\frac{1}{2} + 12 + \cdots$?

11. A metal ball initially at rest falls 5 m in the first second, 15 m in the next second, 25 m in the third second, and so on.

    (a) How far will the metal ball fall in the fifth second?

    (b) Find the total distance fallen by the metal ball by the end of the tenth second.

12. John signed a contract with a company which agreed to pay him $10 000 in the first month as salary, $10 200 in the second month, $10 400 in the third month, and so on. If John received a total salary of $133 200 from the company throughout the contract period,

    (a) find the duration of his contract with the company;

    (b) find, before John's contract ends,
        (i) his last monthly salary;
        (ii) his total salary in the last 6 months.

*13. Calculate the sum of all positive integers less than 100 and

    (a) divisible by 2,

    (b) divisible by 3,

    (c) divisible by 6,

    (d) either divisible by 2 or divisible by 3.

*14.

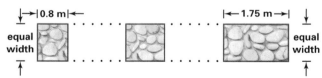

In the figure, rectangular paving slabs of equal widths but different lengths are laid end to end to form a straight path. The slabs are arranged in order of size from small to large and their lengths form an arithmetic sequence. It is known that the shortest slab is 0.8 m long, the longest slab is 1.75 m long and the lengths of adjacent slabs differ by 0.05 m.

    (a) Find the total number of slabs used.

    (b) Find the total length of the straight path.

    (c) Suppose the fifth smallest slab is a square.
        (i) What is the width of the path?
        (ii) Hence find the total area of the path.

2.3   Geometric Series

Consider the series:

$$a + ar + ar^2 + ar^3 + \cdots$$

whose terms form a geometric sequence with $T(1) = a$ and the common ratio $= r$.

◀ *The corresponding geometric sequence is a, ar, ar^2, ar^3, $\cdots$.*

Such a series is called a **geometric series***.

If $S(n)$ denotes the sum to n terms of the series,

then $S(n) = a + ar + ar^2 + \cdots + ar^{n-2} + ar^{n-1}$ . . . .**(i)**

Multiplying both sides of **(i)** by r, we have

$$r \cdot S(n) = ar + ar^2 + ar^3 + \cdots + ar^{n-1} + ar^n \text{ . . . . (ii)}$$

Subtracting **(ii)** from **(i)**,

$$S(n) = a + ar + ar^2 + \cdots + ar^{n-2} + ar^{n-1}$$
$$-) \quad r \cdot S(n) = \quad ar + ar^2 + ar^3 + \cdots + ar^{n-1} + ar^n$$
$$\overline{S(n) - r \cdot S(n) = a + 0 + 0 + \cdots + 0 - ar^n}$$

◀ *All the intermediate terms between a and $-ar^n$ become zero.*

i.e. $S(n)[1 - r] = a(1 - r^n)$

∴ $\boxed{S(n) = \dfrac{a(1 - r^n)}{1 - r}, \text{ where } r \neq 1.}$ . . . . . **(3)**

◀ *If $r = 1$, then the denominator would be zero. Division by zero is not defined.*

Note that $\dfrac{1 - r^n}{1 - r} = \dfrac{-(r^n - 1)}{-(r - 1)}$

$$= \dfrac{r^n - 1}{r - 1}.$$

Hence, alternatively we have

$$\boxed{S(n) = \dfrac{a(r^n - 1)}{r - 1}, \text{ where } r \neq 1.} \quad \text{. . . . . (4)}$$

Note : **(i)** It is more convenient to use formula **(3)** when $r < 1$ and to use formula **(4)** when $r > 1$.

◀ *Do you know why?*

(ii) In particular, when $r = 1$, the series in **(i)** becomes

$$S(n) = a + a + a + \cdots + a \text{ (up to } n \text{ terms)}$$
$$= na.$$

◀ *There are altogether n number of a.*

---

geometric series 等比級數

Example 3 **(a)** Sum the following geometric series to 12 terms:

$$\frac{1}{4} + \frac{1}{2} + 1 + 2 + \cdots .$$

(b) If the sum to n terms of the geometric series in **(a)** is 8 191.75, find the value of n.

Solution Let r be the common ratio of the given geometric series.

$$T(1) = \frac{1}{4} \quad \text{and} \quad T(2) = \frac{1}{2}$$

$$r = \frac{T(2)}{T(1)}$$

$$= \frac{\frac{1}{2}}{\frac{1}{4}}$$

$$= 2$$

(a) Since $r > 1$, we use formula **(4)**:

$$S(n) = \frac{a(r^n - 1)}{r - 1}.$$

◄ $a = T(1)$

When $n = 12$,

$$S(12) = \frac{\frac{1}{4}(2^{12} - 1)}{2 - 1}$$

$$= \frac{1}{4}(2^{12} - 1)$$

◄ 🖩

$$= 1\ 023.75$$

1 $\boxed{a\,{}^b\!/_c}$ 4 $\boxed{\times}$ $\boxed{((\text{---}}$ 2 $\boxed{x^y}$ 12 $\boxed{-}$ 1 $\boxed{\text{---}))}$ $\boxed{=}$
$[1023.75]$

(b) $S(n) = \dfrac{\frac{1}{4}(2^n - 1)}{2 - 1}$

But $S(n) = 8\ 191.75$,

$$\therefore \quad 8\ 191.75 = \frac{1}{4}(2^n - 1)$$

$$\text{i.e.} \quad 32\ 767 = 2^n - 1$$

$$2^n = 32\ 768$$

$$\log 2^n = \log 32\ 768$$

$$n \log 2 = \log 32\ 768$$

$$n = \frac{\log 32\ 768}{\log 2}$$

$$= 15$$

◄ 🖩

32 768 $\boxed{\log}$ $\boxed{\div}$ 2 $\boxed{\log}$ $\boxed{=}$
$[15.]$

Example 4 Given that the first term and the common ratio of a geometric sequence are $\frac{3}{8}$ and -2 respectively and that the sum to n terms of the corresponding geometric series is $-8\,191.875$, find

(a) the value of n,

(b) the nth term of the given geometric sequence.

Solution **(a)** Since $r < 1$, we use formula **(3)**:

$$S(n) = \frac{a(1 - r^n)}{1 - r}$$

But $S(n) = -8\,191.875$,

$$\therefore \quad -8\,191.875 = \frac{\frac{3}{8}[1 - (-2)^n]}{1 - (-2)}$$

$$-65\,535 = 1 - (-2)^n$$

i.e. $\qquad (-2)^n = 65\,536$

Since $65\,536 > 0$, n must be an even number,

and $(-2)^n = (-1)^n (2)^n$

$\qquad\qquad = 2^n$

◀ *When **n** is an even number, $(-1)^n = 1$.*

$$\therefore \qquad 2^n = 65\,536$$

$$\log 2^n = \log 65\,536$$

$$n \log 2 = \log 65\,536$$

$$n = \frac{\log 65\,536}{\log 2}$$

$$= \underline{\underline{16}}$$

◀ 🔢

65 536 [log] [÷] 2 [log] [=]

[I6.]

(b) $\quad T(n) = ar^{n-1}$

$$T(16) = \frac{3}{8}(-2)^{16-1}$$

$$= \underline{\underline{-12\,288}}$$

◀ 🔢

3 [a b/c] 8 [×] 2 [+/−] [x^y] [(---)] 16 [−] 1 [---)] [=]

[-12288.]

Example 5 John invests a sum of $50 000 on the same day at the beginning of each year for 4 consecutive years. If the interest rate is 10% p.a. compounded yearly, find the total amount accumulated at the end of the fourth year.

Solution The last $50 000, which is invested at the beginning of the *fourth* year, earns interest for 1 year only. Hence, it amounts to

$$A(1) = \$50\,000\left(1 + \frac{10}{100}\right)^1 \quad \text{at the end of the 4th year.}$$

The second last $50 000, which is invested at the beginning of the *third* year, earns interest for 2 years only. Hence, it amounts to

$$A(2) = \$50\,000\left(1 + \frac{10}{100}\right)^2 \quad \text{at the end of the 4th year.}$$

Similarly the $50 000 invested at the beginning of the *second* year amounts to

$$A(3) = \$50\,000\left(1 + \frac{10}{100}\right)^3 \quad \text{at the end of the 4th year.}$$

Also, the $50 000 invested at the beginning of the *first* year amounts to

$$A(4) = \$50\,000\left(1 + \frac{10}{100}\right)^4 \quad \text{at the end of the 4th year.}$$

The whole situation is illustrated in the diagram below:

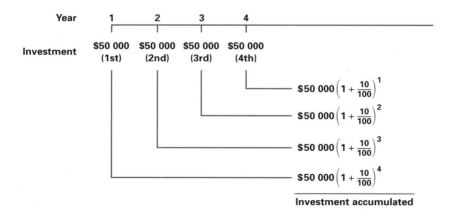

Hence the total amount (in $) accumulated

$$= 50\,000(1.1)^1 + 50\,000(1.1)^2 + 50\,000(1.1)^3 + 50\,000(1.1)^4$$

This is a geometric series, in which the first term $a = 50\,000(1.1)$, the common ratio $r = 1.1$ and $n = 4$.

The total amount (in $) accumulated is $S(4)$ and

$$S(4) = \frac{50\,000(1.1)(1.1^4 - 1)}{1.1 - 1}$$

$$= 255\,255$$

∴   The total amount accumulated is $\$255\,255$.

E X E R C I S E   2B

(Level 1)

1. Find the sum of the following geometric series, leaving the answers in index form if necessary.

   (a) $3 + 12 + 48 + \cdots$ to 7 terms

   (b) $2 - 10 + 50 - \cdots$ to 6 terms

   (c) $36 + 18 + 9 + \cdots$ to 20 terms

2. Find the number of terms in each of the following geometric series having the given sum.

   (a) $1 + 3 + 9 + \cdots = 3\,280$

   (b) $5 + 10 + 20 + \cdots = 2\,555$

3. For the following geometric series, find the number of terms (n) and the sum.

   (a) $4 + 8 + 16 + \cdots + 512$

   (b) $3 + 9 + 27 + \cdots + 6\,561$

4. If the sum of the first seven terms of a geometric series is $1\,093$ and the common ratio is $\frac{1}{3}$, find the first term.

5. David decides to save money in a savings account for retirement. At the beginning of each year, $\$5\,000$ is invested at an interest rate of 5% p.a. compounded annually. How much is the retirement fund, correct to the nearest dollar, at the end of the 40th year?

6. For the geometric series $1 - 3^2 + 3^4 - 3^6 + \cdots + 3^{12}$, find
   (a) the number of terms,
   (b) the common ratio,
   (c) the sum of the series.

7. Given a geometric series $3 + 1 + \frac{1}{3} + \cdots$ such that the sum to k terms of the series is $4\frac{13}{27}$.
   (a) Find the value of k.
   (b) Find the sum to k terms of the geometric series $81 + 27 + 9 + \cdots$.

8. (a) Find the first term and the common ratio of the geometric series whose fifth term is 27 and whose eighth term is 729.
   (b) Hence find the sum of the first 9 terms of the series.

9. (a) Find the sum to n terms of the geometric series $2 + 4 + 8 + \cdots$.
   (b) How many terms of the geometric series in (a) are necessary to give a sum
   (i) equal to 510?
   (ii) greater than 1 000?

10. Rebecca joined a company at the beginning of 1990 at an annual salary of $600 000 and her salary was increased by 10% each year. When Rebecca left the company, her annual salary was $966 306.
    (a) For how long had Rebecca worked for the company?
    (b) Find her total earnings from the company.
        (*Give the answer correct to the nearest $100.*)

11. A long piece of string is cut into 6 portions and their lengths form a geometric sequence. The first and the last portions measure 64 cm and 2 cm respectively.
    (a) What is the original length of the string?
    (b) Suppose the original string is cut into 3 portions. Their lengths form three consecutive terms of an increasing geometric sequence. If the shortest portion measures 18 cm, what is the common ratio of the geometric sequence?

*12. A company invests $x at the beginning of each year. The interest rate is 16% p.a. compounded yearly.

(a) Find, in terms of x, the total value of the investment
   (i) at the end of the first year,
   (ii) at the end of the second year.

(b) Show that the total value of the investment at the end of the nth year is $7.25(1.16^n - 1)x$.

(c) If the total value of the investment at the end of the fifth year is $300\ 000$, find the value of x.
   (*Give the answer correct to the nearest hundred.*)

*13. In the figure, each side of the equilateral triangle ABC is 20 cm. A second equilateral triangle BDE is drawn along BC so that E is the mid-point of BC. A third equilateral triangle DFG is drawn in a similar way, and so on.

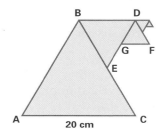

(a) What is the area of the first triangle?

(b) What is the area of the second triangle?

(c) What is the sum of the areas of the first eight triangles formed in this way?
(*Give the answers correct to 1 decimal place.*)

2.4   Sum to Infinity of a Series

Consider the following sequences:

(i) 1, 3, 5, 7, 9;

(ii) 2, 4, 8, 16, 32, 64, 128.

Sequence **(i)** is an arithmetic sequence with five terms;
sequence **(ii)** is a geometric sequence with seven terms.

Each of the two sequences **(i)** and **(ii)** has a <u>finite</u> number of terms, but other sequences can have an <u>infinite</u> number of terms. The sum of a series with an infinite number of terms is called the sum to infinity of the series. We usually denote such a sum by $S(\infty)$, where ∞ is the symbol for infinity.

In the discussions that follow, we shall study the sum to infinity of

(1) arithmetic series,

(2) geometric series.

SUM TO INFINITY OF ARITHMETIC SERIES

Suppose the sequence 1, 3, 5, 7, 9, ⋯ goes on indefinitely.

The common difference of the sequence is 2, which is positive.

For this sequence, as the number of terms increases <u>indefinitely</u>, the magnitude of the terms also increases <u>indefinitely</u>. Consequently the sum of the corresponding series gets larger and larger, we say that it approaches infinity. In symbols, we write

'as $n \to \infty$, $S(n) \to \infty$',

◀ *The symbol '→' stands for 'approaches'.*

which means 'as n approaches infinity, the sum to n terms of the series also approaches infinity'.

On the other hand, consider the arithmetic sequence with a negative common difference:

5, 3, 1, −1, −3, −5, ⋯.

As the number of terms increases indefinitely, the terms will be negative and become smaller and smaller. Hence the sum will be negative and will eventually become smaller and smaller as well. We say that the sum of the series approaches negative infinity.

In symbols, we write

'as $n \to \infty$, $S(n) \to -\infty$'.

Note : **(i)** The symbol '$-\infty$' means 'negative infinity'.

(ii) The fact we have just stated about the sum to infinity of an arithmetic series with a negative common difference is true no matter the first term in the series is positive or negative.

SUM TO INFINITY OF GEOMETRIC SERIES

We have just learnt that for an arithmetic sequence, the sum to infinity is either extremely large, i.e. positive infinity (when the common difference > 0) or extremely small, i.e. negative infinity (when the common difference < 0). Is this also true for geometric sequences?

Consider the geometric series: $\frac{1}{2} + \frac{1}{4} + \frac{1}{8} + \frac{1}{16} + \cdots$.

Here we have the first term, $a = \frac{1}{2}$,

and the common ratio, $r = \frac{1}{2}$.

◀ $r = \frac{T(2)}{T(1)} = \frac{\frac{1}{4}}{\frac{1}{2}} = \frac{1}{2}$

If $S(n)$ denotes the sum to n terms of the series, then

$$S(n) = \frac{1}{2} + \frac{1}{4} + \frac{1}{8} + \cdots + \left(\frac{1}{2}\right)^n$$

$$= \frac{\frac{1}{2}\left[1 - \left(\frac{1}{2}\right)^n\right]}{1 - \left(\frac{1}{2}\right)}$$

$$= 1 - \left(\frac{1}{2}\right)^n.$$

◀ $S(n) = \frac{a(1 - r^n)}{1 - r}$

We can see that as n becomes larger and larger, the value of $\left(\frac{1}{2}\right)^n$ becomes smaller and smaller, and eventually it becomes very close to zero.

e.g. $\left(\frac{1}{2}\right)^{20} \approx 0.000\ 000\ 954$

$\left(\frac{1}{2}\right)^{40} \approx 0.000\ 000\ 000\ 000\ 909$

This fact may be expressed by saying 'as n approaches infinity, $\left(\frac{1}{2}\right)^n$ approaches zero and the sum $S(n)$ approaches 1'.

In symbols, we write

'as $n \to \infty$, $\left(\frac{1}{2}\right)^n \to 0$ and $S(n) \to 1$'.

The value 1 is called the ***sum to infinity*** of the series. And we write

$S(\infty) = 1$.

Note : For simplicity we use '$S(\infty)$' to represent '$S(n)$ when $n \to \infty$'.

Let us now consider the general geometric series with the first term a (assume $a > 0$) and the common ratio r.

$$S(n) = a + ar + ar^2 + \cdots + ar^{n-1}$$

$$= \frac{a(1 - r^n)}{1 - r}$$

$$= \frac{a - ar^n}{1 - r}$$

$$= \frac{a}{1 - r} - \frac{ar^n}{1 - r}$$

Case (1)   **When $-1 < r < 1$**

As $n \to \infty$, $r^n \to 0$ and hence $\dfrac{ar^n}{1 - r} \to 0$,

then $S(n) \to \dfrac{a}{1 - r}$.

We write $S(\infty) = \dfrac{a}{1 - r}$.

> ⌐Refer to the geometric series
> on P. 45 :
> $$\frac{1}{2} + \frac{1}{4} + \frac{1}{8} + \frac{1}{16} + \cdots,$$
> where $r = \frac{1}{2}$ (i.e. $-1 < r < 1$),
> as $n \to \infty$, $\left(\frac{1}{2}\right)^n \to 0$.

> ◀ *Note:*
> *When $r = 0$ $(-1 < 0 < 1)$,*
> $S(\infty) = a$.

Case (2)   **When $r > 1$**

As $n \to \infty$, $r^n \to \infty$ and hence $\dfrac{ar^n}{1 - r} \to -\infty$.

The sum to infinity, i.e. $S(\infty)$, approaches infinity and therefore cannot be determined.

Case (3)   **When $r < -1$**

(i) As n is <u>even</u> and $n \to \infty$, $r^n \to \infty$ and hence $\dfrac{ar^n}{1 - r} \to \infty$.

(ii) As n is <u>odd</u> and $n \to \infty$, $r^n \to -\infty$ and hence $\dfrac{ar^n}{1 - r} \to -\infty$.

In either situation, $S(\infty)$ approaches infinity and therefore cannot be determined.

Case (4)   **When $r = 1$**

The original series now becomes

$$S(n) = a + a + a + \cdots + a \text{ (to } n \text{ terms)}$$

$$= na.$$

As $n \to \infty$, $na \to \infty$, i.e. $S(n) \to \infty$.

Therefore the sum to infinity, i.e. $S(\infty)$, approaches infinity and therefore cannot be determined.

Note : In *Case (4)*, the formula $S(n) = \frac{a(1-r^n)}{1-r}$ cannot be used since when $r = 1$, $1 - r = 0$ and the denominator becomes zero.

As a conclusion, we see that the sum to infinity of a geometric series can be found only in *Case (1)*, i.e. when

$$-1 < r < 1.$$

Thus, when this condition is satisfied, the sum to infinity of the geometric series is $\frac{a}{1-r}$.

We write

$$S(\infty) = \frac{a}{1-r} \quad \text{for} \quad -1 < r < 1. \quad \cdots\cdots\cdots (5)$$

Example 6 Sum the following geometric series to infinity.

(a) $\frac{1}{3} + \frac{1}{9} + \frac{1}{27} + \cdots$

(b) $-4 + 2 - 1 + \cdots$

Solution **(a)** Here the first term $a = \frac{1}{3}$ and the common ratio $r = \frac{1}{3}$.

◀ *Note that* $r = \frac{T(2)}{T(1)} = \frac{\frac{1}{9}}{\frac{1}{3}} = \frac{1}{3}$ *and* $-1 < r < 1$.

Then $S(\infty) = \frac{a}{1-r}$

$$= \frac{\frac{1}{3}}{1 - \frac{1}{3}}$$

$$= \frac{1}{2}$$

(b) Here the first term $a = -4$ and the common ratio $r = -\frac{1}{2}$.

◀ *Note that* $r = \frac{T(2)}{T(1)} = \frac{2}{-4} = -\frac{1}{2}$ *and* $-1 < r < 1$.

Then $S(\infty) = \frac{-4}{1 - \left(-\frac{1}{2}\right)}$

$$= -\frac{8}{3}$$

Example 7 In the figure, $A_1B_1C_1D_1$ is a square. The mid-points of the sides of $A_1B_1C_1D_1$ are joined to form another square $A_2B_2C_2D_2$ as shown. The mid-points of the sides of the square $A_2B_2C_2D_2$ are then joined to form yet another square $A_3B_3C_3D_3$ as shown. This process of forming squares continues indefinitely. Given that the perimeter of $A_1B_1C_1D_1$ is $4\sqrt{2}$ cm.

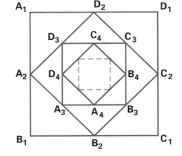

(a) Find the perimeter of the square $A_3B_3C_3D_3$.

(b) Find the area of the square $A_3B_3C_3D_3$.

(c) If the perimeter of $A_1B_1C_1D_1$ is denoted by P_1, the perimeter of $A_2B_2C_2D_2$ by P_2, and so on, find the sum to infinity of $P_1 + P_2 + P_3 + \cdots$.

(d) If the area of $A_1B_1C_1D_1$ is denoted by Q_1, the area of $A_2B_2C_2D_2$ by Q_2, and so on, find the sum to infinity of $Q_1 + Q_2 + Q_3 + \cdots$.

(*Leave the answers in surd form if necessary.*)

Solution   **(a)** The lengths of each side of the squares form a geometric sequence with a common ratio $\dfrac{1}{\sqrt{2}}$.

Hence the perimeters of the squares form a geometric sequence with the first term $4\sqrt{2}$ cm and the common ratio $\dfrac{1}{\sqrt{2}}$.

$\therefore$ Perimeter of $A_3B_3C_3D_3 = 4\sqrt{2}\left(\dfrac{1}{\sqrt{2}}\right)^{3-1}$ cm

$= 2\sqrt{2}$ cm

$\blacktriangleleft$ *Recall:*
$T(3) = ar^{3-1}$

$$A_1B_1 = \frac{4\sqrt{2}}{4}\ cm = \sqrt{2}\ cm$$
$$A_1A_2 = A_1D_2 = \frac{\sqrt{2}}{2}\ cm$$
$$A_2D_2 = \sqrt{\left(\frac{\sqrt{2}}{2}\right)^2 + \left(\frac{\sqrt{2}}{2}\right)^2}\ cm$$
$$= 1\ cm$$
$$\frac{A_2D_2}{A_1B_1} = \frac{1}{\sqrt{2}}$$
Similarly,
$$\frac{A_3D_3}{A_2B_2} = \frac{1}{\sqrt{2}}$$
$$\therefore\ Common\ ratio = \frac{1}{\sqrt{2}}$$

(b) The areas of the squares form a geometric sequence with the first term $2\ cm^2$ and the common ratio $\dfrac{1}{2}$.

$\therefore$ Area of $A_3B_3C_3D_3 = 2\left(\dfrac{1}{2}\right)^{3-1}$ cm^2

$= \dfrac{1}{2}$ cm^2

$$Area\ of\ A_1B_1C_1D_1 = (A_1B_1)^2$$
$$= (\sqrt{2})^2\ cm^2$$
$$= 2\ cm^2$$
$$Area\ of\ A_2B_2C_2D_2 = (A_2D_2)^2$$
$$= 1\ cm^2$$
$$\frac{Area\ of\ A_2B_2C_2D_2}{Area\ of\ A_1B_1C_1D_1} = \frac{1}{2}$$
Similarly,
$$\frac{area\ of\ A_3B_3C_3D_3}{area\ of\ A_2B_2C_2D_2} = \frac{1}{2}$$
$$\therefore\ Common\ ratio = \frac{1}{2}$$

(c) Sum to infinity of $P_1 + P_2 + P_3 + \cdots$

$$= \frac{4\sqrt{2}}{1 - \frac{1}{\sqrt{2}}} \text{ cm}$$

◀ *Recall:*
$S(\infty) = \frac{a}{1-r}$

$$= \frac{8}{\sqrt{2} - 1} \text{ cm}$$

Here $r = \frac{1}{\sqrt{2}}$ *and* $-1 < \frac{1}{\sqrt{2}} < 1$.

$$= 8(\sqrt{2} + 1) \text{ cm}$$

◀ *Rationalization of the denominator.*

(d) Sum to infinity of $Q_1 + Q_2 + Q_3 + \cdots$

$$= \frac{2}{1 - \frac{1}{2}} \text{ cm}^2$$

$$= 4 \text{ cm}^2$$

◀ *Questions:*
(i) *What is the value of Q_1?*
(ii) *From the results obtained in Example 7(d) and (i) above, what is the sum to infinity of $Q_2 + Q_3 + \cdots$? Can you interpret this result geometrically?*

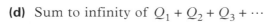

E X E R C I S E   2C

(Level 1)

Find the sum of each of the following infinite geometric series.
[Nos. 1–3]

1. $4 + 2 + 1 + \cdots$ **2.** $1 + \frac{2}{3} + \left(\frac{2}{3}\right)^2 + \cdots$ **3.** $\frac{1}{5} - \frac{1}{20} + \frac{1}{80} - \cdots$

4. For each of the following, find the first term of an infinite geometric series satisfying the given conditions.

(a) $r = 0.02$, $S(\infty) = \frac{50}{49}$ **(b)** $r = -0.6$, $S(\infty) = 2.5$

5. For each of the following, write down the first three terms of an infinite geometric series satisfying the given conditions.

(a) $a = 2$, $S(\infty) = 8$ **(b)** $a = 40$, $S(\infty) = 60$

(Level 2)

6. Given a geometric series $1 + \frac{\sqrt{3}}{3} + \frac{1}{3} + \cdots$.

(a) Find the sum to 5 terms of the given geometric series.

(b) Starting from the 6th term of the given geometric series, find the sum to infinity.
(*Give the answers correct to 2 decimal places.*)

7. (a) Find the sum to infinity of the series

$$\frac{1}{5} + \frac{3}{5^2} + \frac{1}{5^3} + \frac{3}{5^4} + \frac{1}{5^5} + \cdots .$$

(b) Hence find the sum to infinity of the series

$$5 + 3 + \frac{1}{5} + \frac{3}{5^2} + \frac{1}{5^3} + \cdots.$$

8. **(a)** Suppose the recurring decimal $0.1\dot{8}$ is expressed as a geometric series with infinite number of terms such that the first term is 0.18.

   (i) Write down the first three terms of the series.

   (ii) Find the common ratio of the series.

   (b) Hence express each of the following recurring decimals as a fraction.

   (i) $0.1\dot{8}$ **(ii)** $0.08\dot{1}$

9. A wheel rotates through 320 revolutions in the first minute. In each succeeding minute, it rotates $\frac{3}{4}$ as many times as it did in the preceding minute.

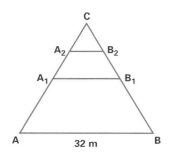

   (a) Find the number of revolutions that the wheel rotates in
      (i) the second minute,
      (ii) the third minute.

   (b) How many revolutions will the wheel make before coming to rest?

10. A hot-air balloon rises 90 m in the first minute after the balloon is released from the ground. In each succeeding minute, the balloon rises through a height which is 25% that in the preceding minute.

   (a) Find the height reached by the balloon 3 minutes after it is released.

   (b) Find the maximum height that the balloon can reach.

   (c) What percentage of the maximum height is the height obtained in **(a)**?
   (*Give the answer correct to 3 significant figures.*)

*11. In the figure, $\triangle ABC$ is equilateral with AB = 32 m. A_1 and B_1 are mid-points of AC and BC respectively, A_2 and B_2 are mid-points of A_1C and B_1C respectively, and so on.

   (a) **(i)** Find the lengths of A_1B_1 and A_2B_2.

      (ii) Hence find the sum to infinity of
         $AB + A_1B_1 + A_2B_2 + \cdots.$

   (b) **(i)** Find the lengths of AB_1, A_1B_2 and A_2B_3.

      (ii) Hence find the sum to infinity of
         $AB_1 + A_1B_2 + A_2B_3 + \cdots.$
      (*Leave the answers in surd form.*)

   (c) Which of the sums obtained in **(a)(ii)** and **(b)(ii)** is larger?

*12. In the figure, a series of semi-circles are drawn indefinitely with all the diameters AB, BC, CD, $\cdots$ lying on a straight line. The lengths of the diameters form a geometric sequence such that AB = 9 cm and BC = 6 cm.

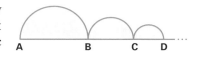

(a) What is the total length of the line segments formed by all the diameters?

(b) Find, in terms of π, the sum to infinity of

$$\overset{\frown}{AB} + \overset{\frown}{BC} + \overset{\frown}{CD} + \cdots .$$

(c) Does the total area of all the semi-circles exceed 18π cm^2 ?

2.5   Summation Notation 'Σ'

A convenient way to write the sum of a series, especially when the series has many terms, is to use the notation 'Σ'.

◀ *The notation 'Σ' is a Greek letter (pronounced as sigma).*

For example, for a given series $T(1) + T(2) + T(3) + \cdots + T(n)$, we write

$$\sum_{r=1}^{n} T(r) = T(1) + T(2) + T(3) + \cdots + T(n) \ldots \ldots \ldots (*)$$

◀ *r is called a 'dummy index' or 'dummy variable'.*

L.H.S. of (*) means the sum of all the terms $T(r)$ when r changes from 1 to n; R.H.S. of (*) is the series itself. We sometimes call the series:

'$\displaystyle\sum_{r=1}^{n} T(r)$ written in the expanded form'.

The following are some examples of writing the sum of a series using the 'Σ' notation and the expanded form:

e.g. (i) $\displaystyle\sum_{r=1}^{5} r = 1 + 2 + 3 + 4 + 5$

(ii) $\displaystyle\sum_{r=11}^{16} r^2 = 11^2 + 12^2 + 13^2 + 14^2 + 15^2 + 16^2$

(iii) $\displaystyle\sum_{r=5}^{n} \frac{b}{r} = \frac{b}{5} + \frac{b}{6} + \frac{b}{7} + \cdots + \frac{b}{n}$

◀ *b is a constant in this series.*

(iv) $\displaystyle\sum_{k=-2}^{2} k(k+1) = -2(-2+1) + (-1)(-1+1) + 0(0+1) +$
$$1(1+1) + 2(2+1)$$

◀ *Note:*
Besides r, we can use other letters like k to denote the dummy variable or index.

(v) $\displaystyle\sum_{k=1}^{\infty} \frac{1}{k} = 1 + \frac{1}{2} + \frac{1}{3} + \cdots$

◀ *This is a sum to infinity of a series.*

Example 8 **(a)** Expand and evaluate $\displaystyle\sum_{r=1}^{5} (2r-8)$.

(b) If $S(n) = \displaystyle\sum_{r=1}^{n} (2r-8)$, find the value of $S(6)$.

Solution **(a)** $\displaystyle\sum_{r=1}^{5} (2r-8) = (2\times1-8) + (2\times2-8) + (2\times3-8) + (2\times4-8) + (2\times5-8)$ ◀
$$= -10$$

This is the expanded form of $\displaystyle\sum_{r=1}^{5} (2r-8)$.

(b) $S(6) = \displaystyle\sum_{r=1}^{6} (2r-8)$

$$= \left[\sum_{r=1}^{5} (2r-8) \right] + (2\times6-8)$$

$$= -10 + 4$$

$$= -6$$

◀ *From* **(a)**,
$\displaystyle\sum_{r=1}^{5} (2r-8) = -10$.

If we know the expression for the general term of a sequence, then we can use the Σ notation to express the series. When the series is expressed in the expanded form, we can find the sum of the series up to a certain term.

Example 9 Use the Σ notation to express the following series:

(a) $1 + \dfrac{1}{2} + \dfrac{1}{3} + \cdots + \dfrac{1}{n}$,

(b) $2 + 4 + 6 + 8 + 10 + 12 + 14$.

Solution **(a)** The general term of the corresponding sequence is $\dfrac{1}{n}$.

◀ *The corresponding sequence is* $1 \left(= \frac{1}{1}\right), \frac{1}{2}, \frac{1}{3}, \cdots, \frac{1}{n}$.

$\therefore$ The required series expressed in Σ notation

$$= \sum_{r=1}^{n} \frac{1}{r}$$

◀ *Here we use r as the dummy variable.*

(b) The corresponding sequence is

2, 4, 6, 8, 10, 12, 14.

[This is an arithmetic sequence with the first term $a = 2$, the common difference $d = 2$. The general term $T(n)$ of the sequence is given by

$$T(n) = 2 + (n-1)(2)$$
$$= 2 + 2n - 2$$
$$= 2n.]$$

◀ For an arithmetic sequence, $T(n) = a + (n-1)d$.

i.e.   The required series expressed in Σ notation

$$= \sum_{r=1}^{7} 2r$$

◀ Here r is the dummy variable.

CLASS PRACTICE

Expand and evaluate each of the following:
(*The first one is done for you as an example.*)

1. $\displaystyle\sum_{i=1}^{4} i = $ _____1 + 2 + 3 + 4_____ $= $ ___10___

2. $\displaystyle\sum_{r=1}^{5} (3r + 1) = $ _____ $= $ _____

3. $\displaystyle\sum_{k=1}^{3} \frac{2k - 3}{k + 1} = $ _____ $= $ _____

4. $\displaystyle\sum_{r=1}^{3} \sin 30r° = $ _____ $= $ _____

5. $\displaystyle\sum_{r=1}^{4} \frac{(-1)^r}{r} = $ _____ $= $ _____

6. $\displaystyle\sum_{i=1}^{\infty} \left(\frac{1}{\sqrt{2}}\right)^i = $ _____ $= $ _____

EXERCISE 2D

(*Level 1*)

Expand and evaluate the following: **[Nos. 1–3]**

1. $\displaystyle\sum_{i=1}^{5} 2^i$

2. $\displaystyle\sum_{k=1}^{4} k^3$

3. $\displaystyle\sum_{m=2}^{4} (3m - 4)^2$

Express each of the following series using the Σ notation and the dummy variable r. **[Nos. 4–5]**

4. $1 + 5 + 9 + 13 + \cdots + (4n - 3)$

5. $4 + 10 + 18 + 28 + \cdots + n(n + 3)$

(Level 2)

Expand and evaluate the following: **[Nos. 6–7]**

6. $3\displaystyle\sum_{r=1}^{4} r^r$

7. $\displaystyle\sum_{k=2}^{4} (k-2)(k-3)(k-4)$

8. **(a)** Evaluate:

   (i) $\displaystyle\sum_{a=1}^{4} (a + a^2)$

   (ii) $\displaystyle\sum_{a=1}^{4} a + \sum_{a=1}^{4} a^2$

   (b) Are the results in **(a)(i)** and **(a)(ii)** equal?

9. **(a)** Find the kth term of the following arithmetic sequences.

   (i) $1,\ 2,\ 3,\ 4,\ 5,\ \cdots$

   (ii) $2,\ 3,\ 4,\ 5,\ 6,\ \cdots$

   (b) Hence, express the series $\dfrac{1}{2} + \dfrac{2}{3} + \dfrac{3}{4} + \dfrac{4}{5} + \dfrac{5}{6}$ using Σ notation and the dummy variable k.

10. **(a)** Find the nth term of the following geometric sequences.

    (i) $9,\ 27,\ 81,\ 243,\ \cdots$

    (ii) $8,\ -8,\ 8,\ -8,\ \cdots$

    (b) Hence, express the series $\dfrac{9}{8} - \dfrac{27}{8} + \dfrac{81}{8} - \dfrac{243}{8}$ using Σ notation and the dummy variable n.

SUPPLEMENTARY
EXERCISE 2

PART I *Further Practice*

(Ex. 2A)

1. Calculate the number of terms and the sum of each of the following arithmetic series.

   (a) $(-10) + (-7) + (-4) + \cdots + 20$

   (b) $7\dfrac{2}{3} + 8 + 8\dfrac{1}{3} + \cdots + 12\dfrac{2}{3}$

2. Find the sum of all two-digit numbers that leave a remainder 1 when divided by 4.

3. In an arithmetic sequence, the ratio $T(9) : T(2) = 3 : 1$. Find the ratio of the sum of the first 30 terms to the sum of the first 20 terms of the corresponding arithmetic series.

4. The interior angles of an n-sided convex polygon form an arithmetic sequence with common difference $10°$. If the smallest interior angle of the polygon is $100°$, find

   (a) the value of n,

   (b) the largest interior angle of the polygon.

5. The sum of the first n terms of an arithmetic series is $3n^2 + 7n$ for all values of n.

   (a) **(i)** Find the sum of the first 8 terms of the arithmetic series.
   (ii) Find the sum of the first 9 terms of the arithmetic series.
   (iii) Hence, or otherwise, find the value of the 9th term of the arithmetic series.

   (b) Find
   (i) the value of the first term of the arithmetic series,
   (ii) the common difference of the corresponding arithmetic sequence.

*6. The sum to n terms of a series is $S(n) = 5n^2 - 3n$.

   (a) Show that the first term of the series is 2 and that the general term of the series is $T(n) = S(n) - S(n-1)$.

   (b) Hence show that the series is an arithmetic series.

   (c) What are the first three terms of the series?

(Ex. 2B)

7. Find $T(1) + T(2) + T(3) + \cdots + T(8)$ if the general term $T(n)$ is 2^n.

8. **(a)** $\dfrac{a}{b}$, -1 and $\dfrac{b}{a}$ are the first 3 terms of a geometric sequence. Find, in terms of a and b, the sum of the first 10 terms of the corresponding geometric series.

   (b) Hence find, correct to 2 decimal places, the sum to 10 terms of the geometric series $\dfrac{3}{2} + (-1) + \dfrac{2}{3} + \cdots$.

9. Given a geometric series where the ratio of the sum of the first 8 terms to the sum of the first 4 terms is $257 : 1$. Find, for the corresponding geometric sequence,

   (a) all the possible values of the common ratio,

   (b) the possible values of the first term if $T(4) - T(2) = 2$.

10. The first term and the common ratio of a geometric sequence are both 2.

    (a) Express each of the following in terms of n.
       (i) The sum of the first n terms.
       (ii) The sum of the first $2n$ terms.

    (b) If the sum of the first $2n$ terms of the geometric series is 65 times the sum of the first n terms,
       (i) show that $2^{2n} - 65 \cdot 2^n + 64 = 0$,
       (ii) hence find the value of n.

*11. The radii of a number of circles are in geometric sequence.

    (a) Show that the areas of the circles are also in geometric sequence.

    (b) If the sum of areas of the first two circles is 25 cm^2 while that of the first four circles is 425 cm^2, find the radii of the first three circles correct to 2 decimal places.

(Ex. 2C)

12. Given the geometric series:
$$2 - \frac{2}{3 - \sqrt{2}} + \frac{2}{11 - 6\sqrt{2}} - \cdots$$

    (a) Find, in surd form, the common ratio of the corresponding geometric sequence.

    (b) Does the common ratio obtained in (a) lie between -1 and 1?

    (c) Find, in surd form, the sum to infinity of the given geometric series.

13. A student was asked to find the sum to infinity of the geometric series $8 + 4 + 2 + \cdots$. Instead he finds the sum of the first 9 terms only.

    (a) What answer does the student obtain?

    (b) What is the correct answer for the sum to infinity?

    (c) Hence find his percentage error correct to 2 significant figures.

14. In the first month of operation, an oil well produced 250 000 barrels of oil. After that, the production in each month was reduced to 95% of that in the preceding month.

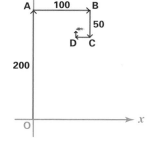

    (a) Find the least number of months of operation required for the well to produce more than 2 000 000 barrels of oil.

    (b) Show that the oil well can never produce more than 5 000 000 barrels of oil no matter how long it operates.

*15. The path of an ant consists of line segments OA, AB, BC, CD, ⋯ which meet at right angles as shown in the given coordinate plane. The line segments OA, AB, BC, CD, ⋯ form a geometric sequence. If A lies on the y-axis and the coordinates of B are $(100, 200)$, find

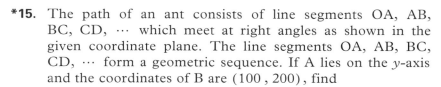

    (a) the total length of the ant's path,

    (b) the coordinates of the final position of the ant.

(Ex. 2D)

16. Evaluate the following:

    (a) $\displaystyle\sum_{i=1}^{6} \frac{(i-1)}{i}$ **(b)** $\displaystyle\sum_{n=1}^{4} (-1)^{n}(1 - n + n^{2})$

17. Express each of the following series using Σ notation and the dummy variable n.

    (a) $1 - 2 + 3 - 4 + 5 - 6 + 7 - 8 + 9 - 10$

    (b) $1 - \dfrac{1}{2} + \dfrac{1}{3} - \dfrac{1}{4} + \dfrac{1}{5} - \dfrac{1}{6} + \dfrac{1}{7}$

18. The general term $T(n)$ of a sequence is $\log \dfrac{n}{n+1}$.

    (a) Find the first 5 terms of the sequence.

    (b) Evaluate $\displaystyle\sum_{n=1}^{99} T(n)$.

Part II | *Miscellaneous*

19. Given a series $2^{-1} + 2^{-2} + 2^{-3} + \cdots + 2^{-n}$.

    (a) Find the sum of the series in terms of n.

    (b) Find the greatest value of n for which the sum of the series is less than $\dfrac{99}{100}$.

    (c) Can we find a value of n for which the sum of the series is greater than 1?

20. Consider all the integers between 1 and 500 inclusive.

    (a) Find the sum of all the integers which are
        (i) multiples of 6,
        (ii) multiples of 9,
        (iii) multiples of 18.

    (b) Find the sum of all the integers between 1 and 500 inclusive which are either multiples of 6 or multiples of 9.

21. A and B are two cities 224 km apart. Mary and John set off on the same day from cities A and B respectively and they travel to meet each other. Mary travels 15 km on the 1st day, 13 km on the 2nd day, 11 km on the 3rd day, and so on. John travels 14 km on the 1st day, 17 km on the 2nd day, 20 km on the 3rd day, and so on.

    (a) After setting off for n days, what is the total distance travelled by **(i)** Mary?　**(ii)** John?
        (*Give the answers in terms of n.*)

    (b) How many days after setting off will Mary and John meet each other?

*22. The terms in the arithmetic sequence 2, 5, 8, 11, $\cdots$ are divided into groups $G_1, G_2, G_3, \cdots$ according to the scheme: $\underbrace{(2)}_{G_1}, \underbrace{(5,8)}_{G_2}, \underbrace{(11,14,17)}_{G_3}, \cdots$

    i.e. There are n terms in the nth group.

    (a) Find, in terms of n, the total number of terms in the first n groups.

    (b) Find, in terms of n, the sum of all the terms in the first n groups.

    (c) To which group does 452 belong?

*23. In the figure, $A_1B_1C_1D_1E_1F_1$ is a regular hexagon of side 12 cm. The mid-points of the sides of $A_1B_1C_1D_1E_1F_1$ are joined to form another regular hexagon $A_2B_2C_2D_2E_2F_2$. This process continues to give an infinite number of regular hexagons. Find

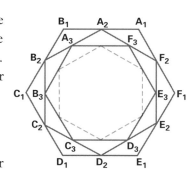

    (a) the area of the regular hexagon $A_1B_1C_1D_1E_1F_1$,

    (b) the area of the regular hexagon $A_2B_2C_2D_2E_2F_2$,

    (c) the sum of the areas of the infinite number of regular hexagons formed in this way.

    (*Leave the answers in surd form.*)

**24. (a) Find the sum to n terms of the series
$$2 + 20 + 200 + 2\,000 + \cdots .$$

(b) Using the result of **(a)**, or otherwise, find the sum to n terms of the series $2 + 22 + 222 + 2\,222 + \cdots .$

(*Give the answers in terms of n.*)

PART III | *HKCEE Questions*

(*Section B Questions*) ————————————————————•

[Note that the terms 'arithmetic progression' (abbreviated as 'A. P.') and 'geometric progression' (abbreviated as 'G. P.') mean the same thing as 'arithmetic sequence' and 'geometric sequence' respectively. From 1997 onwards, the term 'sequence' will be used instead of 'progression' in the HKCE Examinations.]

25. a and b are positive numbers. a, -2, b form a geometric progression and -2, b, a form an arithmetic progression.

(a) Find the value of ab.

(b) Find the values of a and b.

(c) (i) Find the sum to infinity of the geometric progression $a, -2, b, \cdots .$

(ii) Find the sum to infinity of all the terms that are positive in the geometric progression $a, -2, b, \cdots .$

[HKCEE 84]

26. $2, -1, -4, \cdots$ are in A. P.

(a) Find **(i)** the nth term,

(ii) the sum of the first n terms,

(iii) the sum of the progression from the 21st term to the 30th term.

(b) If the sum of the first n terms of the progression is less than $-1\,000$, find the least value of n.

[HKCEE 86]

27. (a) Write down the smallest and the largest multiples of 7 between 100 and 999.

(b) How many multiples of 7 are there between 100 and 999? Find the sum of these multiples.

(c) Find the sum of all positive three-digit integers which are NOT divisible by 7.

[HKCEE 88]

28. The positive integers $1, 2, 3, \cdots$ are divided into groups $G_1, G_2, G_3, \cdots$, so that the kth group G_k consists of k consecutive integers as follows:

$G_1 : 1$

$G_2 : 2, 3$

$G_3 : 4, 5, 6$

$\cdots\cdots\cdots$

$\cdots\cdots\cdots$

$\cdots\cdots\cdots$

$G_{k-1} : u_1, u_2, \cdots, u_{k-1}$

$\quad G_k : v_1, v_2, \cdots, v_{k-1}, v_k$

$\cdots\cdots\cdots$

$\cdots\cdots\cdots$

$\cdots\cdots\cdots$

(a) **(i)** Write down all the integers in the 6th group G_6.

(ii) What is the total number of integers in the first 6 groups $G_1, G_2, \cdots, G_6$?

(b) Find, in terms of k,

(i) the last integer u_{k-1} in G_{k-1} and the first integer v_1 in G_k,

(ii) the sum of all the integers in G_k.

[HKCEE 90]

29. **(a)** Given the G.P. a^n, $a^{n-1}b$, $a^{n-2}b^2$, $\cdots$, a^2b^{n-2}, ab^{n-1}, where a and b are unequal and non-zero real numbers, find the common ratio and the sum to n terms of the G.P.

(b) A man joins a saving plan by depositing in his bank account a sum of money at the beginning of every year. At the beginning of the first year, he puts an initial deposit of $\$P$. Every year afterwards, he deposits 10% more than he does in the previous year. The bank pays interest at a rate of 8% p.a., compounded yearly.

(i) Find, in terms of P, an expression for the amount in his account at the end of

(1) the first year,

(2) the second year,

(3) the third year.

(*Note: You need not simplify your expressions.*)

(ii) Using **(a)**, or otherwise, show that the amount in his account at the end of the nth year is $\$54P(1.1^n - 1.08^n)$.

(c) A flat is worth $1 080 000 at the beginning of a certain year and at the same time, a man joins the saving plan in **(b)** with an initial deposit $P = \$20\,000$. Suppose the value of the flat grows by 15% every year. Show that at the end of the nth year, the value of the flat is greater than the amount in the man's account.

[HKCEE 92]

30. Suppose the number of babies born in Hong Kong in 1994 is 70 000 and in subsequent years, the number of babies born each year increases by 2% of that of the previous year.

(a) Find the number of babies born in Hong Kong
   (i) in the first year after 1994;
   (ii) in the nth year after 1994.

(b) In which year will the number of babies born in Hong Kong first exceed 90 000?

(c) Find the total number of babies born in Hong Kong from 1997 to 2046 inclusive.

(d) It is known that from 1901 to 2099, a year is a leap year if its number is divisible by 4.
   (i) Find the number of leap years between 1997 and 2046.
   (ii) Find the total number of babies born in Hong Kong in the leap years between 1997 and 2046.

[HKCEE 94]

(MC Questions) —————————————————————————————————————

31. Let $a > b > 0$. If a and b are respectively the 1st and 2nd terms of a geometric progression, the sum to infinity of the progression is

A. $\dfrac{1}{a-b}$

B. $\dfrac{a}{1-b}$

C. $\dfrac{ab}{b-a}$

D. $\dfrac{a^2}{a+b}$

E. $\dfrac{a^2}{a-b}$ [HKCEE 90]

32. If the sum to infinity of a G.P. is $\dfrac{81}{4}$ and its second term is -9, the common ratio is

A. $-\dfrac{1}{3}$.   D. $\dfrac{4}{3}$.

B. $\dfrac{1}{3}$.   E. $-\dfrac{4}{9}$.

C. $-\dfrac{4}{3}$.   [HKCEE 94]

33. If the product of the first n terms of the sequence
$$10,\ 10^2,\ 10^3,\ \cdots,\ 10^n,\ \cdots$$
exceeds 10^{55}, find the minimum value of n.

A. 9
B. 10
C. 11
D. 12
E. 56   [HKCEE 94]

As the moon orbits around the earth, the path of the centre of the moon can be regarded as the locus of a moving point.

3

Coordinate Geometry of Circles

This chapter concerns two main topics:

(1) coordinate geometry of circles;

(2) intersection of a circle and a straight line in the rectangular coordinate plane.

3.1 Review

A. *Distance Formula*

The distance between two points $P(x_1, y_1)$ and $Q(x_2, y_2)$ is given by:

$$PQ = \sqrt{(x_1 - x_2)^2 + (y_1 - y_2)^2}$$

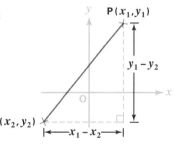

Fig. 1

Note : Alternatively,

$$PQ = \sqrt{(x_2 - x_1)^2 + (y_2 - y_1)^2}.$$

B.   *Slope of a Straight Line*

(1) The slope m of a straight line that passes through two points $P(x_1, y_1)$ and $Q(x_2, y_2)$ is given by:

$$m = \frac{y_2 - y_1}{x_2 - x_1}, \quad \text{where } x_2 \neq x_1$$

Fig. 2

Note : **(i)** Alternatively,

$m = \dfrac{y_1 - y_2}{x_1 - x_2}$, where $x_1 \neq x_2$.

(ii) If $x_1 = x_2$, then PQ is a vertical line. The slope

$m = \dfrac{y_2 - y_1}{0}$, which is undefined.

(2) The slope m of a straight line L making a positive angle θ with the x-axis is given by:

$$m = \tan \theta$$

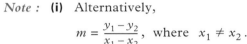

Fig. 3

Note : **(i)** When θ is an <u>acute angle</u>, $\tan \theta$ is positive, hence <u>m is positive</u>.

(ii) When θ is a <u>right angle</u>, $\tan \theta$ is undefined, hence <u>m is undefined</u>.

(iii) When θ is an <u>obtuse angle</u>, $\tan \theta$ is negative, hence <u>m is negative</u>.

C.   *Section Formula*

The x- and y-coordinates of a point $P(x, y)$ which divides the line segment joining the points $A(x_1, y_1)$ and $B(x_2, y_2)$ internally in the ratio $r : s$ are given by:

$$x = \frac{sx_1 + rx_2}{r + s}, \quad y = \frac{sy_1 + ry_2}{r + s}$$

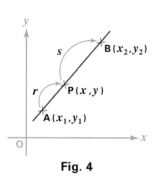

Fig. 4

Note : In particular, if P is the mid-point of AB, then $r : s = 1 : 1$

and
$$x = \frac{x_1 + x_2}{2}, \quad y = \frac{y_1 + y_2}{2}.$$

This formula is known as the mid-point formula.

D. *Different Forms of the Equation of a Straight Line*

(1) Point-slope Form

The equation of the straight line with slope m and passing through a point (x_1, y_1) is given by:

$$y - y_1 = m(x - x_1)$$

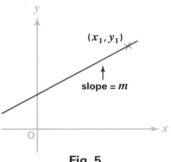

Fig. 5

(2) Two-point Form

The equation of the straight line passing through two points (x_1, y_1) and (x_2, y_2) is given by:

$$\frac{y - y_1}{x - x_1} = \frac{y_2 - y_1}{x_2 - x_1}$$

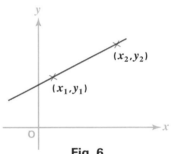

Fig. 6

(3) Intercept Form

The equation of the straight line with x-intercept a and y-intercept b is given by:

$$\frac{x}{a} + \frac{y}{b} = 1$$

Note : a and b may be negative.

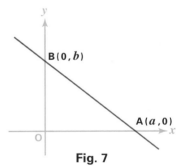

Fig. 7

(4) Slope-intercept Form

The equation of the straight line with slope m and y-intercept c is given by:

$$y = mx + c$$

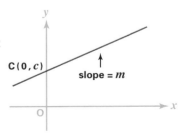

Note : c may be negative.

Fig. 8

(5) General Form

The equation of a straight line can be expressed in the general form:

$$Ax + By + C = 0$$

where A, B and C are constants with A and B not <u>both</u> zero.

Note : **(i)** If $A = 0$ and $B \neq 0$, the line is ***horizontal***.   ◀ *The line is // to the x-axis.*

   (ii) If $A \neq 0$ and $B = 0$, the line is ***vertical***.   ◀ *The line is // to the y-axis.*

   (iii) When $B \neq 0$, $Ax + By + C = 0$ can be expressed as   ◀ $Ax + By + C = 0$
   or $By = -Ax - C$
   $$y = -\frac{A}{B}x - \frac{C}{B}.$$ $y = -\frac{A}{B}x - \frac{C}{B}$

   Now the equation is in slope-intercept form, where

   $$\text{slope} = -\frac{A}{B};$$
   $$y\text{-intercept} = -\frac{C}{B}.$$

   (iv) When $C = 0$, the line passes through the origin.

E. *Parallel Lines and Perpendicular Lines*

(1) If $\ell_1 /\!/ \ell_2$, then $m_1 = m_2$.

Conversely, if $m_1 = m_2$, then $\ell_1 /\!/ \ell_2$.

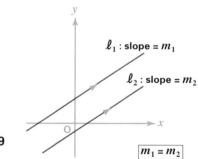

Fig. 9

$$\boxed{m_1 = m_2}$$

(2) If $\ell_1 \perp \ell_2$, then $m_1 m_2 = -1$.

Conversely, if $m_1 m_2 = -1$, then $\ell_1 \perp \ell_2$.

Note : If ℓ_1 or ℓ_2 is parallel to one of the coordinate axes, then the product of the slopes of ℓ_1 and ℓ_2 is undefined, i.e. NOT -1.

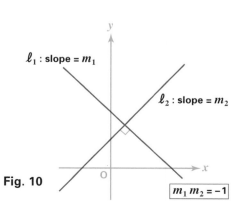

Fig. 10

$$\boxed{m_1 m_2 = -1}$$

1. In each of the following, find
    (i) the distance between the two given points A and B in surd form;
    (ii) the slope m of the straight line joining A and B in fraction if necessary.

    (a) A$(2, -3)$, B$(-4, 9)$

    AB = _____

    m = _____

    (b) A$(-12, 0)$, B$(0, 7)$

    AB = _____

    m = _____

2.

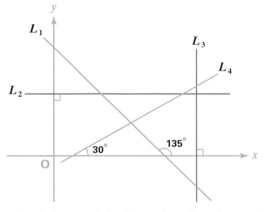

    For each of the straight lines L_1, L_2, L_3 and L_4 in the given figure, find its slope m.

    (*Leave the answer in surd form when appropriate. If the slope is undefined, say so.*)

    For L_1, m is _____ .

    For L_2, m is _____ .

    For L_3, m is _____ .

    For L_4, m is _____ .

3. In the figure,

    (i) P is the mid-point of the line segment RS;

    (ii) Q is a point on RS such that RQ : QS = 3 : 1 .

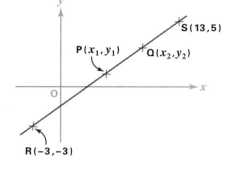

Find the coordinates of P and Q.

For the point P, x_1 =

$$y_1 =$$

For the point Q, x_2 =

$$y_2 =$$

∴   The coordinates of P are _____ .

    The coordinates of Q are _____ .

4. For each of the straight lines in the given figures, write down its equation in the general form.

(a)

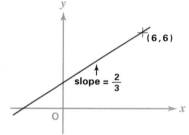

The required equation is

_____ .

(b)

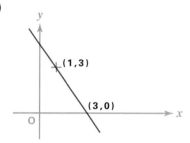

The required equation is

_____ .

(c)

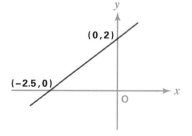

The required equation is

_____ .

(d)

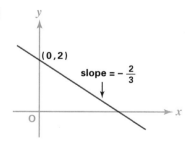

The required equation is

_____ .

5. Find the equation (in general form) of the straight line L in each of the two figures below.

(a)

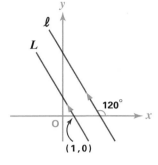

The required equation is

_____ .

(b)

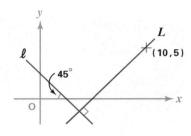

The required equation is

_____ .

3.2　　**Loci**

The Concept of a Locus

> **A locus* is a figure traced by the points which satisfy some specific condition(s).**

◄ *The word locus, in Latin, means location. The plural form of locus is 'loci'.*

Here are some familiar examples of loci in everyday life.

e.g. **(1)** The *locus* of the tip of the second hand of a stop-watch which moves in a minute is a *circle*.

◄ *The condition is that the tip of the second hand moves in a minute.*

Fig. 11

---

locus　軌跡

(2) A metal ball is hung up by a string and swings freely in the air. The *locus* of this swinging metal ball is an *arc of a circle*.

◄ *The condition is that the ball swings back and forth.*

Fig. 12

(3) When a $10 coin is rolled along a straight line on a table, the *locus* of the centre of the coin is a *straight line*.

◄ *The condition is that the $10 coin <u>rolls along a straight line</u>.*

Fig. 13

(4) The *locus* of a satellite moving 1 000 km above the equator of the earth is a *circle* concentric with the earth and with radius 1 000 km greater than that of the earth.

◄ *The condition is that the satellite <u>orbits around the earth at a constant height</u>.*

EARTH

Fig. 14

We have seen some familiar loci in everyday life. In fact, many of the conditions that control the formation of loci can be described in mathematical language. Here are some examples.

(1) **Condition:** In a plane, a point P moves such that it is at a constant distance *r* from a fixed point O.

Locus: *The locus of the point P is a circle with centre O and radius r.*

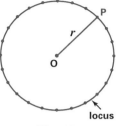

Fig. 15

(2) **Condition:** In a plane, a point Q moves such that it is equidistant from two fixed points A and B.

Locus: *The locus of the point Q is the perpendicular bisector of the line segment AB.*

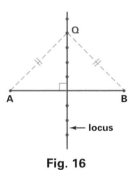

Fig. 16

(3) **Condition:** In a plane, a point R moves such that it is at a constant distance *d* from a fixed line XY.

Locus: *The locus of the point R is a pair of straight lines. They are*
(i)   parallel to XY;
(ii) one on either side of XY;
(iii) each at a distance d from XY.

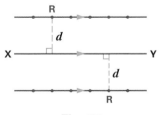

Fig. 17

(4) **Condition:** In a plane, a point S moves such that it is equidistant from two lines CD and EF which intersect at a point T.

Locus: *The locus of the point S is a pair of angle bisectors of the angles formed between the lines CD and EF.*

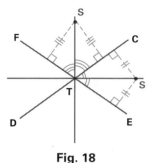

Fig. 18

Note : In each of the above examples, the locus of the point lies *in a plane*. However, objects can move *in space*, i.e. the locus of an object can lie in a three-dimensional space.

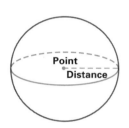

e.g. The locus of an object moving at a constant distance from a fixed point is a sphere with the fixed point as the centre and the constant distance as the radius. [Fig. 19]

At this level we consider only cases where the locus of a point lies in a plane.

Fig. 19

E X E R C I S E 3A

(Level 1)

1. Describe the locus of a ship sailing at a constant distance 10 m from a straight shore.

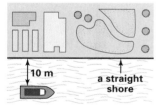

2. In each case below, describe the locus of a point in the square ABCD that is equidistant from:

(a) AB and AD,

(b) A and C,

(c) each of the four sides.

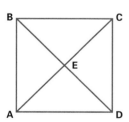

3. Sketch the locus of a point which is at a distance of 1 cm from a line segment 5 cm long.

4. A larger coin is rolled around so that it is in contact with a fixed smaller coin as shown in the picture. Sketch and describe the locus of the centre of the larger coin.

fixed coin

(*Level 2*)

5. Describe the locus formed in each of the following situations.

   (a) The centre of a ball rolling down an inclined plane.

   (b) A certain point on the surface of an inflating spherical balloon whose centre is fixed.

6. In the figure, two line segments OP and OQ intersect at O. ◄ Describe the locus formed by the centres of all the circles touching both OP and OQ.

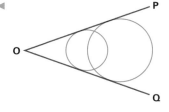

7. Sketch the locus of a point which is at a distance of 1 cm from the perimeter of

   (a) an equilateral triangle of side 5 cm,

   (b) a square of side 5 cm.

8. Given a circle of radius 2 cm, centre O. A point P moves inside the circle so that its shortest distance from the circumference of the circle is always equal to its distance from the centre of the circle. Sketch and describe the locus of the point P.

*9. Given a circle of radius 10 cm. Chord AB moves along the circumference so that the length of AB is always equal to 16 cm. Sketch and describe the locus of the mid-point of AB.

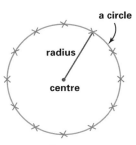

3.3   Equation of a Circle

We have seen in the previous section on loci that:

> **A circle is the locus of a point moving in a plane at a constant distance from a fixed point.**

The fixed point is called the centre of the circle and the constant distance is its radius.

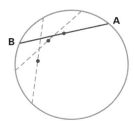

Fig. 20

We have just described a circle as a locus in *a plane* geometrically in the above paragraph. In fact if the circle is in *a rectangular coordinate plane*, then we can work out an equation to describe the circle algebraically. The equation so obtained is called the **equation of the circle**.

A. *Equation of Circle with Centre at the Origin in the Coordinate Plane*

Let $P(x, y)$ be a point in the coordinate plane at a constant distance r from the origin $O(0, 0)$. [**Fig. 21**]

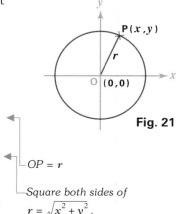

By the distance formula,

$$OP = \sqrt{(x-0)^2 + (y-0)^2}$$

i.e. $r = \sqrt{x^2 + y^2}$

∴

$$\boxed{x^2 + y^2 = r^2}$$

Fig. 21

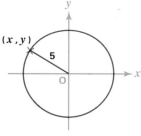

OP = r

Square both sides of
$r = \sqrt{x^2 + y^2}$.

This is the equation of the circle with centre at the origin $(0, 0)$ and radius r.

For different values of r, we have different circles, but all of their centres are located at the origin $(0, 0)$.

e.g. The equation of a circle with centre at the origin and radius equal to 5 units is given by

$$x^2 + y^2 = 5^2$$
$$or \quad x^2 + y^2 = 25.$$

> *Note :* In the above case, the ordered pairs $(3, 4)$, $(4, -3)$, $(0, 5)$, $(-5, 0)$, $(2, \sqrt{21})$, $(\sqrt{24}, -1)$, etc. can be the coordinates of points on the circle.

Fig. 22

B. *Equation of Circle with Centre at (h , k) in the Coordinate Plane*

Let $P(x, y)$ be any point on the circle with centre $C(h, k)$ and radius r. [**Fig. 23**]

◀ *Here we do not consider the case that both h and k are zero.*

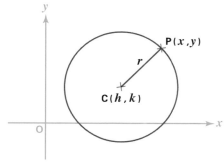

Fig. 23

By the distance formula,

$$CP = \sqrt{(x-h)^2 + (y-k)^2}$$

i.e. $r = \sqrt{(x-h)^2 + (y-k)^2}$ ◀ *CP = r*

∴

$$\boxed{(x-h)^2 + (y-k)^2 = r^2}$$

◀ *Square both sides of*
  $r = \sqrt{(x-h)^2 + (y-k)^2}$.

This equation of the circle is known as in the centre-radius form.   ◀ *Alternatively, people call this equation the standard equation of a circle.*

Note : **(i)** For any point (x, y) lying on a circle, say $\mathcal{C}$, x and y must satisfy the equation of $\mathcal{C}$.

e.g. In Fig. 24, the point $Q(3, 6)$ lies on the circle whose equation is $(x-5)^2 + (y-4)^2 = 8$. Since $(3-5)^2 + (6-4)^2 = (-2)^2 + (2)^2 = 8$, the coordinates of Q satisfy the equation of the given circle.

(ii) The converse of **(i)** is also true, i.e. any point whose coordinates satisfy the equation of a circle must lie on the circle.

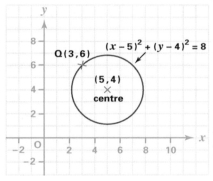

Fig. 24

CLASS PRACTICE

1. Write down the radius and the coordinates of the centre of each of the following circles.

   (*Give the radius in surd form if necessary.*)

	Centre	Radius
(a) $x^2 + (y+3)^2 = 25$	_____	_____
(b) $(x-2)^2 + y^2 = 12$	_____	_____
(c) $(x-5)^2 + (y+3)^2 = 12^2$	_____	_____
(d) $(x+3)^2 + (y-6)^2 = 13$	_____	_____

2. In each of the following, the radius and the coordinates of the centre of a circle are given. Write down the equation of the circle in the centre-radius form.

                                                              Equation

(a) Centre $(0, 8)$, radius $= \dfrac{5}{2}$ _____

(b) Centre $(4, 5)$, radius $= \sqrt{3}$ _____

(c) Centre $(-6, 7)$, radius $= 2\sqrt{2}$ _____

(d) Centre $(-2, -3)$, radius $= \dfrac{2\sqrt{3}}{5}$ _____

C. The General Form of the Equation of a Circle

In the previous section, we have seen that the equation of a circle with centre (h, k) and radius r is given by

$$(x - h)^2 + (y - k)^2 = r^2 \dots\dots\dots (*)$$

Equation $(*)$, when expanded, becomes

$$x^2 - 2hx + h^2 + y^2 - 2ky + k^2 - r^2 = 0$$

or $$x^2 + y^2 - 2hx - 2ky + (h^2 + k^2 - r^2) = 0$$

If we let the letters D, E and F denote any real numbers where

$$D = -2h, \quad E = -2k \quad \text{and} \quad F = h^2 + k^2 - r^2,$$

then the equation of the circle becomes

$$\boxed{x^2 + y^2 + Dx + Ey + F = 0.}$$

This form of equation of a circle is known as the **general form of the equation of a circle.**

Note : In the general form of the equation of a circle, it should be noted that
  (i) the coefficients of x^2 and y^2 are both equal to 1,
  (ii) there are no terms containing xy.

FINDING THE CENTRE AND THE RADIUS FROM THE GENERAL FORM

Comparing the equation (*) for a circle in the centre-radius form and the equation of a circle in the general form, i.e. $x^2 + y^2 + Dx + Ey + F = 0$, where $D = -2h$, $E = -2k$ and $F = h^2 + k^2 - r^2$, we find that

◀ *Equating the coefficients with those in equation (*).*

> **the centre** $(h, k) = \left(-\dfrac{D}{2}, -\dfrac{E}{2}\right)$;
>
> **the radius** $r = \sqrt{\left(\dfrac{D}{2}\right)^2 + \left(\dfrac{E}{2}\right)^2 - F}$.

◀ $\because \quad D = -2h, \quad \therefore \quad h = -\dfrac{D}{2}$;

$\because \quad E = -2k, \quad \therefore \quad k = -\dfrac{E}{2}$.

$\because \quad F = h^2 + k^2 - r^2$

$\therefore \quad r^2 = h^2 + k^2 - F$

i.e. $\quad r = \sqrt{h^2 + k^2 - F}$

$= \sqrt{\left(-\dfrac{D}{2}\right)^2 + \left(-\dfrac{E}{2}\right)^2 - F}$

$= \sqrt{\left(\dfrac{D}{2}\right)^2 + \left(\dfrac{E}{2}\right)^2 - F}$

Note : Consider the expression $\sqrt{\left(\dfrac{D}{2}\right)^2 + \left(\dfrac{E}{2}\right)^2 - F}$ which is the length of the radius.

(a) (i) In the ordinary case, the value under the radical sign is *positive*.

(ii) When the value under the radical sign is *zero*, the equation represents a circle of zero radius. That is, the circle reduces to a point. In this case the circle is known as a *point circle*.

(iii) When the value under the radical sign is *negative*, the circle is *wholly imaginary*.

(b) The expression can be transformed into $\dfrac{1}{2}\sqrt{D^2 + E^2 - 4F}$,

◀ $\sqrt{\left(\dfrac{D}{2}\right)^2 + \left(\dfrac{E}{2}\right)^2 - F}$

$= \sqrt{\dfrac{D^2}{4} + \dfrac{E^2}{4} - F}$

$= \sqrt{\dfrac{1}{4}(D^2 + E^2 - 4F)}$

$= \dfrac{1}{2}\sqrt{D^2 + E^2 - 4F}$

i.e. $\qquad r = \dfrac{1}{2}\sqrt{D^2 + E^2 - 4F}$.

CLASS **PRACTICE**

In each of the following, the general form of the equation of a circle is given. Find the coordinates of the centre and the radius of the circle. (*Give the answer in surd form if necessary.*)

	Centre	Radius
1. $x^2 + y^2 - 6x - 7 = 0$		
2. $x^2 + y^2 + 5y - 14 = 0$		
3. $x^2 + y^2 + 6x - 12y + 32 = 0$		
4. $x^2 + y^2 - 10x + 6y - 110 = 0$		

Example 1 A circle is given by the equation
$$(x+1)^2 + (y-4)^2 = 25.$$

(a) Write down the coordinates of the centre C and the radius r of the circle.

(b) Determine whether the point P$(-3, 0)$ lies inside, outside or on the circle.

Solution **(a)** The coordinates of the centre C = $\underline{(-1, 4)}$

Radius $r = \sqrt{25} = \underline{\underline{5}}$

(b) CP $= \sqrt{[-3-(-1)]^2 + (0-4)^2}$
$= \sqrt{[-2]^2 + (-4)^2}$
$= \sqrt{20}$

Since $\sqrt{20} < 5$ (i.e. CP $< r$),   ◀ $\sqrt{20} = 4.472\ 1\cdots$
the distance of P from the centre $<$ radius.

∴ P lies inside the circle.

Note : When we compare the length of CP with the radius, there are 3 possible cases.

(1)	CP $< r$	P lies inside the circle.
(2)	CP $= r$	P lies on the circle.
(3)	CP $> r$	P lies outside the circle.

Example 2 **(a)** Find the equation, in centre-radius form, of a circle with centre $\left(-\frac{1}{2}, \frac{1}{2}\right)$ and radius $\sqrt{\frac{17}{2}}$.

(b) Hence write the equation in the general form.

(c) Show that the point Q$(2, 2)$ lies on the circle.

Solution **(a)** $\left[\text{Here we have } h = -\frac{1}{2},\ k = \frac{1}{2},\ r = \sqrt{\frac{17}{2}}.\right]$

The required equation is
$$\left[x-\left(-\frac{1}{2}\right)\right]^2 + \left(y-\frac{1}{2}\right)^2 = \left(\sqrt{\frac{17}{2}}\right)^2$$
$$\underline{\left(x+\frac{1}{2}\right)^2 + \left(y-\frac{1}{2}\right)^2 = \frac{17}{2}}.$$

(b) From **(a)**, we have

$$x^2 + x + \frac{1}{4} + y^2 - y + \frac{1}{4} = \frac{17}{2}$$

or $\qquad x^2 + y^2 + x - y - 8 = 0.$

(c) For the point Q$(2 , 2)$,

substituting $x = 2$ and $y = 2$ into the L.H.S. of the equation $x^2 + y^2 + x - y - 8 = 0$, we have

$$2^2 + 2^2 + 2 - 2 - 8 = 4 + 4 + 2 - 2 - 8$$
$$= 0$$

Since the coordinates of Q satisfy the equation, the point Q must lie on the circle.

◄ *Note:*
In order to show that a point lies on the circle, we need to show that the coordinates of the point satisfy the equation of the given circle.

Example 3 A circle, centre G, passes through the points A$(-8 , 8)$ and B$(6 , 10)$. If G lies on the y-axis,

(a) find the coordinates of G,

(b) hence find the equation of the circle in the general form.

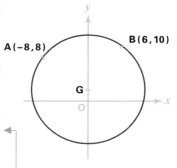

Solution **(a)** Since the centre G lies on the y-axis, we let the centre G be $(0 , k)$.

Radius $=$ GA $=$ GB

$$\therefore \quad \sqrt{[0 - (-8)]^2 + (k - 8)^2} = \sqrt{(0 - 6)^2 + (k - 10)^2}$$
$$8^2 + (k - 8)^2 = 6^2 + (k - 10)^2$$
$$64 + k^2 - 16k + 64 = 36 + k^2 - 20k + 100$$
$$128 - 16k = 136 - 20k$$
$$4k = 8$$
$$k = 2$$

◄ *The x-coordinate of any point on the y-axis must be 0.*

$\therefore$ The coordinates of G are $(0 , 2)$.

(b) Radius $=$ GB

$$= \sqrt{(0 - 6)^2 + (2 - 10)^2}$$
$$= 10$$

The required equation is

$$(x - 0)^2 + (y - 2)^2 = 10^2$$

i.e. $\qquad x^2 + y^2 - 4y + 4 = 100$

or $\qquad x^2 + y^2 - 4y - 96 = 0.$

Example 4 Find the equation of the circle passing through the points $(0,1)$, $(2,-1)$ and $(3,0)$. Write the equation in the general form.

Solution   Let the equation of the circle be
$$x^2 + y^2 + Dx + Ey + F = 0 \ldots\ldots\ldots\ldots(*)$$

The points $(0,1)$, $(2,-1)$ and $(3,0)$ must satisfy the equation $(*)$. Therefore, we have
$$0 + 1 + 0 + E + F = 0 \ldots\ldots\ldots \text{ (i)}$$
$$4 + 1 + 2D - E + F = 0 \ldots\ldots\ldots \text{(ii)}$$
$$9 + 0 + 3D + 0 + F = 0 \ldots\ldots\ldots \text{(iii)}$$

(i) + (ii): $6 + 2D + 2F = 0$ ◀ *Eliminate E from* (i) *and* (ii).
$$3 + D + F = 0 \ldots\ldots\ldots \text{(iv)}$$

(iii) − (iv): $6 + 2D = 0$ ◀ *Eliminate F from* (iii) *and* (iv).
$$\therefore \qquad\qquad\qquad D = -3$$

Substituting $D = -3$ into **(iv)**,
$$3 - 3 + F = 0$$
$$F = 0$$

Substituting $F = 0$ into **(i)**,
$$1 + E + 0 = 0$$
$$E = -1$$

$\therefore$ The required equation of the circle is
$$\underline{x^2 + y^2 - 3x - y = 0.}$$

Alternative Method

Let the centre of the circle be (h, k) and the radius be r. Then
$$(h-0)^2 + (k-1)^2 = (h-2)^2 + (k+1)^2 \ldots\ldots\text{(i)}$$
and $(h-0)^2 + (k-1)^2 = (h-3)^2 + (k-0)^2 \ldots\ldots\text{(ii)}$

From **(i)** and **(ii)**, we have
$$h - k = 1 \ldots\ldots\ldots\ldots\ldots \text{(iii)}$$
$$3h - k = 4 \ldots\ldots\ldots\ldots\ldots \text{(iv)}$$

Solving **(iii)** and **(iv)**, we have
$$h = \frac{3}{2}, \ k = \frac{1}{2}.$$

$$\therefore \ r^2 = \left(\frac{3}{2} - 0\right)^2 + \left(\frac{1}{2} - 1\right)^2$$
$$= \frac{5}{2}$$

Thus, the equation of the circle is
$$\left(x - \frac{3}{2}\right)^2 + \left(y - \frac{1}{2}\right)^2 = \frac{5}{2}$$
or $\underline{x^2 + y^2 - 3x - y = 0.}$

Example 5 **(a)** Show that the equation $4x^2 + 4y^2 + 12x - 40y + 45 = 0$ represents a circle with a positive radius.

(b) **(i)** Using the method of completing the square, convert the equation in **(a)** into an equation of a circle in the centre-radius form.

(ii) Hence find the centre of the circle.

Solution **(a)** $4x^2 + 4y^2 + 12x - 40y + 45 = 0$ is equivalent to

$$x^2 + y^2 + 3x - 10y + \frac{45}{4} = 0.$$

◀ *This equation represents a circle since the coefficients of x^2 and y^2 are both equal to 1, and there is NOT a term containing xy.*

$$\left[\text{Here we have } D = 3, E = -10, F = \frac{45}{4}.\right]$$

$$\text{Radius} = \sqrt{\left(\frac{D}{2}\right)^2 + \left(\frac{E}{2}\right)^2 - F}$$

$$= \sqrt{\left(\frac{3}{2}\right)^2 + \left(\frac{-10}{2}\right)^2 - \frac{45}{4}}$$

$$= \sqrt{16}$$

$$= 4$$

i.e. The radius of the circle is positive.

∴ The equation $4x^2 + 4y^2 + 12x - 40y + 45 = 0$ represents a circle with a positive radius.

(b) **(i)** $x^2 + y^2 + 3x - 10y + \frac{45}{4} = 0$

∴ $x^2 + 3x + y^2 - 10y + \frac{45}{4} = 0$

$$x^2 + 3x + \left(\frac{3}{2}\right)^2 + y^2 - 10y + \left(-\frac{10}{2}\right)^2 - \left(\frac{3}{2}\right)^2 - \left(-\frac{10}{2}\right)^2 + \frac{45}{4} = 0$$

i.e. $\left(x + \frac{3}{2}\right)^2 + (y - 5)^2 - \frac{9}{4} - 25 + \frac{45}{4} = 0$

The technique of completing the square is used here.

∴ The required equation of a circle in centre-radius form is

$$\left(x + \frac{3}{2}\right)^2 + (y - 5)^2 = 16.$$

(ii) From the equation obtained in **(i)**, the centre of the circle is $\left(-\frac{3}{2}, 5\right)$.

Note : As shown in the earlier part of this section on P. 76, we can obtain the equation of a circle in *general form* from the *centre-radius form* by *expansion*.

On the other hand, as shown in **(b)(i)** of **Example 5**, we can obtain the equation of a circle in *centre-radius form* from the *general form* by the method of *completing the square*.

EXERCISE **3B**

[In this exercise, **(i)** give the answers for the equations of circles in the general form unless otherwise stated, **(ii)** leave the answers in surd form if necessary.]

(Level 1)

1. Find the centre and the radius of each of the following circles.

   (a) $x^2 + y^2 = 16$

   (b) $(x-2)^2 + (y+4)^2 = 9$

   (c) $(2x+1)^2 + (2y-3)^2 = 16$

2. Find the centre and the radius of each of the following circles.

   (a) $x^2 + y^2 + 8x - 2y - 8 = 0$

   (b) $x^2 + y^2 + 6x - 7 = 0$

   (c) $6y + 1 - x^2 = y^2$

3. Find the equations of the following circles in centre-radius form.

   (a) 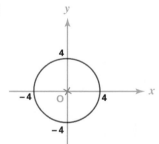 **(b)** 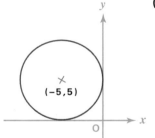 **(c)**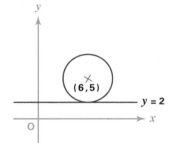

4. In each of the following, write down the equation of the circle with the given centre and radius.

   (a) Centre $= (4, -1)$, radius $= 3$.

   (b) Centre $= (5, 0)$, radius $= 4$.

5. Find the equation of each of the following circles.

   (a) The circle has centre at $(-2, 5)$ and passes through $(1, -2)$.

   (b) The circle has centre at $(4, -3)$ and cuts the y-axis at $(0, 2)$.

6. The line segment joining $(5, -7)$ and $(1, -3)$ is a diameter of a circle. Find

   (a) the coordinates of the centre,

   (b) the radius,

   (c) the equation of the circle.

7. Find the equation of the circle passing through the points $(0,0)$, $(0,-3)$ and $(5,0)$.

(Level 2)

8. Find the centre and the radius of each of the following circles.

   (a) $2x + 6y - x^2 - y^2 = 1$

   (b) $2y + 48 = \dfrac{x^2 + y^2}{2}$

9. Find the equation of each of the following circles.

   (a) The circle has an area of 5π and its centre locates at $(1,6)$.

   (b) The circle with centre lying on the x-axis touches both the lines $x = 4$ and $y = 2$.

10. **(a)** Show that the equation $16x^2 - 8x + 16y^2 + 96y + 65 = 0$ represents a circle.

    (b) Find the centre and the radius of the circle in **(a)**.

11. In the figure, the circle $\mathcal{C}_1 : x^2 + y^2 - 2x + 6y - 15 = 0$ cuts the x-axis at two points A and B.

    (a) Find the coordinates of A and B.

    (b) Hence find the equation of another circle $\mathcal{C}_2$ with AB as diameter.

    (c) Does $\mathcal{C}_2$ pass through the centre of $\mathcal{C}_1$?

12. A triangle has vertices $A(3,2)$, $B(-5,6)$ and $C(-3,10)$.

    (a) Show that $\triangle ABC$ is right-angled.

    (b) Find the equation of the circumscribed circle of $\triangle ABC$.

    (c) What is the distance of AB from the centre of the circle?

13. A circle with centre C on the x-axis passes through the points $A(-1,1)$ and $B(0,-2)$.

    (a) Find the coordinates of the centre.

    (b) Find the length of the radius.

    (c) Find the equation of the circle.

    (d) Hence determine whether the point $P(3,-2)$ lies on, outside or inside the circle.

*14. $A(3,-1)$ and $B(4,-4)$ are two points on a circle.

    (a) Find the equation of the perpendicular bisector of AB.

    (b) If the centre of the circle lies on the line $2x + 3y + 5 = 0$, find the coordinates of the centre of the circle.

    (c) Hence find the equation of the circle.

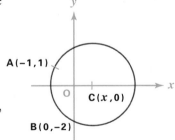

3.4   Intersection of a Straight Line and a Circle

A straight line and a circle on the same plane may intersect at two points, one point or no points. [Fig. 25]

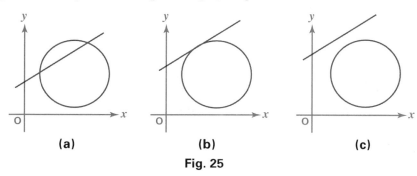

(a)   **(b)**   **(c)**

Fig. 25

When we are given the equation of a circle and the equation of a straight line, we can find

(I)   the **number of point(s)** of intersection,
(II) the **coordinates** of the point(s) of intersection.

Conversely, when we are given the equation of a circle and the coordinates of the point(s) of intersection of a circle and a straight line, we can find **the equation of the straight line.**

◀ *The straight line may be a chord of the circle or a tangent to the circle at the point of contact.*

A.   *Finding*   (I)   *Number of Point(s) of Intersection*
                     (II) *Coordinates of Point(s) of Intersection*

Given the equations of a straight line and a circle, the number of points of intersection of the straight line and the circle can be determined by the 'discriminant method'.

Let the equation of the straight line be $y = mx + c$ . . . . **(i)**

and the equation of the circle be $x^2 + y^2 + Dx + Ey + F = 0$ . . . **(ii)**

Considering **(i)** and **(ii)** as a pair of simultaneous equations and eliminating y from these equations (by substituting **(i)** into **(ii)**), we have

$$x^2 + (mx + c)^2 + Dx + E(mx + c) + F = 0$$
$$x^2 + m^2x^2 + 2mcx + c^2 + Dx + Emx + Ec + F = 0$$
$$(1 + m^2)x^2 + (2mc + D + Em)x + c^2 + Ec + F = 0 . . . .$$ **(iii)**

Equation **(iii)** is a quadratic equation in x. The roots of **(iii)** clearly satisfy both **(i)** and **(ii)**, hence these roots are the x-coordinates of the points of intersection. As a result, the number of points of intersection is the number of roots of **(iii)**.

Without actually solving equation **(iii)**, we can determine the number of points of intersection by simply evaluating the discriminant (Δ) of equation **(iii)**.

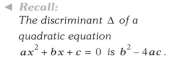
◄ *Recall:*
The discriminant Δ of a quadratic equation
$ax^2 + bx + c = 0$ *is* $b^2 - 4ac$.

> **(a) When $\Delta > 0$, there are two points of intersection.**
>
> **(b) When $\Delta = 0$, there is only one point of intersection.**
>
> **(c) When $\Delta < 0$, there are no points of intersection.**

However, when it is required to find the coordinates of the points of intersection, we must first solve the quadratic equation **(iii)** to find the x-coordinates, then the next step is to find the y-coordinates. Study the following examples.

Example 6 The equation $x^2 + y^2 = 25$ represents a circle. For each of the following straight lines, find the number of points of intersection with the circle.

(a) $L_1 : y + x + 8 = 0$

(b) $L_2 : x - 2y + 10 = 0$

(c) $L_3 : 3y + 4x + 25 = 0$

Solution   **(a)** Consider the simultaneous equations:
$$\begin{cases} y + x + 8 = 0 \dots\dots\dots\dots \text{(i)} \\ x^2 + y^2 = 25 \dots\dots\dots\dots \text{(ii)} \end{cases}$$

From **(i)**, $y = -x - 8$.

Substituting $y = -x - 8$ into **(ii)**, we have
$$x^2 + (-x - 8)^2 = 25$$
$$x^2 + x^2 + 16x + 64 = 25$$
i.e. $2x^2 + 16x + 39 = 0 \dots\dots \text{(iii)}$

The discriminant of **(iii)**, $\Delta = 16^2 - 4(2)(39)$
$$= -56 < 0.$$

Hence there are no points of intersection.

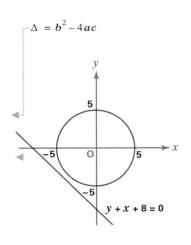

$\Delta = b^2 - 4ac$
$y + x + 8 = 0$

(b) Consider the simultaneous equations:

$$\begin{cases} x - 2y + 10 = 0 \dots\dots\dots\dots \text{(iv)} \\ x^2 + y^2 = 25 \dots\dots\dots\dots\dots \text{(v)} \end{cases}$$

From **(iv)**, $x = 2y - 10$.

Substituting $x = 2y - 10$ into **(v)**, we have

$$(2y - 10)^2 + y^2 = 25$$
$$4y^2 - 40y + 100 + y^2 = 25$$
$$5y^2 - 40y + 75 = 0$$

i.e. $y^2 - 8y + 15 = 0 \dots\dots\dots \text{(vi)}$

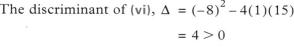

The discriminant of **(vi)**, $\Delta = (-8)^2 - 4(1)(15)$
$$= 4 > 0$$

Hence there are two points of intersection.

◀ *Can you find out the coordinates of these two points of intersection?*

(c) Consider the simultaneous equations:

$$\begin{cases} 3y + 4x + 25 = 0 \dots\dots\dots\dots \text{(vii)} \\ x^2 + y^2 = 25 \dots\dots\dots\dots \text{(viii)} \end{cases}$$

From **(vii)**, $y = \dfrac{-4x - 25}{3}$.

Substituting $y = \dfrac{-4x - 25}{3}$ into **(viii)**, we have

$$x^2 + \left(\frac{-4x - 25}{3}\right)^2 = 25$$
$$x^2 + \frac{16x^2 + 200x + 625}{9} = 25$$
$$9x^2 + 16x^2 + 200x + 625 = 225$$
$$25x^2 + 200x + 400 = 0$$

i.e. $x^2 + 8x + 16 = 0 \dots\dots \text{(ix)}$

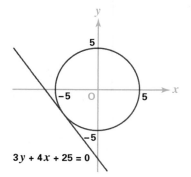

$3y + 4x + 25 = 0$

The discriminant of **(ix)**, $\Delta = 8^2 - 4(1)(16)$
$$= 0$$

Hence there is only one point of intersection.

◀ *Again, can you find out the coordinates of the point of contact?*

Example 7   Given the equation of a circle:
$$x^2 + y^2 - 4x - 6y - 13 = 0.$$

(a) Show that $P(1, -2)$ is a point on the circle.

(b) Show that the straight line joining P and another point $Q(10, 7)$ intersects the circle at two points.

(c) Find the coordinates of the two points of intersection in **(b)**.

Solution   **(a)** Substituting $(1, -2)$ into the L.H.S. of the given equation of the circle
$$x^2 + y^2 - 4x - 6y - 13 = 0,$$
we have $1^2 + (-2)^2 - 4(1) - 6(-2) - 13 = 0$.   ◀ $1 + 4 - 4 + 12 - 13 = 0$

∵ $(1, -2)$ satisfies the given equation,

∴ $\underline{P(1, -2) \text{ is a point on the given circle.}}$

(b) The equation of the straight line joining $P(1, -2)$ and $Q(10, 7)$ is

$$\frac{y - (-2)}{x - 1} = \frac{7 - (-2)}{10 - 1}$$

or $\dfrac{y + 2}{x - 1} = 1$

i.e. $y = x - 3$

Substituting $y = x - 3$ into $x^2 + y^2 - 4x - 6y - 13 = 0$, we have

$$x^2 + (x - 3)^2 - 4x - 6(x - 3) - 13 = 0$$
$$x^2 + x^2 - 6x + 9 - 4x - 6x + 18 - 13 = 0$$
$$2x^2 - 16x + 14 = 0$$
$$x^2 - 8x + 7 = 0 \ \cdots\cdots (*)$$

The discriminant of $(*)$, $\Delta = (-8)^2 - 4(1)(7)$
$$= 36 > 0$$

$\underline{\text{Hence there are two points of intersection.}}$

(c) Solving the quadratic equation $(*)$, we have
$$(x - 1)(x - 7) = 0$$
i.e. $x = 1$ and $y = -2$
or $x = 7$ and $y = 4$

$\underline{\text{Hence the required coordinates are } (1, -2) \text{ and}}$ ◀ $(1, -2)$ *are the coordinates*
$\underline{(7, 4).}$ *of the point P.*

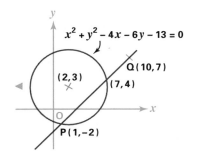

B. *Finding Equations of Tangents and Chords*

Example 8 Given that C is the centre of the circle $x^2 + y^2 - 8x - 12y + 47 = 0$.

(a) Find the coordinates of C and the radius of the circle.

(b) If $A(3, 8)$ is a point on the circle, find the equation of the tangent to the circle at A.

(c) $B(5, b)$ is another point on the circle. Find
   (i) the possible values of b;
   (ii) the equation of the chord that passes through $A(3, 8)$ and $B(5, b)$.

Solution   (a) The coordinates of $C = \left(-\dfrac{(-8)}{2}, -\dfrac{(-12)}{2}\right)$

$$= \underline{\underline{(4, 6)}}$$

The radius $= \sqrt{\left(\dfrac{-8}{2}\right)^2 + \left(\dfrac{-12}{2}\right)^2 - 47}$

$$= \underline{\underline{\sqrt{5}}}$$

(b) Slope of $CA = \dfrac{8-6}{3-4}$

$$= -2$$

If m is the slope of the tangent at A, then
$$m(-2) = -1$$
$$\therefore \qquad m = \frac{1}{2}$$

The equation of the tangent is
$$y - 8 = \frac{1}{2}(x - 3)$$

or $\underline{x - 2y + 13 = 0}$.

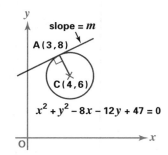

(c) (i) Since the point B lies on the circle, its coordinates $(5, b)$ must satisfy the equation of the circle.

i.e. $5^2 + b^2 - 8(5) - 12(b) + 47 = 0$

$$25 + b^2 - 40 - 12b + 47 = 0$$

$$b^2 - 12b + 32 = 0$$

$$(b - 4)(b - 8) = 0$$

$$\therefore \qquad\qquad\qquad b = \underline{\underline{4}} \;\; or \;\; \underline{\underline{8}}$$

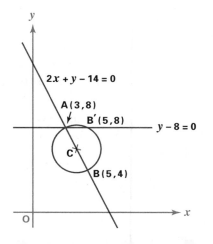

(ii) There are two possible chords: one passes through A(3 , 8) and B(5 , 4), and the other passes through A(3 , 8) and B′(5 , 8).

∴ The required equation is
$$2x + y - 14 = 0 \quad or \quad y - 8 = 0.$$

- For the points A(3 , 8) and B(5 , 4), by the two-point form,
  $$\frac{y-8}{x-3} = \frac{4-8}{5-3}$$
  i.e. $\frac{y-8}{x-3} = -2$
  ∴ $y - 8 = 6 - 2x$
  $2x + y - 14 = 0$

- For the points A(3 , 8) and B′(5 , 8), by the two-point form,
  $$\frac{y-8}{x-3} = \frac{8-8}{5-3}$$
  i.e. $\frac{y-8}{x-3} = 0$
  ∴ $y - 8 = 0$

Example 9 Given that the equation of a circle $\mathcal{C}$ is $x^2 + y^2 + 40x - 20y + 400 = 0$ and the origin O lies outside the circle. L is a line with slope m and passing through O.

(a) Find the equation of L in terms of m.

(b) For what values of m is the line L tangent to the circle $\mathcal{C}$? Hence write down the equations of the tangents to the circle $\mathcal{C}$ from O.

(c) Find the coordinates of the point of contact for each tangent found in **(b)**.

Solution **(a)** The equation of L is
$$y = mx + 0$$
◀ By the slope-intercept form.

i.e. $y = mx.$

(b) We have
$$x^2 + y^2 + 40x - 20y + 400 = 0 \dots\dots\dots \textbf{(i)}$$
$$y = mx \dots\dots\dots \textbf{(ii)}$$

Substituting **(ii)** into **(i)**,
$$x^2 + (mx)^2 + 40x - 20(mx) + 400 = 0$$
$$(1 + m^2)x^2 + 20(2 - m)x + 400 = 0 \dots \textbf{(iii)}$$

For L to be tangent to $\mathcal{C}$, the discriminant of **(iii)** must be zero.

i.e. $[20(2 - m)]^2 - 4(1 + m^2)(400) = 0$
$$(2 - m)^2 - 4(1 + m^2) = 0$$
$$4 - 4m + m^2 - 4 - 4m^2 = 0$$
$$-4m - 3m^2 = 0$$
$$-m(4 + 3m) = 0$$
∴ $m = 0 \quad or \quad m = -\frac{4}{3}$

Hence the equations of tangents are
$$y = 0 \quad and \quad y = -\frac{4}{3}x.$$

◀ $y = 0$ is a tangent means that the x-axis is tangent to the circle $\mathcal{C}$.

(c) For the tangent $y = 0$, we have $m = 0$.

Substitute $m = 0$ into **(iii)**,

$$x^2 + 40x + 400 = 0$$

$$(x + 20)^2 = 0$$

$$x = -20 \ (repeated)$$

$\therefore$ The point of contact is $(-20, 0)$.

For the tangent $y = -\dfrac{4}{3}x$, we have $m = -\dfrac{4}{3}$.

Substitute $m = -\dfrac{4}{3}$ into **(iii)**,

$$\left(1 + \frac{16}{9}\right)x^2 + 20\left(2 + \frac{4}{3}\right)x + 400 = 0$$

$$x^2 + 24x + 144 = 0$$

$$(x + 12)^2 = 0$$

$$x = -12 \ (repeated)$$

$\therefore \quad y = -\dfrac{4}{3}(-12)$

$\qquad = 16$

$\therefore$ The point of contact is $(-12, 16)$.

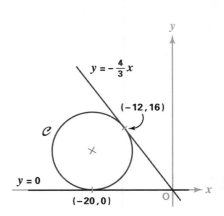

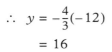

E X E R C I S E   3C

(Level 1)

1. In each of the following, find the number of points of intersection of the circle $\mathcal{C}$ and the line L without finding the coordinates of the points of intersection.

   (a) $\mathcal{C} : x^2 + y^2 = 10$, $L : x + 3y - 10 = 0$.

   (b) $\mathcal{C} : x^2 + y^2 + 4x - 5 = 0$, $L : x + y - 3 = 0$.

2. In each of the following, find the point(s) of intersection of the circle $\mathcal{C}$ with the line L.

   (a) $\mathcal{C} : x^2 + y^2 = 50$, $L : x - 2y - 5 = 0$.

   (b) $\mathcal{C} : x^2 + y^2 + 2x + 4y = 0$, $L : 2x + y - 1 = 0$.

3. Find the equation of the tangent to the circle $\mathcal{C}$ at the point P in each of the following.

   (a) $\mathcal{C} : x^2 + y^2 = 29$, $P : (-2, 5)$.

   (b) $\mathcal{C} : (x - 4)^2 + (y + 3)^2 = 13$, $P : (1, -5)$.

4. It is given that $\mathcal{C} : x^2 + y^2 - 8x = 0$ and $L : x + y - 8 = 0$. If L cuts $\mathcal{C}$ at A and B as shown in the figure, find

   (a) the coordinates of A and B,

   (b) the length, in surd form, of the chord AB.

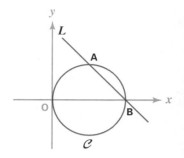

5. In the figure, AB is parallel to the x-axis and is a chord of the circle $x^2 + y^2 - 25 = 0$. If $AB = 8$, find the coordinates of A and B.

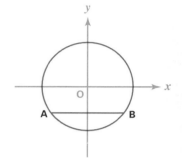

(Level 2)

6. **(a)** For what value(s) of m is the line $y = mx$ tangent to the circle $x^2 + y^2 + 6x - 3y = 0$?

   (b) Hence find the coordinates of the point(s) of contact.

7. It is given that a circle $\mathcal{C}$ is represented by the equation $x^2 + y^2 + 6x - 7 = 0$ and the coordinates of a point P are $(2, 0)$.

   (a) Write down, in terms of m, the equation of the line L which passes through P and has a slope m.

   (b) If L is a tangent to $\mathcal{C}$, find the values of m.

   (c) Find the equations of the tangents from point P to circle $\mathcal{C}$.

8. In the figure, L is the line $y = \frac{1}{2}x + k$. $\mathcal{C}$ is a circle passing through the origin and centred at $(2, -1)$. L is the tangent to the circle at $A(p, q)$.

   (a) Find the equation of the circle $\mathcal{C}$ in the general form.

   (b) **(i)** Show that $5q^2 - (6 + 8k)q + (4k^2 + 8k) = 0$.
   (ii) Hence find the values of k and write down the possible equations of L.

   (c) Find the coordinates of A when k is positive.

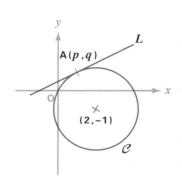

9. Given a circle $\mathcal{C} : (x-6)^2 + (y-4)^2 = 8$ and a line $L_1 : y = mx + 2$ where m is positive. L_1 is a tangent to $\mathcal{C}$.

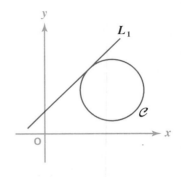

   (a) (i) Show that $7m^2 - 6m - 1 = 0$.

   (ii) Hence find the value of m.

   (b) L_2 is a line perpendicular to L_1 and tangent to $\mathcal{C}$.

   (i) Find the slope of L_2.

   (ii) Write down two possible equations of L_2.

10. Let $\mathcal{C}$ be the circle $x^2 + y^2 + 6x - 31 = 0$ and L be the line $3x - y - 11 = 0$.

   (a) Show that L is a tangent to $\mathcal{C}$.

   (b) If the point of contact between L and $\mathcal{C}$ is P, find the coordinates of P.

   (c) If Q is a point on $\mathcal{C}$ such that PQ is a diameter, find

   (i) the equation of PQ,

   (ii) the coordinates of Q.

11. In the figure, the circle has an equation
$$x^2 + y^2 + 5x - 4y + 4 = 0.$$

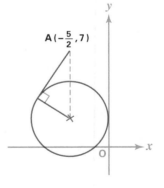

   (a) Find the length of the chord which lies on the x-axis.

   (b) A is the point $\left(-\dfrac{5}{2}, 7\right)$ outside the circle.

   (i) What is the distance of A from the centre of the circle?

   (ii) Find the length of a tangent segment from A to the circle.
   (*Leave the answer in surd form.*)

*12. It is given that a circle $\mathcal{C} : x^2 + y^2 - 4x - 8y + 4 = 0$ and a line $L : x - y - 2 = 0$ intersect at two points A and B.

   (a) Find the coordinates of the mid-point of AB.

   (b) XY is another chord of the circle. If XY is parallel to AB and $XY = AB$, find

   (i) the coordinates of the mid-point of XY,

   (ii) the equation of XY.

[In this exercise, **(i)** give the answers for the equations of circles in the general form unless otherwise stated, **(ii)** leave the answers in surd form if necessary.]

PART I| *Further Practice*

(Ex. 3A)

1. In a plane, two fixed points A and B are 6 cm apart. Sketch and describe the locus of a point C moving in the same plane so that the area of $\triangle ABC$ is always 18 cm^2.

2. In the figure, AB is a ladder 2 m long and G is the mid-point of AB. The ladder is leaning against a vertical wall with its foot resting on a horizontal floor.

   (a) Is OG = GB? Give reasons.

   (b) If the ladder slides down with the top and the foot always touching the wall and the floor respectively, sketch and describe the locus of G.

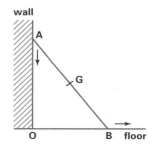

(Ex. 3B)

3. Find the radius and the coordinates of the centre of each of the following circles.

   (a) $x^2 + y^2 - 6x + 6y = 12$ **(b)** $2x^2 + 2y^2 = 12x - 2y - 17$

4. Find the equation of each of the following circles.

   (a) The circle has centre at $(-4, 3)$ and diameter 10.

   (b) The circle has centre at $(-3, -2)$ and is tangent to the y-axis.

5. **(a)** Find the equation of the circle $\mathcal{C}_1$ which is concentric with the circle $\mathcal{C}_2 : x^2 + y^2 - 2x - 4y - 4 = 0$ and passes through the point $P(4, 7)$.

   (b) Which circle is larger, $\mathcal{C}_1$ or $\mathcal{C}_2$?

6. A circle $\mathcal{C}_1$ passes through the points $A(6, -1)$, $B(2, -9)$ and $C(2, -1)$.

   (a) Find the equation of the circle $\mathcal{C}_1$.

   (b) $\mathcal{C}_2$ is another circle whose diameter is AC. Find the equation of the circle $\mathcal{C}_2$.

   (c) Does the circle $\mathcal{C}_2$ pass through the centre of the circle $\mathcal{C}_1$?

7. Given three points A$(-2, -1)$, B$(1, 3)$ and C$(9, -3)$.

   (a) Show that AB $\perp$ BC.

   (b) Find the coordinates of the centre of a circle passing through A, B and C.

   (c) Find the equation of the circle.

   (d) Hence show that D$(8.5, 0.5)$ is a point on the circle.

   (e) What is $\angle$ADC?

8. In the figure, two equal circles $\mathcal{C}_1$ and $\mathcal{C}_2$ touch each other at P$(-3, 1)$. The y-axis is a tangent to both $\mathcal{C}_1$ and $\mathcal{C}_2$. The centres of $\mathcal{C}_1$ and $\mathcal{C}_2$ are A and B respectively.

   (a) Find the radius of each of the two circles.

   (b) Write down the coordinates of A and B.

   (c) Find the equations of $\mathcal{C}_1$ and $\mathcal{C}_2$.

   (d) Find the equation of another circle $\mathcal{C}_3$ which passes through A, B and has centre on the y-axis.

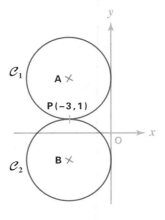

*9. Given a circle $\mathcal{C}$ which passes through a point P$(4, 2)$ and touches the x- and y-axes at points A and B respectively.

   (a) Find the coordinates of A and B.

   (b) Find the two possible equations of the circle $\mathcal{C}$.

   (c) Which equation in **(b)** represents a circle such that BA $\perp$ AP?

   (d) Hence find the diameter of the circle in **(c)**.

*10. The figure shows two concentric circles with the same centre N. The equation of the larger circle $\mathcal{C}_1$ is $x^2 + y^2 - 8x + 10y + 16 = 0$. Find the equation of the smaller circle $\mathcal{C}_2$ for each of the following given conditions.

   (a) The difference between the radius of $\mathcal{C}_1$ and the radius of $\mathcal{C}_2$ is 3 units.

   (b) The ratio of the area of $\mathcal{C}_1$ to the area of $\mathcal{C}_2$ is $4 : 1$.

(Ex. 3C)

11. Find the equation of the tangent to the circle $\mathcal{C}$ at the point P in each of the following.

   (a) $\mathcal{C} : x^2 + y^2 + 2x + 2y - 16 = 0$, P$: (2, 2)$.

   (b) $\mathcal{C} : x^2 + y^2 - 3x - y - 18 = 0$, P$: (-3, 1)$.

12. In the figure, the circle with centre K cuts the x-axis at two points A and B, and touches the y-axis at a point C. If the equation of the circle is $x^2 + y^2 + 10x - 6y + 9 = 0$,

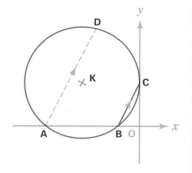

(a) find the coordinates of A, B and C;

(b) (i) find the equation of the chord AD which is parallel to the line BC,

    (ii) find the coordinates of the point D.

13. The line $L : x + y - 2 = 0$ cuts the circle $\mathcal{C} : x^2 + y^2 - 8x + 8y + 23 = 0$ at P and Q.

(a) Find the mid-point M of the chord PQ.

(b) Find the perpendicular distance of the chord PQ from K, the centre of $\mathcal{C}$.

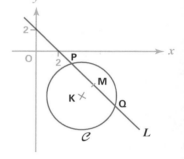

*14. Given a circle $\mathcal{C} : x^2 + y^2 + 6x - 10y + 24 = 0$.

(a) Find the coordinates of the centre(M) of the circle $\mathcal{C}$.

(b) Show that A$(-4, 6)$ lies inside the circle $\mathcal{C}$.

(c) Find the equation of a chord of the circle with A as the mid-point.

(d) If P and Q are the end points of the chord obtained in (c), find their coordinates.

(e) Two straight lines ℓ_1 and ℓ_2 are tangents to the circle $\mathcal{C}$ at P and Q respectively. If ℓ_1 and ℓ_2 intersect at a point R, find the coordinates of R.

(f) Find the area of the quadrilateral PRQM.

Part II | *Miscellaneous*

15. A circle $\mathcal{C}$ is given by the equation
$$x^2 + y^2 - 10x - 10y + 25 = 0.$$

(a) Show that the line segment joining A$(2, 1)$ and B$(5, 0)$ is a chord of $\mathcal{C}$.

(b) If one end point of a diameter of $\mathcal{C}$ is A, find the coordinates of the other end point P of this diameter.

(c) Find the equation of the circle passing through B, P and the centre of $\mathcal{C}$.

16. P(2 , 4), Q(4 , −6) and R(8 , 0) are the vertices of △PQR.

  (a) Find the equation of the circle circumscribing △PQR.

  (b) Find the radius and the coordinates of the centre of the circle.

  (c) Hence show that
   (i) PQ is a diameter of the circle,
   (ii) the origin lies inside the circle.

17. In the figure, A(0 , 0), B(2 , 2$\sqrt{3}$) and C(4 , 0) are vertices of an equilateral triangle and D is the centroid of △ABC.

  (a) Find the coordinates of D.

  (b) Find the length of AD.

  (c) Hence, or otherwise, find the equation of the circumscribed circle of △ABC in centre-radius form.
    [*Hint: In an equilateral triangle, the distance of each vertex from the centroid is the same.*]

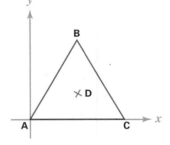

18. Given a circle $\mathcal{C} : x^2 + y^2 + 6x - 8y + 15 = 0$ and a line $L : x - y + 3 = 0$.

  (a) If $\mathcal{C}$ and L intersect at A on the y-axis and a point B, find the coordinates of A and B.

  (b) Hence find the equation of the smallest circle passing through points A and B.

19. Given two circles $\mathcal{C}_1 : x^2 + y^2 - 2x + 4y - 20 = 0$ and $\mathcal{C}_2 : x^2 + y^2 - 6x + 4y + 4 = 0$. A and B are the centres of $\mathcal{C}_1$ and $\mathcal{C}_2$ respectively. Both $\mathcal{C}_1$ and $\mathcal{C}_2$ pass through a point P.

  (a) Find the coordinates of A and B.

  (b) Find the lengths of AB, BP and AP.

  (c) Are the points A, B and P collinear?

  (d) If a line L is the tangent to $\mathcal{C}_1$ at P, show that L is also the tangent to $\mathcal{C}_2$ at P. Draw a rough diagram to show this information.

*20. The figure shows a circle with centre at $A(5, k)$ in the first quadrant of the coordinate plane. The circle touches the y-axis at a point B, and $C(2, 0)$ is a point on the circumference of the circle.

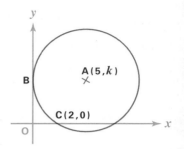

(a) Find the value of k.

(b) If CD is a diameter of the circle, find the coordinates of the point D.

(c) Find the equation of the circumscribed circle of $\triangle BAD$.

*21. $\mathcal{C} : x^2 + y^2 + Dx + Ey + F = 0$ is a circle which passes through two points $P(-4, 0)$ and $Q(3, 7)$.

(a) Show that

(i) $F = 4D - 16$,

(ii) $E = -(D + 6)$.

(b) Suppose the radius of $\mathcal{C}$ is 5 units.

(i) Show that $D^2 + E^2 - 4F = 100$.

(ii) Find all possible values of D, E and F.

(iii) Hence find the equation of $\mathcal{C}$ if its diameter lies on the y-axis.

*22. Given a circle $\mathcal{C} : x^2 + y^2 + 4x - 6y + 3 = 0$ and a line $L : x + 2y + k = 0$. Suppose L cuts $\mathcal{C}$ at $A(x_1, y_1)$ and $B(x_2, y_2)$.

(a) Find the coordinates of the centre and the radius of $\mathcal{C}$.

(b) Show that

(i) x_1 and x_2 are the roots of the equation $5x^2 + (2k + 28)x + k^2 + 12k + 12 = 0$,

(ii) y_1 and y_2 are the roots of the equation $5y^2 + (4k - 14)y + k^2 - 4k + 3 = 0$.

(c) Hence find the coordinates of the mid-point of AB in terms of k.

(d) If the length of the chord AB is $\sqrt{20}$, find the possible values of k.

PART III | *HKCEE Questions*

(Section A Questions)

23. In the figure, the circle $\mathcal{C}$ has equation

$$x^2 + y^2 - 4x + 10y + k = 0,$$

where k is a constant.

(a) Find the coordinates of the centre of $\mathcal{C}$.

(b) If $\mathcal{C}$ touches the y-axis, find the radius of $\mathcal{C}$ and the value of k.   [HKCEE 88]

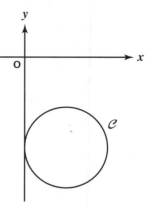

24. L_1 is the line passing through the point $A(10, 5)$ and perpendicular to the line $L_2 : x - 2y + 5 = 0$.

(a) Find the equation of L_1.

(b) Find the intersection point of L_1 and L_2.   [HKCEE 92]

(Section B Questions)

25. Let L be the line $y = k - x$ (k being a constant) and $\mathcal{C}$ be the circle $x^2 + y^2 = 4$.

(a) If L meets $\mathcal{C}$ at exactly one point, find the two values of k.

(b) If L intersects $\mathcal{C}$ at the points $A(2, 0)$ and B,
(i) find the value of k and the coordinates of B;
(ii) find the equation of the circle with AB as diameter.
    [HKCEE 84]

26. The line $y - x - 6 = 0$ cuts the circle $x^2 + y^2 - 6x - 8y = 0$ at the points B and C as shown in the figure. The circle cuts the x-axis at the origin O and the point A; it also cuts the y-axis at D.

(a) Find the coordinates of B and C.

(b) Find the coordinates of A and D.

(c) Find $\angle ADO$, $\angle ABO$ and $\angle ACO$, correct to the nearest degree.

(d) Find the area of $\triangle ACO$.   [HKCEE 86]

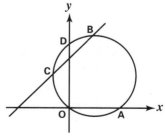

27. Let $(\mathcal{C}_1)$ be the circle $x^2 + y^2 - 2x + 6y + 1 = 0$ and A be the point $(5, 0)$.

    (a) Find the coordinates of the centre and the radius of $(\mathcal{C}_1)$.

    (b) Find the distance between the centre of $(\mathcal{C}_1)$ and A. Hence determine whether A lies inside, outside or on $(\mathcal{C}_1)$.

    (c) Let s be the shortest distance from A to $(\mathcal{C}_1)$.
        (i) Find s.
        (ii) Another circle $(\mathcal{C}_2)$ has centre A and radius s. Find its equation.

    (d) A line touches the above two circles $(\mathcal{C}_1)$ and $(\mathcal{C}_2)$ at two distinct points E and F respectively. Draw a rough diagram to show this information. Find the length of EF.

                                  [HKCEE 90]

28.

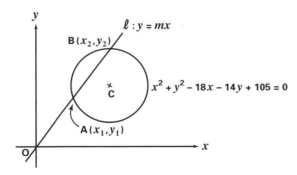

In the figure, the line $\ell : y = mx$ passes through the origin and intersects the circle $x^2 + y^2 - 18x - 14y + 105 = 0$ at two distinct points $A(x_1, y_1)$ and $B(x_2, y_2)$.

    (a) Find the coordinates of the centre C and the radius of the circle.

    (b) By substituting $y = mx$ into $x^2 + y^2 - 18x - 14y + 105 = 0$, show that $x_1 x_2 = \dfrac{105}{1 + m^2}$.

    (c) Express the length of OA in terms of m and x_1 and the length of OB in terms of m and x_2.
    Hence find the value of the product of OA and OB.

    (d) If the perpendicular distance between the line ℓ and the centre C is 3, find the lengths of AB and OA.

                                    [HKCEE 92]

29.

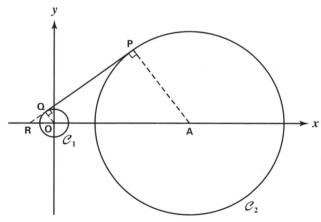

The figure shows two circles
$$\mathcal{C}_1 : x^2 + y^2 = 1,$$
$$\mathcal{C}_2 : (x-10)^2 + y^2 = 49.$$

O is the origin and A is the centre of $\mathcal{C}_2$. QP is an external common tangent to $\mathcal{C}_1$ and $\mathcal{C}_2$ with points of contact Q and P respectively. The slope of QP is positive.

(a) Write down the coordinates of A and the radius of $\mathcal{C}_2$.

(b) PQ is produced to cut the *x*-axis at R. Find the *x*-coordinate of R by considering similar triangles.

(c) Using the result in **(b)**, find the slope of QP.

(d) Using the results of **(b)** and **(c)**, find the equation of the external common tangent QP.

(e) Find the equation of the other external common tangent to $\mathcal{C}_1$ and $\mathcal{C}_2$. [HKCEE 94]

(MC Questions) ───────────────────────────────■

30. If the lines $y = mx + b$ and $\frac{x}{a} + \frac{y}{b} = 1$ are perpendicular, find *m*.

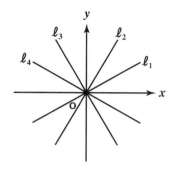

A. $\frac{a}{b}$ **D.** $-\frac{a}{b}$

B. $\frac{b}{a}$ **E.** $-\frac{b}{a}$

C. ab [HKCEE 90]

31. In the figure, the slopes of the straight lines ℓ_1, ℓ_2, ℓ_3 and ℓ_4 are m_1, m_2, m_3 and m_4 respectively. Which of the following is true?

A. $m_1 > m_2 > m_3 > m_4$

B. $m_2 > m_1 > m_3 > m_4$

C. $m_1 > m_2 > m_4 > m_3$

D. $m_2 > m_1 > m_4 > m_3$

E. $m_4 > m_3 > m_2 > m_1$ [HKCEE 90]

32.

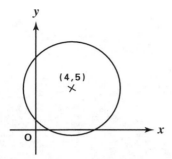

In the figure, a circle cuts the *x*-axis at two points 6 units apart. If the circle has centre (4 , 5), then its equation is

A. $(x-4)^2 + (y-5)^2 = 25$

B. $(x-4)^2 + (y-5)^2 = 34$

C. $(x-4)^2 + (y-5)^2 = 52$

D. $(x+4)^2 + (y+5)^2 = 34$

E. $(x+4)^2 + (y+5)^2 = 25$ [HKCEE 90]

33. If the two lines $2x - y + 1 = 0$ and $ax + 3y - 1 = 0$ do not intersect, then $a =$

A. -6.

B. -2.

C. 2.

D. 3.

E. 6.   [HKCEE 92]

34. If $0 < k < h$, which of the following circles intersect(s) the *y*-axis?

I. $(x-h)^2 + (y-k)^2 = k^2$

II. $(x-h)^2 + (y-k)^2 = h^2$

III. $(x-h)^2 + (y-k)^2 = h^2 + k^2$

A. I only

B. II only

C. III only

D. I and II only

E. II and III only   [HKCEE 92]

35. If the line $y = mx + 3$ divides the circle $x^2 + y^2 - 4x - 2y - 5 = 0$ into two equal parts, find *m*.

A. $-\dfrac{1}{4}$

B. -1

C. 0

D. $\dfrac{5}{4}$

E. 2 [HKCEE 92]

36. The points A(4 , -1), B(-2 , 3) and C(*x* , 5) lie on a straight line. Find *x*.

A. -5

B. -4

C. 0

D. 2

E. 5 [HKCEE 94]

37. AB is a diameter of the circle $x^2 + y^2 - 2x - 2y - 18 = 0$. If A is (3 , 5), then B is

A. (2 , 3).

B. (1 , -1).

C. (-1 , -3).

D. (-5 , -7).

E. (-7 , -9).   [HKCEE 94]

38. The equations of two circles are

$$x^2 + y^2 - 4x - 6y = 0,$$
$$x^2 + y^2 + 4x + 6y = 0.$$

Which of the following is/are true?

I. The two circles have the same centre.

II. The two circles have equal radii.

III. The two circles pass through the origin.

A. I only

B. II only

C. III only

D. I and III only

E. II and III only   [HKCEE 94]

The linear inequality $15 < T < 25$ describes a range of temperatures ($T\,^{\circ}$C) in which the flowers in the picture will blossom beautifully.

4

Inequalities in One Unknown

CHAPTER 4

4.1 Review

A. The Concepts of Inequality

I. Meaning of Inequality

> An inequality is a mathematical sentence in which two expressions are connected by a symbol of inequality.

e.g. $7 > 3$, $-b < -1$, $x \geqslant 0$ and $y \leqslant x + 1$, etc. are inequalities.

II. Symbols of Inequality

Symbol	Meaning
$\neq$	is not equal to
$>$	is greater than
$<$	is less than
$\geqslant$	is greater than or equal to
$\leqslant$	is less than or equal to

III. Law of Trichotomy

For any two given **real numbers** a and b, one of the following three statements must be true.

> (i) $a > b$,
> (ii) $a < b$,
> (iii) $a = b$.

◀ *Note that the sharp end of a symbol of inequality always points to the smaller number in an inequality. Hence the order in which the numbers in an inequality are written is very important. And $a > b$ means the same thing as $b < a$.*

This is known as the *law of trichotomy* 三分律. Obviously, **(i)** and **(ii)** are inequalities while **(iii)** is an equation.

We have the following fundamental properties for inequalities related to the law of trichotomy.

IV. Fundamental Properties of Inequalities

For any three real numbers, a, b and c:

(i) Transitive Property

> **If $a > b$ and $b > c$, then $a > c$.**

◀ *e.g.* $10 > 7$ *and* $7 > 2$ *are true,*
$10 > 2$ *is also true.*

(ii) Additive Property

> **If $a > b$, then $a + c > b + c$.**

◀ *e.g.* $\because$ $10 > 7$,
$\therefore$ $10 + (-2) > 7 + (-2)$.

(iii) Multiplicative Property

> **If $a > b$, then**
>
> **(a) $ac > bc$ when $c > 0$;**
>
> **(b) $ac < bc$ when $c < 0$.**

◀ *e.g.* $\because$ $10 > 7$,
$\therefore$ **(a)** $10(2) > 7(2)$,
and **(b)** $10(-2) < 7(-2)$.

Note : According to property **(iii)(b)** above, when we multiply or divide an inequality by a negative number, the direction of the inequality symbol should be '*reversed* '.

Besides the three fundamental properties mentioned above, there are also two very important facts about inequalities. They are:

> **If $a \neq 0$, then $a^2 > 0$.**

◀ *e.g.* $10^2 > 0$ *and* $(-10)^2 > 0$,
but $0^2 = 0$.

> **If $a > b$ and $ab > 0$, then $\dfrac{1}{a} < \dfrac{1}{b}$.**

◀ *e.g.* $10 > 7$, *but* $\frac{1}{10} < \frac{1}{7}$.

Note : The above properties and facts for inequalities also hold when the symbols of inequality '$>$' and '$<$' are replaced by '$\geqslant$' and '$\leqslant$' respectively.

CLASS PRACTICE

In each of the following, fill in the blank with an appropriate symbol of inequality.

1. If $a > b$, then $a - b$ _____ 0.

2. If a and b are positive and $\dfrac{a}{b} > 1$, then a _____ b.

3. If a and b are two real numbers, then $(a-b)^2$ _____ 0 .

4. If $a > b$ and $c > d$, then $a + c$ _____ $b + d$.

B. *Solving Linear Inequalities*

I.   Solving Linear Inequalities in One Variable

An inequality involving only one variable in the first degree is called a linear inequality in one variable.

For a linear inequality in one variable, say x, the values of x that satisfy the inequality are called the solution of the inequality.

e.g. For the linear inequality $x - 1 > 5$, the solution is the values of x like 7, 8.5, $9\frac{1}{4}$, etc.

Recall:
Such an inequality is in fact an 'open sentence'. Do you remember the meaning of 'open sentence'?

Using the skills similar to those we use in *solving linear equations*, we can solve linear inequalities easily. Let us study the following example.

Question:
Is 6 a solution to the given inequality?

Example 1 Solve each of the following inequalities:

(a) $3(x - 5) < -2(5 - 2x)$

(b) $\dfrac{2x - 5}{3} - \dfrac{5}{2} \geq \dfrac{x + 1}{2} + \dfrac{3x - 4}{3}$

Solution   (a)

$$3(x - 5) < -2(5 - 2x)$$
i.e. $3x - 15 < -10 + 4x$

$3x - 4x < -10 + 15$ ◀ *Transpose terms.*

$-x < 5$

∴ $\underline{x > -5}$ ◀ *Multiply both sides of the inequality by -1 and reverse the symbol of inequality.*

(b)

$$\dfrac{2x - 5}{3} - \dfrac{5}{2} \geq \dfrac{x + 1}{2} + \dfrac{3x - 4}{3}$$

i.e. $2(2x - 5) - 15 \geq 3(x + 1) + 2(3x - 4)$ ◀ *Multiply both sides of the inequality by the L.C.M. of the denominators 2 and 3, i.e. 6.*

$4x - 10 - 15 \geq 3x + 3 + 6x - 8$

$4x - 25 \geq 9x - 5$

$4x - 9x \geq -5 + 25$

$-5x \geq 20$

∴ $\underline{x \leq -4}$

In our example above, we have demonstrated one way to express the solution of a linear inequality, i.e. to give the range of values of x that satisfy the given inequality. The solution is also in the form of an inequality.

Another way to express the solution of a linear inequality is to make use of the number line. In this way, we say that we represent the solution on the number line or represent the solution graphically.

REPRESENTATION OF SOLUTION ON THE NUMBER LINE

We can represent the solution of inequalities that involve the variable x, the positive constants a and b on the number line in the following ways.

Inequality	Representation on Number Line

(a) $x \leqslant a$

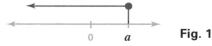

Fig. 1

(The symbol '●' means that a is included in the solution.)

(b) $x > -b$

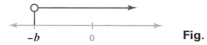

Fig. 2

(The symbol 'O' means that $-b$ is **NOT** included in the solution.)

(c) $-b \leqslant x \leqslant a$

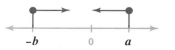

Fig. 3

Note : $-b \leqslant x \leqslant a$ is an *interval* 區間. Since the end points a and $-b$ are included in the solution, the interval is called a *closed interval* 閉區間.

(d) $-b < x < a$

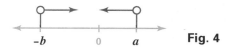

Fig. 4

Note : For the interval $-b < x < a$, since the end points a and $-b$ are **NOT** included in the solution, $-b < x < a$ is called an *open interval* 開區間.

MORE! Something More

We must be careful NOT to write an inequality in the form $-b > x < a$ *or* $-b < x > a$*, etc. The narrow ends of the symbol of inequality must point to the same direction in an inequality.*

(e) $-b < x \leqslant a$

Fig. 5

Note : For the interval $-b < x \leqslant a$, since the end point a is included in the solution while $-b$ is **NOT**, $-b < x \leqslant a$ is called a *half-open interval* 半開區間 (or a *half-closed interval* 半閉區間).

CLASS PRACTICE

1. Represent the solution of the linear inequality obtained in **Example 1(a)** [P. 105] on the number line below.

◀ *This is also known as the graphical representation of the solution.*

2. Represent the solution of the linear inequality obtained in **Example 1(b)** [P. 105] on the number line below.

3. Solve the linear inequality $\frac{1}{2}(x+3) \geqslant \frac{3x}{4}$ and represent the solution on the number line below.

Solution

II. Solving Compound Linear Inequalities in One Variable

Compound linear inequalities are two or more linear inequalities related together by the words '*and*' or '*or*'.

COMPOUND INEQUALITIES INVOLVING '*AND*'

When we are asked to solve two inequalities related together by '*and*', we have to find those values of x which can satisfy BOTH inequalities. In other words, a value of x which satisfies one inequality but not the other cannot be included in the solution.

Example 2 Solve $5x + 7 > 11$ *and* $2x - 5 < 9$ and represent the solution on the number line.

Solution   Solving $5x + 7 > 11$, we have

$$5x > 4$$

$$x > \frac{4}{5} \; \ldots \ldots \text{ (i)}$$

Solving $2x - 5 < 9$, we have

$$2x < 14$$

$$x < 7 \ldots \ldots \ldots \text{(ii)}$$

Combining **(i)** and **(ii)**, we have

$$\frac{4}{5} < x < 7.$$

Graphical representation of the solution:

0    $\frac{4}{5}$ 7

Note : When we are asked to solve the system of inequalities

$$\begin{cases} 5x + 7 > 11 \\ 2x - 5 < 9, \end{cases}$$

it means that we have to find the values of x which satisfy *both* $5x + 7 > 11$ *and* $2x - 5 < 9$. The method used would be exactly the same as that stated in **Example 2** above.

─ *What is Wrong?* ─

Given the inequalities:
$5x + 7 > 2x - 5 > 9$.
A student solves the inequalities in the following way:

$$5x + 7 > 9 \; \ldots \ldots \text{ (i)}$$
$$and \; 5x + 7 > 2x - 5. \; \ldots \text{(ii)}$$

From (i),

$$5x > 2,$$
$$x > \frac{2}{5}.$$

From (ii),

$$3x > -12$$
$$x > -4$$
$$\therefore \; x > \frac{2}{5}.$$

Is his answer correct? Why?

COMPOUND INEQUALITIES INVOLVING 'OR'

On the other hand, when we are asked to solve two inequalities related together by '*or*', any value of x satisfying any **one** of the two inequalities can be included in the solution.

Example 3 Solve $3x - 8 > \dfrac{18 - 5x}{3}$ *or* $5(x + 2) > x + 2$ and represent the solution on the number line.

Solution   Solving $3x - 8 > \dfrac{18 - 5x}{3}$, we have

$$9x - 24 > 18 - 5x$$
$$14x > 42$$
$$\therefore \qquad x > 3 \ldots \ldots \ldots \text{(i)}$$

Solving $5(x + 2) > x + 2$, we have
$$5x + 10 > x + 2$$
$$4x > -8$$
$$\therefore \qquad x > -2 \ldots \ldots \ldots \text{(ii)}$$

◄ *Caution:*
Do NOT try to solve the inequality by dividing both sides of the inequality by $x + 2$! Do you know why?

Combining **(i)** and **(ii)**, we have
$$x > 3 \quad or \quad x > -2.$$

$$\therefore \quad \underline{\text{The solution is } x > -2.}$$

◄ *Note:*
The solution $x > -2$ includes the solution $x > 3$.

Graphical representation of the solution:

-2 0

EXERCISE   4A

(*Level 1*)

Solve each of the following inequalities and represent the solution on the number line. **[Nos. 1–4]**

1. $2\left(\dfrac{4}{3}x - 2\right) \geqslant 20$

2. $3x - 2 < \dfrac{15x + 4}{4}$

3. $\dfrac{3(x - 4)}{5} \leqslant \dfrac{4 - x}{3}$

4. $\dfrac{3x + 1}{2} + \dfrac{x + 3}{4} < x + 2$

Solve each of the following inequalities and represent the solution on the number line. **[Nos. 5–8]**

5. $\begin{cases} 2x - 7 < 3x - 2 \\ 5x - 1 < 4x + 2 \end{cases}$

6. $-1 \leqslant \frac{1}{2}x - 7$ *and* $\frac{3}{2}x - 9 > 0$

7. $2 < \frac{2x + 3}{6} < \frac{5}{2}$

8. $3x - 7 > 8$ *or* $5x + 1 < 11$

(Level 2)

9. Solve the inequality

$$-2\left(\frac{3x + 4}{3} - \frac{x - 2}{5}\right) \geqslant 4$$

and represent the solution graphically.

10. **(a)** Solve the inequality

$$2x - \frac{3x}{2} < \frac{x}{4} + 3.$$

(b) Using the result of **(a)**, solve the inequality

$$2(2y + 3) - \frac{3}{2}(2y + 3) < \frac{2y + 3}{4} + 3.$$

Solve each of the following systems of compound inequalities and represent the solution on the number line. **[Nos. 11–16]**
(*State which system of inequality, if any, has no solution.*)

11. $\begin{cases} \frac{3}{4}(x - 3) - x \leqslant -5 \\ 2 - \frac{2}{3}(3 - x) > 4 \end{cases}$

12. $\frac{x - 8}{7} + 2 \geqslant 0$ *and* $2 \leqslant \frac{1}{2} - \frac{x}{4}$

13. $2 + \frac{x}{2} \leqslant \frac{2x + 1}{3} \leqslant \frac{x + 1}{2}$

14. $x + \frac{1}{2} > \frac{x + 1}{3}$ *or* $3x < \frac{2x + 1}{2} + 1$

15. $\frac{1 - x}{2} > 0$ *and* $3x - 2 \geqslant 5x + 6$ *and* $7 + x \leqslant \frac{2}{3}x$

16. $x - \frac{1}{2} \leqslant 2x + 1 < 6$ *or* $x > \frac{2 + x}{3}$

17. **(a)** Solve the compound inequality

$$\begin{cases} \frac{2x - 1}{3} \leqslant 4 - \frac{3x}{2} \\ 3x + 4 > x - 2. \end{cases}$$

(b) In addition, if x is a positive integer, find the possible values of x.

*18. **(a)** Solve the compound inequality

$$x + 2 > \frac{3x + 2}{4} \geqslant 2x + 1.$$

(b) In addition, if x is an integer, find the greatest and the least values of x.

4.2 Quadratic Inequalities in One Variable

A *quadratic* inequality in one variable is an inequality involving only one variable in the *second* degree.

◄ *Recall:*
A linear inequality in one variable is an inequality involving only one variable in the first degree.

The following are some common types of quadratic inequalities in x.

(1) $ax^2 + bx + c \geqslant 0$,

(2) $ax^2 + bx + c > 0$,

(3) $ax^2 + bx + c \leqslant 0$,

(4) $ax^2 + bx + c < 0$,

where a is non-zero.

Quadratic inequalities can be solved by methods related to the methods for solving quadratic equations, namely **(i)** the graphical method and **(ii)** the algebraic method.

We shall discuss the graphical method first because it can help us understand the concept of solving quadratic inequalities better.

A. Solution by the Graphical Method

Consider the quadratic inequality $x^2 - 2x - 3 > 0$.

We can solve this inequality from the graph of the corresponding quadratic function $y = x^2 - 2x - 3$. [**Fig. 6**]

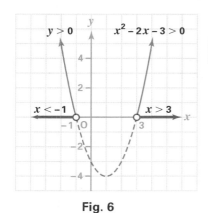

Fig. 6

$y > 0$

◄ i.e. $x^2 - 2x - 3 > 0$

when $x < -1$ *or* $x > 3$.

∴ The solution of $x^2 - 2x - 3 > 0$ is $x < -1$ *or* $x > 3$.

Consider the quadratic inequality $x^2 - 2x - 3 < 0$. We can also use the graph of $y = x^2 - 2x - 3$ to solve $x^2 - 2x - 3 < 0$. [Fig. 7]

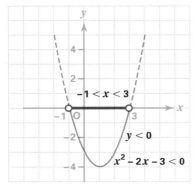

Fig. 7

when $-1 < x < 3$.

$\therefore$ The solution of $x^2 - 2x - 3 < 0$ is

$-1 < x < 3$.

Recall:
$y = 0$ (*i.e.* $x^2 - 2x - 3 = 0$) *when* $x = -1$ *or* $x = 3$.
Graphically, we have

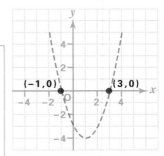

$\therefore$ *The solution of the equation* $x^2 - 2x - 3 = 0$ *are* $x = -1$ *or* $x = 3$.

i.e. $x^2 - 2x - 3 < 0$

Having understood the concepts of solving quadratic inequalities from the above discussions, we can follow the steps listed below to solve any given quadratic inequality *graphically*:

Step (1): | Write the corresponding quadratic function of the given inequality.

Step (2): | Use the factor method to find the x-intercepts of the quadratic function.

Step (3): | Draw a *sketch* of the quadratic function to show where the graph cuts the x-axis.

Step (4): | Read the solution of the quadratic inequality from the sketch.

Example 4 Solve the quadratic inequality $x^2 + 2x - 15 < 0$ graphically and represent the solution on the number line.

Solution   The corresponding quadratic function is

◀ **Step (1)**

$$y = x^2 + 2x - 15.$$

When $y = 0$, we have

$$x^2 + 2x - 15 = 0$$

i.e. $(x - 3)(x + 5) = 0$

◀ **Step (2):**
Put $y = 0$ to find the x-intercepts of the quadratic function.

∴ The x-intercepts are 3 and -5.

Step (3):
Draw a sketch of $y = x^2 + 2x - 15$ to show where the graph cuts the x-axis.

Sketch:

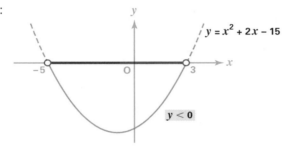

◀ *Recall:*
The graph of $y = x^2 + 2x - 15$ is a parabola opening upwards because the coefficient of x^2 is 1, greater than 0.

From the sketch,

$y < 0$ when $-5 < x < 3$.

∴ The required solution is $-5 < x < 3$.

◀ **Step (4)**

◀ *We can also write $3 > x > -5$.*

Graphical representation of the solution:

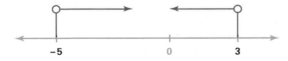

◀ *Recall:*
The symbol 'O' indicates that the numbers -5 and 3 are NOT included in the solution.

Note : With enough practice, **Steps (1)** and **(2)** can be combined to find the x-intercepts of the corresponding quadratic function directly.

Example 5 Solve the quadratic inequality $2x - x^2 \leqslant 0$ graphically and represent the solution on the number line.

Caution:
Reverse the direction of the symbol of inequality after we multiply the whole inequality by −1.

Solution [First we rewrite the inequality as $x^2 - 2x \geqslant 0$ to make the coefficient of x^2 positive.]

◄ *It is customary and convenient to keep the coefficient of x^2 positive so that the graph always opens upwards.*

The corresponding quadratic function is $y = x^2 - 2x$.

When $y = 0$, we have

$$x(x - 2) = 0$$

∴ $x = 0 \quad or \quad x = 2$

◄ *These are the x-intercepts of the quadratic function.*

Sketch:

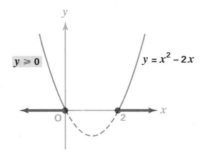

$y \geqslant 0$ $y = x^2 - 2x$

From the sketch,
$y \geqslant 0$ when $x \leqslant 0 \quad or \quad x \geqslant 2$.

∴ The required solution is $x \leqslant 0 \quad or \quad x \geqslant 2$.

◄ *Note:*
$x = 0$ or $x = 2$ are included in the solution since $y = 0$ when $x = 0$ or $x = 2$.

Graphical representation of the solution:

0   2

◄ *Note:*
The symbol '●' indicates that the numbers 0 and 2 are included in the solution.

Note : In our examples above, we can use the factor method to find the x-intercepts easily because the x-intercepts are integers. However, when the factors CANNOT be found easily, we will have to find the x-intercepts using the quadratic formula.

e.g. For the inequality $x^2 - 2x - 2 \geqslant 0$, the corresponding quadratic function is $y = x^2 - 2x - 2$.

To find the x-intercepts, we let $x^2 - 2x - 2 = 0$.

∴ $x = \dfrac{-(-2) \pm \sqrt{(-2)^2 - 4(1)(-2)}}{2(1)}$

$= 1 + \sqrt{3} \quad or \quad 1 - \sqrt{3}$

Recall:
The quadratic formula for solving a quadratic equation in the form of
$$ax^2 + bx + c = 0 \text{ is}$$
$$x = \dfrac{-b \pm \sqrt{b^2 - 4ac}}{2a}.$$

Example 6 Solve the quadratic inequality $x^2 + 4x + 4 > 0$ graphically and represent the solution on the number line.

Solution The corresponding quadratic function is

$$y = x^2 + 4x + 4.$$

When $y = 0$, we have

$$x^2 + 4x + 4 = 0$$

i.e. $(x + 2)^2 = 0$

$\therefore$ $x = -2$ (*repeated*)

Sketch:

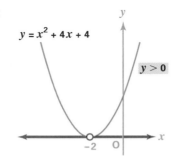

◀ *Note:*
The symbol '○' indicates that the number -2 is NOT included in the solution.

From the sketch,

$y > 0$ when $x > -2$ *or* $x < -2$ but not at $x = -2$.

$\therefore$ The required solution is ALL values of x except -2.

Graphical representation of the solution:

◀ *Question:*
Can you guess what the solution of the quadratic inequality $x^2 + 4x + 4 \geqslant 0$ is?

Note : We have seen in **Example 6** above what happens when a quadratic function has only **one** x-intercept. However, a quadratic function can have **NO** x-intercepts at all.

e.g. For the quadratic inequality $x^2 + 4x + 5 > 0$, the corresponding quadratic function is $y = x^2 + 4x + 5$.

The discriminant of $x^2 + 4x + 5 = 0$ is $4^2 - 4(1)(5) < 0$, therefore the corresponding quadratic function $y = x^2 + 4x + 5$ has no x-intercepts.

The sketch of $y = x^2 + 4x + 5$ also shows that $y = x^2 + 4x + 5$ has NO x-intercepts:

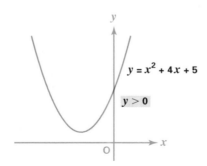

The solution of $x^2 + 4x + 5 > 0$ is ALL values of x since $y > 0$ for ALL values of x.

◄ *Question:*
Relating to the sketch of
$y = x^2 + 4x + 5$, *can you*
find the solution of
$x^2 + 4x + 5 < 0$?

CLASS PRACTICE

1. Solve $x^2 + x - 6 > 0$ graphically and represent the solution on the number line.

   Step (1): Find the x-intercepts of $y = x^2 + x - 6$.

   Step (2): Draw a sketch to show where the graph of $y = x^2 + x - 6$ cuts the x-axis.

   From the sketch, $y > 0$ (i.e. $x^2 + x - 6 > 0$) when _____ .

   ∴ The solution is _____ .

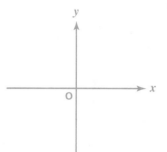

   Graphical representation of the solution:

2. Solve $x^2 - 6x + 5 < 0$ graphically and represent the solution on the number line.

Step (1): Find the x-intercepts of $y = x^2 - 6x + 5$.

Step (2): Draw a sketch to show where the graph of $y = x^2 - 6x + 5$ cuts the x-axis.

From the sketch, $y < 0$ (i.e. $x^2 - 6x + 5 < 0$) when

_____ .

∴ The solution is _____ .

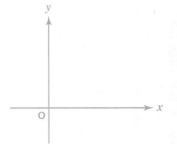

Graphical representation of the solution:

3. Solve $x^2 - 2\sqrt{3}x + 3 < 0$ graphically.

Step (1): Find the x-intercept of $y = x^2 - 2\sqrt{3}x + 3$.

Step (2): Draw a sketch to show where the graph of $y = x^2 - 2\sqrt{3}x + 3$ cuts the x-axis.

From the sketch,

E X E R C I S E **4B**

(Level 1)

Solve each of the following quadratic inequalities graphically and represent the solution on the number line. **[Nos. 1–6]**
(*State which inequality, if any, has no solution.*)

1. $(2x - 1)(3x - 1) > 0$ 2. $x^2 - x - 12 < 0$ 3. $x^2 + 2x - 3 < 0$

4. $x^2 \leqslant 9$ 5. $6x^2 \geqslant 12x$ 6. $(x - 1)(x + 1) < -2$

(Level 2)

Solve each of the following quadratic inequalities graphically and represent the solution on the number line. **[Nos. 7–13]**
(*State which inequality, if any, has no solution.*)

7. $-2x^2 - 3x + 2 \leqslant 0$ 8. $\dfrac{2x(x + 2)}{7} < 10$ 9. $x^2 - 2x - 1 \leqslant 0$

10. $4x^2 - 12x + 9 > 0$ 11. $x^2 + \dfrac{1}{2}x + \dfrac{1}{4} < 0$ 12. $3x(x + 3) \geqslant 2(x + 3)$

*13. $2x(x + 6) \geqslant (3x + 2)(x + 2)$

B. *Solution by the Test Value Method*

Besides the graphical method, here we have another method of solving a quadratic inequality in one variable.

Let us study the following quadratic inequality as an example:

$$x^2 - x - 12 > 0$$

i.e. $(x + 3)(x - 4) > 0$.   ◀ *Factorize the quadratic expression.*

Notice that when $x = -3$ *or* $x = 4$,

$$(x + 3)(x - 4) = 0.$$

The points corresponding to the two values -3 and 4 divide the number line into *three* intervals, as shown in the figure below.   ◀ *Note:*
These two points are usually known as the critical points.

Fig. 8

In fact, only *one value of x* in each *interval* is needed to determine whether or not *all the values of x in that interval* are the solution of the given inequality.

Hence we may select *any* value of x from *each interval* to test whether it satisfies the inequality $(x+3)(x-4) > 0$. From this result we can determine the solution of the inequality.

Note : We do NOT test the value of $x^2 - x - 12$ for $x = -3$ *or* $x = 4$ because $x^2 - x - 12 = 0$ when $x = -3$ *or* 4.

The procedure is illustrated below.

In interval A: $(x < -3)$

◀ *In other words, x lies between $-\infty$ and -3.*

e.g. Take $x = -4$.

Then $(-4+3)(-4-4) = 8 > 0$,

i.e. $(x+3)(x-4) > 0$ is true when $x = -4$.

Hence all the values of x in *interval A* are the *solution of the given inequality.*

In interval B: $(-3 < x < 4)$

◀ *In other words, x lies between -3 and 4.*

e.g. Take $x = 0$.

Then $(0+3)(0-4) = -12 \not> 0$,

i.e. $(x+3)(x-4) > 0$ is *not* true when $x = 0$.

◀ *The symbol '$\not>$' means 'is not greater than'.*

Hence all the values of x in *interval B* are <u>not</u> the *solution of the given inequality.*

In interval C: $(x > 4)$

◀ *In other words, x lies between 4 and ∞.*

e.g. Take $x = 5$.

Then $(5+3)(5-4) = 8 > 0$,

i.e. $(x+3)(x-4) > 0$ is true when $x = 5$.

Hence all the values of x in *interval C* are the *solution of the given inequality.*

From the above discussions, we see that the solution includes the points in either interval A *or* interval C. This can be written as

$$x < -3 \quad or \quad x > 4.$$

Graphical representation of the solution:

To conclude, for any quadratic inequality, if we can find the two critical points which divide the number line into *three* intervals, then the solution of the inequality *MUST* be one of the following cases.

Case 1: 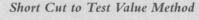 *Case 2:*

Case 3: *Case 4:*

From this conclusion, we derive a '*Short Cut to Test Value Method*' which is stated as follows.

Short Cut to Test Value Method

Interval A   Interval B   Interval C

critical points

Refer to the figure above:

We may take any value of x in the interval B and test this value in the given inequality. There are TWO possible results:

(i) The inequality holds for the chosen value of x, then the solution is all the values of x in interval B. [*Case 1 or Case 2*]

(ii) The inequality does NOT hold for the chosen value of x, then the solution is all the values of x in interval A *or* in interval C. [*Case 3 or Case 4*]

Example 7 Solve $2x^2 + 13x - 7 \geqslant 0$.

Solution Factorizing $2x^2 + 13x - 7$, we have $(2x - 1)(x + 7)$.

∴ The critical points are $\frac{1}{2}$ and -7.

i.e.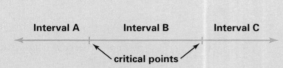

In interval B: $\left(-7 \leqslant x \leqslant \frac{1}{2}\right)$

Take $x = 0$, then $[2(0) - 1](0 + 7) = -7 < 0$

Thus the solution is $x \leqslant -7$ or $x \geqslant \frac{1}{2}$.

◀ *Interval A is $x \leqslant -7$ and interval C is $x \geqslant \frac{1}{2}$.*

◀ *i.e. The solution must lie in either interval A or interval C.*

Note : **(i)** When there is only **one** critical point in a quadratic inequality, the Short Cut to Test Value Method does **NOT** work but the Test Value Method still works to solve the inequality.

cf. **Example 6** *on P.* 115 .

e.g. For $x^2 + 4x + 4 > 0$, -2 is the only critical point. Using the Test Value Method, we see that $x^2 + 4x + 4 > 0$ is true when $x > -2$ or $x < -2$. Hence the solution is ALL values of x except -2.

For $x > -2$, take $x = 3$ and $x^2 + 4x + 4 > 0$; for $x < -2$, take $x = -3$ and $x^2 + 4x + 4 > 0$.

(ii) When there are **NO** critical points in a quadratic inequality, both the Short Cut to Test Value Method and the Test Value Method do **NOT** work, but the '*method of completing the square*' can be used to solve the inequality.

◀ *The discriminant of $x^2 + 4x + 5 = 0$ is $4^2 - 4(1)(5) = -4 < 0$, hence there are no critical points.*

e.g. $x^2 + 4x + 5 = x^2 + 4x + 4 + 1$
$$= (x + 2)^2 + 1$$

∵ $(x + 2)^2 + 1 > 0$ for ALL values of x.

∴ The solution of $x^2 + 4x + 5 > 0$ is **all values of x**.

◀ *cf. The note after* **Example 6** *on P.* 115 .

CLASS PRACTICE

In each of the following, solve the given quadratic inequality algebraically.

Solution

1. $x^2 - 2x - 3 \leqslant 0$ _____

2. $x^2 - 2x - 15 \geqslant 0$ _____

3. $2x - x^2 > 0$ _____

4. $x^2 - 2x - 2 < 0$ _____

5. $2x^2 + 13x - 7 \leqslant 0$ _____

6. $x^2 + 4x + 4 \leqslant 0$ _____

7. $x^2 + 4x + 5 \leqslant 0$ _____

(Level 1)

Solve each of the following quadratic inequalities algebraically and represent the solution on the number line. **[Nos. 1–8]**

1. $(3x+4)(x+8) < 0$

2. $(x+0.3)(8-x) \le 0$

3. $x^2 - 14x + 33 > 0$

4. $x^2 - 16 \le 0$

5. $12x^2 - 3x > 0$

6. $(x-2)^2 < 16$

7. $\dfrac{x(x-1)}{2} \le 3$

8. $(2x-1)(x-2) - (x+2)(x-2) \ge 0$

(Level 2)

Solve each of the following quadratic inequalities algebraically and represent the solution on the number line. **[Nos. 9–19]**

(State which inequality, if any, has no solution.)

9. $6x^2 - 5x - 4 > 0$

10. $-6x^2 + x + 1 > 0$

11. $\dfrac{1}{3} + x^2 \le \dfrac{7x}{6}$

12. $(5-3x)^2 \ge 49$

13. $x^2 - 4x - 3 > 0$

14. $x^2 - 6x + 10 \le 0$

15. $(x-2)(2-x) \ge 0$

16. $\dfrac{x(x-3)}{2} + \dfrac{2x-1}{3} < 0$

17. $(3-2x)(x+3) + 3x(2x-3) \ge 0$

18. $(2x-1)(x+2) \le (3x+2)(x-1)$

*19. $x^2 + 12.8x + 24.15 \le 0$

*20. (a) Solve the system of inequalities:
$$\begin{cases} x(x+1) \le 3(x+1) \\ 4x^2 + 4x - 3 < 0 \end{cases}$$

(b) In addition, if x is an integer, find the maximum value of x.

C. Practical Problems Involving Quadratic Inequalities in One Variable

Example 8 The product of two consecutive even integers is less than or equal to 24. Find all the possible pairs of even numbers.

Solution Let x be the smaller even integer. Then $x + 2$ is the larger even integer.

$$x(x + 2) \leqslant 24$$
$$x^2 + 2x - 24 \leqslant 0$$
$$(x - 4)(x + 6) \leqslant 0$$

Thus $-6 \leqslant x \leqslant 4$

The possible even integers that lie within this range are:

-6, -4, -2, 0, 2 and 4.

∴ The possible pairs of consecutive even integers are $(-6, -4)$, $(-4, -2)$, $(-2, 0)$, $(0, 2)$, $(2, 4)$ and $(4, 6)$.

Use the short cut method:
The critical points are 4 and -6.
Choose $x = 0$, then
$(0 - 4)(0 + 6) = -24 < 0$.

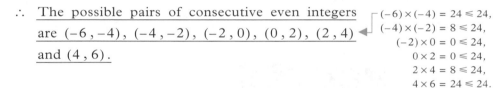

-6 0   4

$(-6) \times (-4) = 24 \leqslant 24$,
$(-4) \times (-2) = 8 \leqslant 24$,
$(-2) \times 0 = 0 \leqslant 24$,
$0 \times 2 = 0 \leqslant 24$,
$2 \times 4 = 8 \leqslant 24$,
$4 \times 6 = 24 \leqslant 24$.

Example 9 Find the range of values of k for which the quadratic equation $x^2 + kx + k = 0$ has

(a) two distinct real roots,

(b) no real roots.

Solution **(a)** For the quadratic equation $x^2 + kx + k = 0$ to have two distinct real roots, the discriminant of the equation $= k^2 - 4(1)(k) > 0$.

$$k^2 - 4k > 0$$
$$k(k - 4) > 0$$

∴ $k < 0$ or $k > 4$

Use the short cut method:
The critical points are 0 and 4.
Choose $k = 2$,
then $2(2 - 4) = -4 < 0$.

0   4

(b) For $x^2 + kx + k = 0$ to have no real roots, the discriminant of the equation $= k^2 - 4(1)(k) < 0$.

$$k^2 - 4k < 0$$
$$k(k - 4) < 0$$

∴ $0 < k < 4$

Example 10 A housewife is going to put 116 m of fence around a plot of land. The plot of land to be enclosed is rectangular in shape. If the area to be enclosed is at least 760 m^2, find the maximum length of the plot.

Solution   Let the length of the plot be ℓ m. Then the width is $\left(\dfrac{116}{2} - \ell\right)$ m, i.e. $(58 - \ell)$ m.

The area of the plot of land is at least 760 m^2,

i.e. $\ell(58 - \ell) \geqslant 760$

$58\ell - \ell^2 - 760 \geqslant 0$

$\ell^2 - 58\ell + 760 \leqslant 0$

$(\ell - 20)(\ell - 38) \leqslant 0$

$\therefore \qquad\qquad 20 \leqslant \ell \leqslant 38$

$\therefore$ The maximum length is 38 m.

> $\because$ *Total length of the fence*
> *= (width + length) × 2*
> $\therefore$ *Width + length*
> *= $\frac{1}{2}$ × total length of the fence*
>
> *i.e.   Width*
> *= $\frac{1}{2}$ × $\begin{array}{c}\text{total length of}\\ \text{the fence}\end{array}$ − length*

> *Use the short cut method:*
> *The critical points are 20 and 38.*
>
> *Choose $\boldsymbol{\ell}$ = 30,*
> *then   (30 − 20)(30 − 38)*
> *   = (10)(−8)*
> *   = −80 < 0.*

E X E R C I S E   4D

(Level 1)

1. Find the range of values of k for which the equation $kx^2 + kx - 9 = 0$ has

   (a) real roots,
   (b) two distinct real roots,
   (c) no real roots.

2. If $x = 3$ is a solution of $(x - k)(x - 2k) < 2$, find the range of values of k.

3. A ball is thrown upwards from the ground so that its height h (in m) after t seconds is given by $h = 15t - 5t^2$. For what range of values of t will the ball be at a height of more than 10 m?

4. A circle with radius r cm has an area ranging from 100 cm^2 to 105 cm^2 inclusive. Find the range of values of r.
   (*Give the answer correct to 3 significant figures.*)

5. The sum of the squares of two consecutive positive integers is less than or equal to 25. Find the possible values of the smaller integer.

(Level 2)

6. The sum S of the first n natural numbers,
$$S = 1 + 2 + 3 + \cdots + n,$$
is given by the formula $S = \frac{1}{2}n(n + 1)$.

    (a) For what values of n will the sum S be less than 66?

    (b) What is the least value of n such that the sum S is more than 190?

7. The difference of two prime numbers is 2. If the product of these two prime numbers is not greater than 143, find all the possible pairs of prime numbers.

8. One side of a rectangular field is bounded by a river. A farmer has 100 m of fencing and wants to fence the other three sides of the field. If he wants to enclose an area of at least 800 m^2, what will be the maximum length of the field along the river?

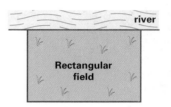

9. The dimensions of a rectangular sheet of cardboard are 16 cm by 10 cm. Squares of equal sizes are cut from each corner and the edges of the cardboard are folded up to form an open box. What is the maximum height of this box if the base has an area of at least 72 cm^2?

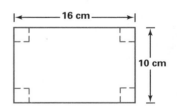

10. The total cost $\$C$ in producing x units of a certain product is given by $C = 20x + 1\,000$. The total income $\$R$ obtained by selling x units of the same product is given by $R = x^2 + 5x$. Find the range of values of x that will give a profit.

*11. To make a cubic lantern of side x cm which is open at the top, one has to build a framework by using pieces of metal wire. Pieces of cloth are then mounted on the framework. The costs of metal wire and mounting cloth are \$4 per 10 cm and \$30 per m^2 respectively.

    (a) Find the total cost of materials for the lantern in terms of x.

    (b) Find the range of values of x if the lantern costs at least \$100 and at most \$150.
        (Give the answer correct to 1 decimal place.)

PART I| *Further Practice*

(*Ex. 4A*)

Solve each of the following inequalities and represent the solution on the number line. **[Nos. 1–3]**
(*State which system of inequality, if any, has no solution.*)

1. $10 - 3x > 2x - \dfrac{1}{2}$ *and* $3x + \dfrac{x}{2} < \dfrac{x + 10}{2}$

2. $-\dfrac{3}{2} < \dfrac{5 - 2x}{4} < \dfrac{1}{2}$

3. $\dfrac{1}{2}(x - 3) \leqslant 2x - 6$ *and* $2(5x - 1) < 13$

4. **(a)** Simplify $x + 2x + 3x + \cdots + 14x + 15x$.

   (b) Solve the inequality $2x + 4x + 6x + \cdots + 30x \leqslant 240$ and represent the solution on a number line.

5. If $10 \leqslant \dfrac{2}{5}(x - 4) + 4 \leqslant 14$, find the possible values of x for each of the following conditions.

   (a) x is an integer greater than 25.

   (b) x is a multiple of 3 smaller than 25.

(*Ex. 4B*)

Solve the following quadratic inequalities graphically and give the answers in surd form if necessary. **[Nos. 6–9]**

6. $x^2 - x - 6 < 0$

7. $2x^2 - 6x - 3 > 0$

8. $(2x + 5)(x - 1) \leqslant (x + 3)^2 + x + 10$

9. $\begin{cases} 12x(x - 1) \leqslant x + 4 \\ x \text{ is an integer.} \end{cases}$

(Ex. 4C)

Solve each of the following quadratic inequalities and represent the solution on the number line. [**Nos. 10–12**]

10. $3(x-1) < x(x-1)$ **11.** $x(5x+37)+14 \geqslant 0$

12. $(4x+1)^2 - (2x+19) \geqslant (5x-3)^2$

*13. **(a)** Solve $y^2 - y - 6 \leqslant 0$.

     (b) Hence, or otherwise, solve
$$(x^2 - 4x - 2)^2 - (x^2 - 4x - 2) - 6 \leqslant 0.$$

(Ex. 4D)

14. The sum of a positive integer n and its reciprocal is not greater than 100. Find the maximum value of n.

15. **(a)** Find the minimum value of k if $2x^2 - 4x + k \geqslant 0$ for all values of x.

     (b) Find the maximum value of k if $-x^2 - 4x + k \leqslant 8$ for all values of x.

16. The figure shows a circle inscribed in a square. If the area of the shaded part is not greater than 100 cm^2, find the maximum length of a diagonal of the square.

(Give the answer correct to 2 decimal places.)

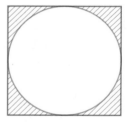

17. The width of a rectangle is shorter than its length by 20 cm. If both the width and the length of the rectangle are increased by 5 cm, the area is at most $1\,925 \text{ cm}^2$. What is the greatest possible area of the original rectangle and what are the corresponding dimensions?

*18. Find the range of values of k so that the quadratic equation
$$2x^2 + (k-4)x = 2(k-1)$$
has two unequal positive roots.

*19. In the figure, ABCD is a square of side 4 cm. E and F are two points on the sides AD and BA respectively such that $BF = ED = x$ cm.

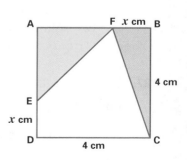

     (a) Find the range of values of x if the area of $\triangle$AFE is not less than 2 cm^2.

     (b) If the area of $\triangle$AFE is less than that of $\triangle$BFC and the difference between their areas is less than 2 cm^2, find the range of values of x.

     (Leave the answer in surd form if necessary.)

PART II | *Miscellaneous*

20. Solve $(12x+1)^2 + (5x-1)^2 \geqslant (13x-1)^2$.

21. **(a)** Expand $(a-b)^2$.

(b) Hence, show that $\dfrac{a+b}{2} \geqslant \sqrt{ab}$ for any positive real numbers a and b.

22. In $\triangle ABC$, $AB = AC = x$ cm and the perimeter is equal to 40 cm. Knowing that the length of each side of a triangle is always less than the sum of the lengths of the other two sides, find the range of values of x in $\triangle ABC$.

23. The radius of a cylinder is r cm and its height is $(r-2)$ cm. The surface area of the cylinder is less than 48π cm^2. Find the range of values of r.

*24. If $\sin\theta = 2x+1$ where θ represents any angle, find the range of values of x.

*25. The height (h) of a right circular cone is related to the radius (r) of the cone such that $h = 4\sqrt{3}r$. If the curved surface area of the right circular cone is greater than 88 cm^2 but less than 198 cm^2, find the range of values of the slant height of the cone.
$\left(Take \ \pi = \dfrac{22}{7}. \right)$

*26. The sides a, b, c and the angle A of $\triangle ABC$ in the figure are related by the cosine formula:
$$a^2 = b^2 + c^2 - 2bc\cos A.$$

(a) Show that there are two solutions for c if
$$\cos^2 A > 1 - \dfrac{a^2}{b^2}.$$

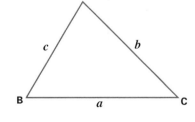

(b) Find the range of values of A if $a = 3$, $b = 4$ and c has two solutions.
(*Give the answer correct to the nearest degree.*)

*27. Solve the following inequalities:

(a) $\dfrac{2x}{x-4} < 0$

[*Hint: Multiply both sides of the inequality by $(x-4)^2$.*]

(b) $\dfrac{2x+1}{x+2} > 1$

PART III | *HKCEE Questions*

(Section A Questions)

28. Solve the inequality $2x^2 \geqslant 5x$. [HKCEE 88]

29. (a) Solve the following inequalities:
 (i) $6x + 1 \geqslant 2x - 3$,
 (ii) $(2 - x)(x + 3) > 0$.

 (b) Using **(a)**, find the values of x which satisfy
 both $6x + 1 \geqslant 2x - 3$ *and* $(2 - x)(x + 3) > 0$.

[HKCEE 90]

(MC Questions)

30. If $a < b < 0$, which of the following must be true?

 A. $-a < -b$

 B. $\frac{a}{b} < 1$

 C. $a^2 < b^2$

 D. $10^a < 10^b$

 E. $a^{-1} < b^{-1}$ [HKCEE 90]

31. How many integers x satisfy the inequality $6x^2 - 7x - 20 \leqslant 0$?

 A. 0
 B. 1
 C. 2
 D. 3
 E. 4 [HKCEE 92]

32.

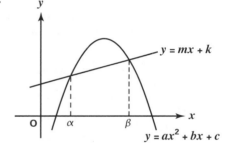

From the figure, if $\alpha \leqslant x \leqslant \beta$, then

 A. $ax^2 + (b - m)x + (c - k) \leqslant 0$.
 B. $ax^2 + (b - m)x + (c - k) < 0$.
 C. $ax^2 + (b - m)x + (c - k) = 0$.
 D. $ax^2 + (b - m)x + (c - k) > 0$.
 E. $ax^2 + (b - m)x + (c - k) \geqslant 0$.

[HKCEE 92]

33. If $x(x + 1) < 5(x + 1)$, then

 A. $x < 5$.
 B. $x < -5$ *or* $x > 1$.
 C. $x < -1$ *or* $x > 5$.
 D. $-5 < x < 1$.
 E. $-1 < x < 5$. [HKCEE 94]

Tsing Ma Bridge is the longest suspension bridge for combined vehicle and rail traffic in the world. The building of this bridge is subject to many restrictions which can be expressed in the form of inequalities.

If we want to minimize the cost of building the bridge subject to the above-mentioned restrictions, then we need the knowledge of a special branch of mathematics called Linear Programming.

CHAPTER

5

Inequalities in Two Unknowns and Linear Programming

5.1 Solving Linear Inequalities in Two Variables Graphically

Fig. 1 below shows the straight line graph of the linear equation
$y = x + 1$.

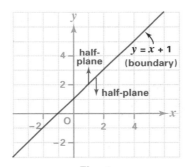

Fig. 1

The straight line divides the coordinate plane into *two* regions:

(i) a region '*above*' the line, and

(ii) a region '*below*' the line.

Each of the regions '*above*' and '*below*' the line is called a
half-plane* and the straight line itself is the **boundary*** of each
half-plane.

---

half-plane 半平面
boundary 邊界

If we start at any point on the line, say P(2, 3), and move vertically *upwards*, the y-coordinate of that point *increases* while the x-coordinate remains the same. [**Fig. 2**] Thus every point in the half-plane 'above' the line satisfies the inequality $y > x + 1$.

Therefore, the 'upper' half-plane is the graph of $y > x + 1$.

Similarly, the 'lower' half-plane is the graph of $y < x + 1$.

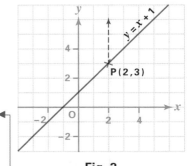

Fig. 2

⌐The y-coordinate decreases as we move vertically downwards from the point P.

Normally the solution of inequalities is indicated by shading on their graphs. If the boundary line is a part of the solution, it is drawn as a *solid* line. If the boundary line is *not* a part of the solution, it is drawn as a *dotted* line. Hence the solutions of $y > x + 1$ [**Fig. 3**] and $y < x + 1$ [**Fig. 4**] are drawn and indicated as shown below.

◄ **Note:**
The graphs of $y > x + 1$, $y < x + 1$ and $y = x + 1$ together cover the whole coordinate plane.

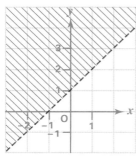

Fig. 3 $y > x + 1$

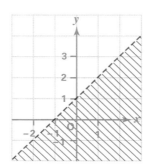

Fig. 4 $y < x + 1$

On the other hand, the **upper** half-plane **and** the **boundary line** in **Fig. 2** together give the graph of $y \geqslant x + 1$. We draw the solution as shown in **Fig. 5**.

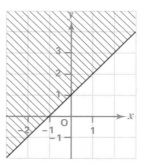

Fig. 5
$y \geqslant x + 1$

The **lower** half-plane **and** the **boundary line** in **Fig. 2** together give the graph of $y \leqslant x + 1$. We draw the solution as shown in **Fig. 6**.

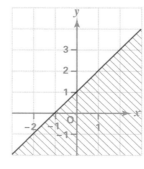

Fig. 6
$y \leqslant x + 1$

Something More

When the boundary line is included in the solution, the region that contains the solution is called a closed *half-plane. When the boundary line is NOT included in the solution, the region that contains the solution is called an* open *half-plane.*

The following examples show how to solve any linear inequality in two variables graphically.

Example 1 Solve $2x + y \geqslant 5$ graphically.

Suggested scale for both axes:
2 divisions = 2 units.

Solution   **Method 1**

[**Step (1)**: Draw the line $2x + y = 5$ as a *solid* line.

Step (2): Shade the half-plane *above* the line, since $2x + y \geqslant 5$ can be written as $y \geqslant 5 - 2x$.]

◀ *Since the symbol '$\geqslant$' is used in the inequality, a solid line should be drawn.*

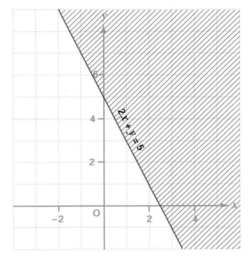

The solution lies on the solid line and in the shaded half-plane.

Method 2

[**Step (1)**: Draw the line $2x + y = 5$ as a *solid* line.

Step (2): We know that the graph of $2x + y \geqslant 5$ is a half-plane. To determine which half-plane to shade, we select a point *not* on the line and check whether its coordinates satisfy the inequality. If so, we shade the half-plane containing the point; otherwise we shade the other half-plane.]

Test the point $(0, 0)$:
$$2(0) + (0) = 0 \not\geqslant 5$$

It is most convenient to take the point $(0, 0)$ as long as it does <u>not</u> lie on the line.

This shows that the point $(0, 0)$ is *not* a solution of $2x + y \geqslant 5$. Thus we shade the half-plane *not* containing the point $(0, 0)$.

Example 2 Solve $x > 3$ graphically.

Solution   [Draw the vertical line $x = 3$ as a *dotted* line. The ◀ *Since the symbol '>' is used*
coordinates of any point on the right of the vertical line   *in the inequality, a dotted*
satisfy $x > 3$. Hence the solution of $x > 3$ lies in the   *line should be drawn.*
half-plane on the right of the line $x = 3$.]

Suggested scale for both axes:
2 divisions = 2 units.

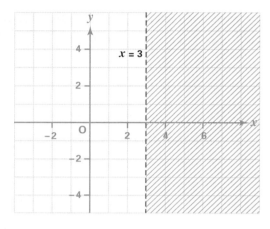

The solution lies in the shaded half-plane.

After we have learnt how to solve a single linear inequality in two
variables graphically, our next example shows how we can solve a
system of inequalities consisting of two linear inequalities in two
variables graphically.

Example 3 Solve graphically the system of linear inequalities

$$\begin{cases} x + y \geqslant 5 \\ y < 2x + 2. \end{cases}$$

Suggested scale for both axes:
2 divisions = 2 units.

Solution   [**Step (1):** Graph $x + y \geqslant 5$.   ◀ *The line $x + y = 5$ should be*
Step (2): Graph $y < 2x + 2$.   ◀ *drawn as a solid line.*
Step (3): The common part of the two graphs gives the
required solution.]   *The line $y = 2x + 2$ should*
be drawn as a dotted line.

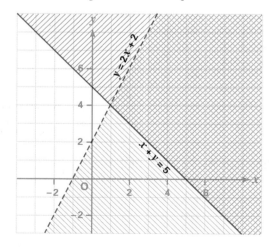

The solution lies in the double shaded
region and on the part of the solid line
$x + y = 5$ within this region.

Note : Too many shadings in the same coordinate plane tend to be confusing. We can avoid this by using arrows to indicate the region in which the solution of **each** individual inequality lies. [**Fig. 7**]

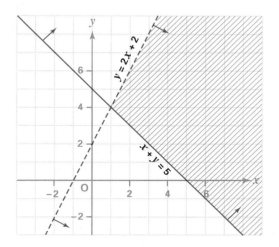

The arrow convention is particularly useful when we solve a system of two or more linear inequalities in two variables.

Fig. 7

CLASS *PRACTICE*

1. The figure shows the graph of $3y = 2x + 12$. Indicate (by shading) on the diagram the solution of $3y \geqslant 2x + 12$.

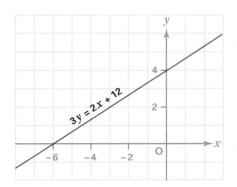

2. The figure shows the graph of $x + 2y = 6$. Indicate (by shading) on the diagram the solution of the following system of inequalities:

$$\begin{cases} x \geqslant 0 \\ y \geqslant 0 \\ x + 2y \leqslant 6 \end{cases}$$

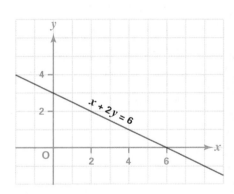

3. The figure shows the graphs of $y = x + 2$ and $y = 5 - x$. Indicate (by shading) on the diagram the solution of the following system of inequalities:

$$\begin{cases} x \geqslant 0 \\ y \geqslant 0 \\ y \leqslant x + 2 \\ y \leqslant 5 - x \end{cases}$$

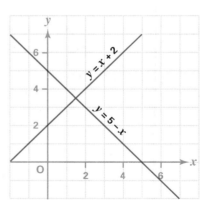

The shaded region in each of the following graphs shows the solution of an inequality or a system of inequalities. Write down the appropriate inequality or the system of inequalities for each case. **[Nos. 4–7]**

4.

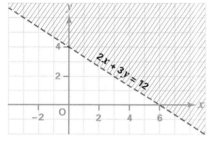

Answer: _____

5.

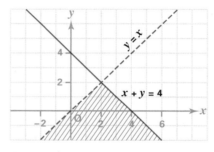

Answer: _____

_____

6.

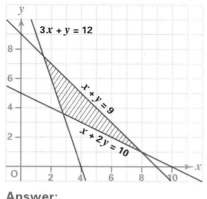

Answer: _____

_____

_____

7.

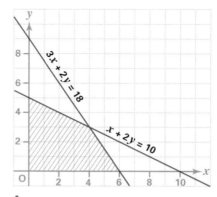

Answer: _____

_____

_____

EXERCISE 5A

[In this exercise, suggested scale for both axes : 10 divisions (1 cm) = 1 unit.]

(Level 1)

Solve the following inequalities graphically. **[Nos. 1–6]**

1. $x \geqslant 4$ **2.** $y \leqslant 2$

3. $3x < y$ **4.** $y - 2x > 6$

5. $-4 \geqslant x + 2y$ **6.** $3x - 2y < 10 + 2y$

Solve the following systems of inequalities graphically. **[Nos. 7–8]**

7. $x \leqslant 3$ *and* $y > 4$ **8.** $\begin{cases} x + y < 0 \\ x - y \geqslant 0 \end{cases}$

(Level 2)

Solve the following systems of inequalities graphically. **[Nos. 9–17]**

9. $x + y \leqslant 1$ *and* $x + y \geqslant -1$ **10.** $2x - y \leqslant 2$ *and* $2y - x \leqslant 2$

11. $\begin{cases} y \leqslant x + 1 \\ y > 1 - x \end{cases}$ **12.** $\begin{cases} 2x - 3y \geqslant 6 \\ 2x \leqslant 3y + 6 \end{cases}$

13. $x > 0$, $y < 0$, $x + 2y > 8$ **14.** $x \geqslant -2$, $y > 2$, $x + 2y \leqslant 4$

15. $\begin{cases} x + y \geqslant 1 \\ x + y \leqslant 4 \\ x - y \leqslant 0 \end{cases}$ **16.** $\begin{cases} x + 1 \geqslant 3 \\ x - y \leqslant 1 \\ x < 3 \end{cases}$

17. $\begin{cases} 4 \leqslant x \leqslant 7 \\ 3 \leqslant y < 5 \end{cases}$

18. Graph the system of inequalities:
$$\begin{cases} x + y \leqslant 5 \\ x + y + 5 \geqslant 0 \\ x \geqslant y + 5 \\ y \geqslant x + 5 \end{cases}$$

*19. Solve graphically $x > 3$, $y > 2$, $x + y \leqslant 8$. Find all possible pairs of values of x and y if they are both integers.

*20. Shade the region determined by the inequalities $x + 2 \geqslant y$, $2x + 5y \geqslant 0$, $15 \geqslant 3x + 4y$. Hence state the coordinates of the corner points of the region. ⌐ *The corner points are the points of intersection of the boundary lines.*

5.2   Linear Programming

A function of the form $y = x + 1$ is a linear function in x. In this function, the values of y *depend* on the values of x. We say that y is a function of x.

On the other hand, a function of the form $P = 4x + y$ is a linear function in x and y. In this function, the values of P *depend* on the values of **both** x and y. We say that P is a function of x and y.

For the linear function $y = x + 1$, the dependent variable y may have a maximum or minimum value according to the restrictions put on the values of x.

e.g. **(i)** If x is an integer with a value not greater than 10, then y has a maximum value of 11 when $x = 10$.

(ii) If x is an integer with a value not less than 0, then y has a minimum value of 1 when $x = 0$.

Very often the restrictions on the variables are given in the form of inequalities, and each inequality is called a **constraint*** to the function.

The branch of Mathematics that deals with maximizing or minimizing a linear function subject to a number of constraints (linear in order) is called '**linear programming***'.

In our discussion that follows, we shall make use of the linear function $P = 4x + y$ as an example to illustrate the concept of linear programming.

The table below [**Table 1**] shows different values of x and y for the function $P = 4x + y$, and the corresponding values of P.

x	0	1	3	6	7
y	0	4	4	4	3
P	0	8	16	28	31

Table 1

Suppose we want to minimize $P = 4x + y$ subject to the constraints $x + y \geqslant 5$ and $y \leqslant 2x + 2$. Then we make use of the values of P in **Table 1** and plot different straight lines of $P = 4x + y$ on the same graph.

Something More

To denote a function of x, we can use the function notation $f(x)$ instead of using the letter y, e.g. $f(x) = x + 1$. Similarly, to denote a function of x and y, we can use the function notation $f(x, y)$ instead of using the letter P, e.g. $f(x, y) = 4x + y$.

Note:
We <u>cannot</u> find a minimum value for y under these restrictions since x can have any value less than 10.

Note:
We <u>cannot</u> find a maximum value for y under these restrictions since x can have any value greater than 0.

In our examples,
$x \leqslant 10$ is a constraint for **(i)**;
$x \geqslant 0$ is a constraint for **(ii)**.

constraint 約束
linear programming 綫性規劃

The result is **Fig. 8** below.

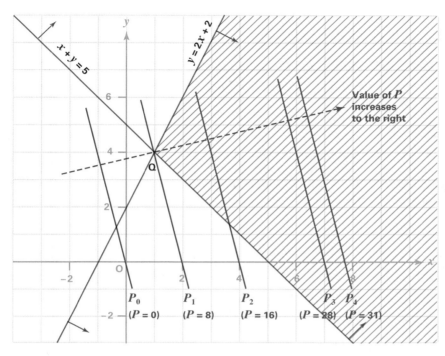

For easy reference, we have labelled the lines that correspond to different values of P as P_0, P_1, P_2, etc.

The solution region of a system of linear inequalities in two variables is also known as the feasible region. The intersections of the boundaries for the system of linear inequalities are called the vertices (i.e. corner points) of the feasible region.

Fig. 8

From **Fig. 8**, we observe that:

(i) for the function $P = 4x + y$, the lines corresponding to different values of the function P are parallel to one another with slopes -4;

◀ P_0: $4x + y = 0$,
P_1: $4x + y = 8$,
P_2: $4x + y = 16$,
$\vdots$

(ii) the lines P_2, P_3, P_4, $\cdots$ that lie on the *right* of the line P_1 intersect the solution region;

Since the slopes of these straight lines are the same, i.e. -4, they are parallel to one another.

(iii) the line P_0 that lies on the *left* of the line P_1 does **NOT** intersect the solution region;

(iv) the greater the value of P, the further the lines to the right.

◀ *Note:*
This is true when the coefficient of x in the function is positive.

From these observations, we conclude that among all the lines that lie in the solution region, P_1 which passes through the vertex $Q(1, 4)$ of the solution region corresponds to the smallest value of P, which is 8.

Using the language of linear programming, we say that the function $P = 4x + y$ has a minimum value of 8 at the vertex $Q(1, 4)$ of the solution region defined by the constraints.

◀ *Question:*
Is it possible to find the maximum value of P subject to the given constraints?

Note : In our example above, we have actually solved a linear programming problem by the graphical method.

Here are some more examples of linear programming.

Example 4 Find graphically the maximum and the minimum values of the linear function $C = 2x + y$ subject to the following system of inequalities.

$$\begin{cases} x \leqslant 7 \dots \dots \dots \text{ (i)} \\ y \leqslant 6 \dots \dots \dots \text{(ii)} \\ x + y \geqslant 8 \dots \dots \text{(iii)} \end{cases}$$

Suggested scale for both axes:
2 divisions = 2 units .

Solution   [**Step (1)**: Draw all the boundary lines and shade the solution region for the given system of inequalities. The coordinates of every point in this region satisfy the given constraints.]

The boundary lines are
$x = 7$, $y = 6$ and $x + y = 8$.

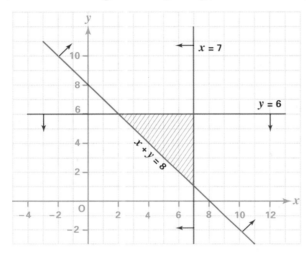

[**Step (2)**: Draw the line $2x + y = 0$ and use the ruler and set square method to obtain a set of parallel lines $2x + y = C$ for different values of C.]

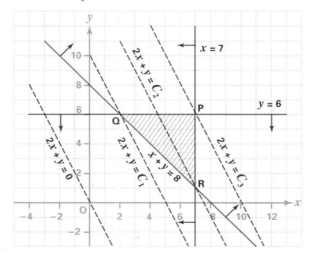

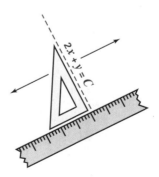

[**Step (3)**: For ALL the lines that lie *in the solution region*, we know, from our previous discussion on linear programming, that $C_3 > C_2 > C_1$. Hence there are no points in the solution region other than the two vertices $P(7, 6)$ and $Q(2, 6)$ that will give the largest or the smallest value of the function C respectively.]

◄ C_3 *lies on the* right *of* C_2; C_1 *lies on the* left *of* C_2.

Thus the function C attains its maximum value at $P(7, 6)$ and its minimum value at $Q(2, 6)$.

∴ Maximum value of $C = 2(7) + 6 = \underline{\underline{20}}$

   Minimum value of $C = 2(2) + 6 = \underline{\underline{10}}$

Alternative Method

[Since a function which is subject to a number of constraints often attains its minimum and maximum values at the vertices of the solution region, we can obtain the maximum and the minimum values of the function by testing the values of C at the vertices.]

◄ *Caution:*
There are exceptions:
(i) *When the graph of the function is parallel to one of the boundary lines.*
(ii) *When one of the constraints requires that x and y are integers.*
[*See* **Example 5(c)** *on next page.*]

Thus at $P(7, 6)$, $C = 2(7) + 6 = 20$,

at $Q(2, 6)$, $C = 2(2) + 6 = 10$,

at $R(7, 1)$, $C = 2(7) + 1 = 15$.

∴ Maximum value of $C = \underline{\underline{20}}$

   Minimum value of $C = \underline{\underline{10}}$

Example 5 **(a)** Graph the system of inequalities:

$$\begin{cases} x \geqslant 0 \\ y \geqslant 0 \\ x - y \geqslant -2 \\ x + y \leqslant 11 \\ 3x + y \geqslant 12 \end{cases}$$

(b) Given a linear function $P(x, y) = x + 2y$. Under the constraints given by the inequalities in **(a)**, find the maximum and the minimum values of P.

(c) Repeat **(b)** if x and y are integers.

Solution   **(a)**

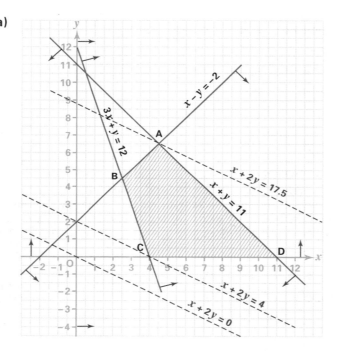

◀ **Question:**
What is the scale for both axes?

(b) [Draw the line $x + 2y = 0$ and use the ruler and set square method to obtain the set of parallel lines $x + 2y = P$ for different values of P.]

From the graph, P is maximum at A(4.5, 6.5) and minimum at C(4, 0).

Maximum value of $P = 4.5 + 2(6.5) = \underline{\underline{17.5}}$

Minimum value of $P = 4 + 2(0) = \underline{\underline{4}}$

Alternative Method

In the diagram, the vertices of the solution region are A(4.5, 6.5), B(2.5, 4.5), C(4, 0) and D(11, 0).

At A(4.5, 6.5), $P = 4.5 + 2(6.5) = 17.5$.

At B(2.5, 4.5), $P = 2.5 + 2(4.5) = 11.5$.

At C(4, 0), $P = 4 + 2(0) = 4$.

At D(11, 0), $P = 11 + 2(0) = 11$.

∴ Maximum value of $P = \underline{\underline{17.5}}$

Minimum value of $P = \underline{\underline{4}}$

(c) [In the diagram below, the points satisfying the constraints are the points whose x- and y-coordinates are integers in the shaded region, i.e. the set of points marked with black dots.]

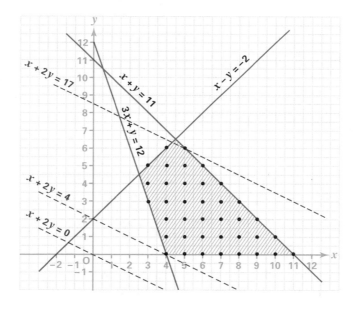

[Draw the line $x + 2y = 0$ and use the ruler and set square method to obtain the set of parallel lines $x + 2y = P$ for different values of P.]

From the graph, P is maximum at (5, 6) and minimum at (4, 0).

◄ *Note:*
Since the additional constraint is that x and y are integers, the alternative method in (b) is not applicable here.

∴ Maximum value of $P = 5 + 2(6) = \underline{\underline{17}}$

Minimum value of $P = 4 + 2(0) = \underline{\underline{4}}$

EXERCISE 5B

[In this exercise, suggested scale for both axes : 10 divisions (1 cm) = 1 unit.]

(Level 1)

In each of the following, the shaded region shows the solution of a system of inequalities. Find the maximum and the minimum values of the given function P. **[Nos. 1–2]**

1. $P = 2x + y$

2. $P = x - 3y$

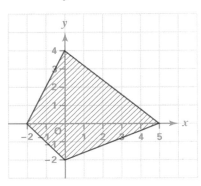

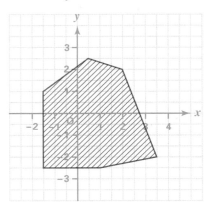

3. Find graphically the minimum value of $f(x, y) = 2x + 3y$ when $2x + y \geqslant 0$, $x + 3y \geqslant 6$.

4. Find graphically the maximum value of the linear function $f(x, y) = 5x + 3y$ subject to the constraints $x \geqslant 0$, $y \geqslant 0$, $x + y \leqslant 8$, $2x + y \leqslant 10$.

(Level 2)

5. Find the values of x and y which maximize $f(x, y) = x + 2y$ when $x \geqslant 0$, $y \geqslant 0$, $x + y \leqslant 6$, $2x + y \leqslant 10$, $x + 3y \leqslant 16$.

6. **(a)** Show graphically the solution region of the following system of inequalities:
$x + y \leqslant 5$, $x + 3y \leqslant 6$, $x \geqslant 1$, $y \geqslant 0$.

(b) Find the maximum value of the linear function $P = x + 1.5y$ subject to the constraints given in **(a)**.

7. **(a)** Graph the inequalities $3x + 5y \leqslant 15$, $x + y \leqslant 4$, $x \geqslant 0$, $y \geqslant 0$.

(b) If x and y are integers, find the maximum and the minimum values of $P = 3x + 4y$ subject to the constraints given in **(a)**.

8. **(a)** Draw and shade the region defined by the following inequalities: $3x + 6 \geqslant 2y$, $2x + 3y \leqslant 12$, $x - 4y \leqslant 4$.

(b) Hence determine the smallest and the greatest values of $f(x, y) = x + y$ subject to the constraints given in **(a)** if x and y are integers.

9. **(a)** Draw and shade the region represented by $y + 2 \geqslant 0$, $x \leqslant 2$, $x + y \leqslant 7$, $2x + 4 \geqslant y$.

   (b) Write down the coordinates of each vertex of the shaded region in **(a)**.

   (c) Find the maximum and the minimum values of the linear function $f(x, y) = 3x - 2y$ subject to the constraints given in **(a)**.

*10. **(a)** Graph the inequalities $-1 \leqslant y \leqslant 3$, $x \leqslant 4$, $2x + y \leqslant 2$, $3x - 2y \geqslant -3$.

   (b) Find the smallest and the greatest values of $W = 4x + 8y - 11$ subject to the constraints given in **(a)**.

5.3	**Applications of Linear Programming**

Problems concerning linear programming often arise in everyday practical situations.

Many practical problems in business, science and industry can be solved using the knowledge of linear programming. In most of these cases, the variables are often non-negative integers as they are usually numbers of certain items.

In general, to solve a problem on linear programming in a practical situation, we can follow the steps below:

Step (1): Identify the variables and represent them by x and y.

Step (2): Express the function to be maximized or minimized in terms of x and y.

Step (3): All the constraints that restrict the function are expressed in inequalities, also in terms of x and y.

Step (4): Check whether x and y can only be integers or whether they can only be non-negative.

Step (5): Graph the solution region in the rectangular coordinate plane.

Step (6): Maximize or minimize the function by sliding the line representing the function on the graph in the *correct* direction.

Example 6 A bookseller has to display two different sizes of books on a bookshelf. The books are 8 cm and 4 cm thick. The thicker book weighs 1 kg each and the thinner book weighs 0.75 kg each. The bookshelf is 0.8 m long and can support a total weight of 12 kg. The bookseller decides that the total number of thinner books on the bookshelf can exceed the total number of thicker books by 9 at most.

(a) Write down the function that represents the total number of books on the bookshelf.

(b) Write down the constraints imposed on the function obtained in (a).

(c) Draw suitable lines on a graph paper and shade the region which is under the constraints in (b).

Suggested scale for both axes: 5 divisions = 5 units .

(d) Find the maximum number of books that can be put on the bookshelf.

Solution (a) Let x be the number of thicker books displayed and y be the number of thinner books displayed.

Then the function $F = x + y$.

(b) The constraints are

(i) x, y: non-negative integers,

(ii) $8x + 4y \leqslant 80$,

(iii) $x + 0.75y \leqslant 12$,

(iv) $y - x \leqslant 9$.

(c)

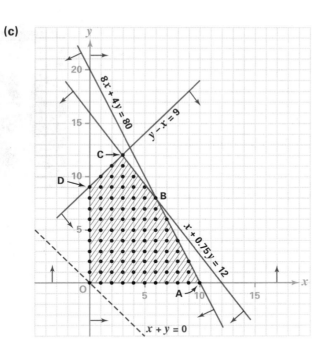

(d) [Draw the line $x + y = 0$. Then use the ruler and set square method and find that the maximum value of F occurs at $C(3, 12)$.]

The corresponding maximum value of F $= 3 + 12 = 15$

∴ The maximum number of books that can be put on the bookshelf is 15.

Example 7 A tailor shop takes orders for dresses and pantsuits. The resources in the shop allow for making at most 7 dresses and 3 pantsuits in a week. It takes the tailor 10 hours to make a dress and 20 hours to make a pantsuit. The tailor intends to work for at most 80 hours in a week. Let x and y be the number of dresses and the number of pantsuits made in a week respectively.

(a) Write down the four constraints on x and y.

(b) Draw and shade on a piece of graph paper the region which satisfies the constraints in (a).

Suggested scale for both axes: 10 divisions = 1 unit.

(c) If the profit on making a dress and that on making a pantsuit are the same, determine the values of x and y that will maximize the profit.

(d) If the profit on making a dress is one-third that on making a pantsuit, find the values of x and y that will maximize the profit.

Solution   (a) The four constraints are

(i) x, y: non-negative integers,

(ii) $x \leqslant 7$,

(iii) $y \leqslant 3$,

(iv) $10x + 20y \leqslant 80$.

(b)

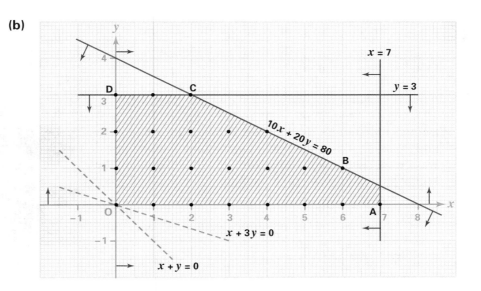

(c) The profit function is denoted by $P_1 = kx + ky$, where k is a non-zero constant.

[Draw the line $P_1 = 0$, i.e. $x + y = 0$. Then use the ruler and set square method to find that the maximum value of P_1 occurs at A(7, 0) and B(6, 1).]

◀ *For $P_1 = 0$,*
$$kx + ky = 0,$$
or $k(x + y) = 0$.
Since $k \neq 0$, we draw the line $x + y = 0$.

$x = \underline{\underline{7}}$, $y = \underline{\underline{0}}$ *or* $x = \underline{\underline{6}}$, $y = \underline{\underline{1}}$

(d) The profit function is denoted by $P_2 = kx + 3ky$, where k is a non-zero constant.

[Draw the line $P_2 = 0$, i.e. $x + 3y = 0$. Then use the ruler and set square method to find that the maximum value of P_2 occurs at C(2, 3).]

◀ *For $P_2 = 0$,*
$$kx + 3ky = 0,$$
or $k(x + 3y) = 0$.
Since $k \neq 0$, we draw the line $x + 3y = 0$.

$x = \underline{\underline{2}}$, $y = \underline{\underline{3}}$

Example 8 The numbers of units of vitamins B_1, B_2 and B_3 in 1 kilogram of food P and those in 1 kilogram of food Q are shown in the table.

Vitamins	B_1	B_2	B_3
Food P	6	2	2
Food Q	2	4	2

The minimum recommended intake per week is 12 units of vitamin B_1, 10 units of vitamin B_2 and 8 units of vitamin B_3. If food P costs \$8 a kilogram and food Q costs \$7 a kilogram, find the cheapest way and also the minimum cost to provide the recommended intake each week.

Solution Let x be the number of kilograms of food P required,
y be the number of kilograms of food Q required.

The constraints are

$$x \geqslant 0 \quad \ldots\ldots \text{ (i)}$$
$$y \geqslant 0 \quad \ldots\ldots \text{(ii)}$$
$$6x + 2y \geqslant 12 \quad \ldots\ldots \text{(iii)}$$
$$2x + 4y \geqslant 10 \quad \ldots\ldots \text{(iv)}$$
$$2x + 2y \geqslant 8 \quad \ldots\ldots \text{(v)}$$

The cost $C = 8x + 7y$

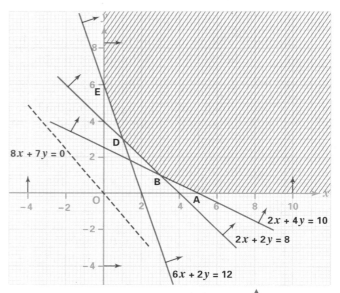

Scale for both axes:
10 *divisions* = 2 *units*.

[The shaded region is the solution region for the inequalities. Note that this region is unbounded and consequently the cost function $8x + 7y$ does not attain a maximum value. To obtain the minimum value of C, the line $8x + 7y = C$ should be as near to the origin as possible because the nearer it is, the smaller the value of C is.]

It is found that the minimum value of C occurs at D$(1, 3)$.

The corresponding minimum value of $C = 8(1) + 7(3) = 29$

∴ The cheapest way to provide the desired intake each week is 1 kilogram of food P and 3 kilograms of food Q.

The minimum cost is \$29.

CLASS PRACTICE

A sports goods manufacturer decides to produce x basketballs and y *water polo balls* 水球 each day subject to the following conditions:

(1) The number of basketballs produced daily should be at least 30 and at most 80.

(2) The number of water polo balls produced daily should be at least 10 and at most 30.

(3) In order to maintain high quality, the total number of balls produced each day should not exceed 80.

(a) Write down all the constraints that represent the above conditions:

(i) _____

(ii) _____

(iii) _____

(iv) _____

(b) Draw suitable lines on the graph paper provided below and shade the region which contains all the points satisfying the above constraints.

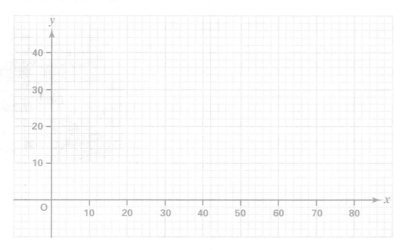

(c) If the manufacturer makes a profit of $8 on each basketball and $15 on each water polo ball, find, from the graph above, how many balls of each kind should be produced daily for maximum profit and state this profit.

Answer: Number of basketballs = _____

Number of water polo balls = _____

Maximum profit = _____

EXERCISE 5C

(Level 1)

1. A bookstore is holding an annual sale. Each student can buy books at $35 each and CD records at $80 each. Let x be the number of books and y be the number of CD records a student buys. Write the following conditions as inequalities.

    (a) Each student is allowed to buy at most 5 books and 10 records.

    (b) A student has $450 to buy books and records.

2. A manufacturer wants to make two types of machines, A and B. Type A machine requires 10 man-hours to make and $150 of raw materials. Type B machine requires 9 man-hours to make and $240 of raw materials. The manufacturer finds out that he has at most 1 000 man-hours and $24 000 worth of raw materials available for these machines. Let x be the number of type A machines made and y be the number of type B machines made. Write down a system of constraints that represent the above conditions.

3. The parking area in a small car park is 720 m^2. The average area for a car is 6 m^2 and for a truck is 24 m^2. Not more than 60 vehicles can be parked in this car park at the same time.

    (a) Supposing that x is the number of cars and y is the number of trucks to be parked in the car park, write down a system of inequalities in x and y.

    (b) Show on a graph the solution of the system of inequalities.

    (c) If the parking charge for a car is $20 per hour and for a truck is $50 per hour, in order to maximize income, how many of each vehicle should be allowed in the car park per hour? State this income.

◄ *Suggested scales:*
x-axis,
10 *divisions* (1 *cm*) = 20 *units*;
y-axis,
10 *divisions* (1 *cm*) = 5 *units* .

4. A grocer sells at least 6 kg of lettuces whenever he sells 1 kg of carrots. Carrots and lettuces cost $15 per kg and $12.5 per kg respectively. He has a capital of $4 500.

   (a) Let x kg and y kg be the weights of carrots and lettuces he buys respectively. Write down the four constraints on x and y.

   (b) On a graph paper, draw and shade the region satisfying the constraints in (a).

   ◄ *Suggested scale for both axes:*
   10 divisions (1 cm) = 50 units .

   (c) If the profits on 1 kg of carrots and 1 kg of lettuces are $4 and $2 respectively, find the weight of each of them that he should buy to secure a maximum profit.

5. A toy factory employs a man and a boy to make two types of toys. The man can make 10 toy cars and 4 toy guns per hour. The boy can make 6 toy cars and 4 toy guns per hour. The factory needs to make at least 60 toy cars and 32 toy guns a day.

   (a) If the man and the boy work for x hours and y hours a day respectively, write down a set of inequalities in x and y.

   (b) Draw suitable lines on a graph paper and shade the region that satisfies the inequalities in (a).

   ◄ *Suggested scale for both axes:*
   10 divisions (1 cm) = 2 units .

   (c) If the man and the boy are paid $20 and $15 per hour respectively, find the number of hours worked by the man and the boy respectively in order to minimize the cost.

(*Level 2*)

6. 500 television sets are transported by a lorry and a van. The lorry can take 100 sets at a time and the van can take 40 sets at a time. It is decided that the van will make at least as many journeys as the lorry.

   (a) Let x and y denote the number of journeys made by the lorry and the van respectively. Write down a system of inequalities in x and y.

   (b) Graph the inequalities in (a).

   ◄ *Suggested scales:*
   x-axis,
   10 divisions (1 cm) = 1 unit ;
   y-axis,
   10 divisions (1 cm) = 2 units .

   (c) The cost of each journey is $320 for the lorry and $150 for the van. How many journeys should each vehicle make to keep the cost to a minimum? What is the minimum cost?

   (d) Repeat part (c) if the cost of each journey for the van reduces to $120.

7. A woman knits pullovers and *jerseys* 毛織運動衫 from red and green wool. Each pullover needs 200 g of red wool and 100 g of green wool. Each jersey needs 80 g of red wool and 250 g of green wool. The woman has 1 000 g of wool for each colour. Suppose she makes x pullovers and y jerseys.

(a) Write down the constraints on x and y for the above conditions.

(b) Draw and shade the region described by the constraints in **(a)** on a graph paper.

◄ *Suggested scale for both axes: 10 divisions (1 cm) = 2 units.*

(c) If the woman makes a profit of $120 on each pullover and $144 on each jersey, find the most profitable combination of the numbers of pullovers and jerseys she should knit.

8. A camera company is having a sale on print film and slide film. The company can make a profit of $4 on each roll of slide film and a profit of $3 on each roll of print film. Sales records indicate that the company should have enough film in stock to sell at least 5 rolls of print film for every 3 rolls of slide film. The company has room to keep a maximum of 12 000 rolls of film.

(a) Let the company store x rolls of print film and y rolls of slide film. Write down the constraints on x and y in the form of inequalities.

(b) Graph the constraints in **(a)**.

(c) How many rolls of each type of film must the company sell in order to make the greatest profit?

Suggested scale for both axes: 10 divisions (1 cm) = 2 000 units.

9. Mrs. Chan decides to hold a birthday party for her daughter and expects to invite x boys and y girls.

(a) Write down the inequalities in x and y for the following statements.
  (i) At least 5 girls will be invited.
  (ii) Mrs. Chan will invite at least 2 boys, but not more than 7.
  (iii) The number of girls will be at least 2 more than the number of boys.

(b) On a sheet of graph paper, draw and shade the region that satisfies the inequalities in **(a)**.

◄ *Suggested scale for both axes: 10 divisions (1 cm) = 1 unit.*

(c) If each boy and each girl are expected to drink 3 and 2 cans of soft drinks respectively, find the minimum number of cans of soft drinks Mrs. Chan should buy for her guests. Also, find the numbers of boys and girls invited in this case.

10. A nutritionist is planning a menu consisting of two main foods A and B. The number of units of vitamins in one gram of each food is given in the table below:

Food	Vitamin A	Vitamin B	Vitamin C
A	2	1	4
B	3	3	3

The nutritionist wants the meal to provide at least 18 units of vitamin A, 12 units of vitamin B and 24 units of vitamin C.

(a) Let x grams be the weight of food A served and y grams be the weight of food B served. Set up all the above constraints on x and y.

(b) On a sheet of graph paper, draw and shade the region that satisfies the constraints in **(a)**.

◄ *Suggested scale for both axes: 10 divisions (1 cm) = 2 units.*

(c) If one gram of A costs 20 cents and one gram of B costs 25 cents, how many grams of each food should be served to minimize the cost of the meal yet satisfy the nutritionist's requirements?

11. You are about to take a test which contains two sections: section A and section B. There are 10 questions in each section, the marks and time required for each question in the two sections are given in the following table:

Section	Marks	Time
A	7 points	8 minutes
B	12 points	10 minutes

You must attempt at least 9 questions and the maximum time available for the test is 80 minutes.

(a) Let x questions from section A and y questions from section B be attempted, write down all the constraints in terms of x and y.

(b) Draw suitable straight lines on a sheet of graph paper and shade the region which satisfies the constraints in **(a)**.

◄ *Suggested scale for both axes: 10 divisions (1 cm) = 1 unit.*

(c) In order to maximize your score, how many questions in each section should you do? What is the maximum score?

*12. For 'Tasty' mixed rice, the percentages by weight of Chinese rice and Japanese rice are 70% and 30% respectively. For 'Chewy' mixed rice, the percentages by weight of Chinese rice and Japanese rice are 40% and 60% respectively. A merchant wishes to produce at least 10 kg of a new product called 'Super Rice' by mixing 'Tasty' and 'Chewy' together. For the new product, the least percentages by weight of Chinese rice and Japanese rice are 50% and 35% respectively.

    (a) If 'Super Rice' contains x kg of 'Tasty' and y kg of 'Chewy', write down the inequalities in x and y.

    (b) Show on a graph the solution of the set of inequalities in **(a)**.

◀ *Students should choose a suitable scale for each axis by themselves.*

    (c) If the costs of 'Tasty' and 'Chewy' per kg are $8 and $10 respectively, how should the merchant blend 'Tasty' and 'Chewy' in order to minimize the cost of 'Super Rice'?

*13. Mr. Wong plans to buy two types of machines A and B. Type A takes 2 m^2 of space and type B takes 3 m^2. Together the two types of machines cannot take up more than 35.5 m^2 of space. Type A costs $1 000 each and type B costs $6 000 each. Mr. Wong plans to spend an amount not more than $47 000 on the machines. The ratio of the number of type A machines to that of type B machines cannot be greater than 2 : 1 .

    (a) If Mr. Wong buys x machines of type A and y machines of type B, write down all the above constraints for x and y.

    (b) Draw and shade the region that satisfies the constraints in **(a)** on a graph paper.

    (c) Find the maximum number of machines that can be bought.

    (d) If type A and type B machines depreciate each year by 10% and 25% respectively, find the numbers of type A and type B machines should be bought in order to keep the value of the machines to a maximum after one year.

PART I | *Further Practice*

(Ex. 5A)

1. (a) Graph the solution region of the following system of inequalities:

$$\begin{cases} x + y \leqslant 5 \\ 3x - 2y \geqslant 0 \\ 4y \geqslant x \end{cases}$$

◀ *Suggested scale for both axes:*
10 divisions (1 cm) = 1 unit .

(b) Find the area of this solution region.

2. (a) Solve graphically the system of inequalities:

$$\begin{cases} y + 2x > 3 \\ y + x \leqslant 5 \\ 3y - 2x \geqslant -3 \\ -x + 2y < 4 \end{cases}$$

◀ *Suggested scale for both axes:*
10 divisions (1 cm) = 1 unit .

(b) Hence, find all possible pairs of values of x and y satisfying the system of inequalities in **(a)**, if x and y are integers.

3. The shaded region determined by a number of straight lines in each of the following figures shows the solution of a system of inequalities. Write down the appropriate system of inequalities for each case.

(a)   **(b)**

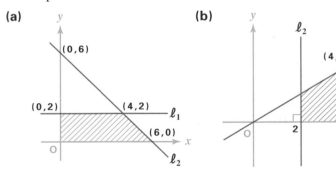

*4. Write down the system of inequalities which has a solution region as shaded in the figure.

[*Hint: You may use 'or'.*]

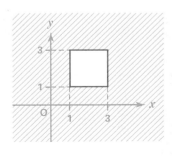

(Ex. 5B)

5. Find graphically the maximum and the minimum values of $x + 3y$ subject to $x + y \leqslant 8$, $5x + 2y \geqslant 14$, $x \geqslant 2$, $y \geqslant 0$. ◀ *Suggested scale for both axes:* *10 divisions (1 cm) = 1 unit.*

6. Find graphically the maximum and the minimum values of the linear function $f(x, y) = 20 - 3x + 2y$ subject to the constraints $-2 \leqslant x \leqslant 5$ *and* $-2 \leqslant y \leqslant 5$. ◀ *Suggested scale for both axes:* *10 divisions (1 cm) = 1 unit.*

7. **(a)** Graph the system of inequalities:
$$x + y \geqslant 4,$$
$$4x - 3y - 9 \leqslant 0,$$
$$3x \geqslant 2y - 3,$$
$$x + 3y - 21 \leqslant 0.$$
◀ *Suggested scale for both axes:* *10 divisions (1 cm) = 1 unit.*

   (b) Find the maximum and the minimum values of the linear function $f(x, y) = 300 - x - 3y$ subject to the above constraints.

*8. **(a) (i)** On a sheet of graph paper, draw the straight lines
$$\ell_1 : 2x + y = 8,$$
$$\ell_2 : x + y = 6.$$

   (ii) On the graph, use dots (•) to mark the points with integral coordinates that satisfy all the following constraints:
$$x > 0,$$
$$y > 0,$$
$$2x + y > 8,$$
$$x + y \leqslant 6.$$

   (b) It is given that $P = x + 4y$, where x and y are integers. Under the constraints given in **(a)(ii)**, find

   (i) the values of x and y when P is a maximum,

   (ii) the minimum value of P.

*9. In the figure, the three straight lines ℓ_1, ℓ_2 and ℓ_3 intersect at three points A$(1,5)$, B$(-3,-1)$ and C$(8,-3)$.

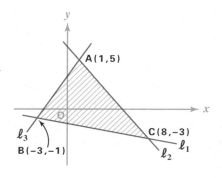

(a) Write down the inequalities that determine the shaded region, including the boundary, in the given figure.

(b) Find the maximum and the minimum values of the linear function $f(x,y) = 2x - 3y - 1$ subject to the constraints obtained in **(a)**.

(c) Find the maximum and the minimum values of the linear function $f(x,y)$ if there is an additional constraint that $x \leqslant -1$.

(Ex. 5C)

10. Ben has \$300 for buying comic books and story books. He wants to buy at least 6 books altogether. Each comic book costs \$25 and each story book costs \$30.

(a) Represent these information on a graph.

◄ *Suggested scale for both axes:*
10 divisions (1 cm) = 2 units .

(b) If he buys the same number of books of each kind, what is the possible total number of books he buys?

11. To grow top quality apples, a farmer needs to use at least 8.4 kg of chemical N and 6.6 kg of chemical P in his fertilizers. The percentages of chemicals N and P in two types of fertilizers A and B that the farmer uses are different. This information together with the cost per kg of the fertilizers are shown in the table below.

Fertilizer	Percentage of chemical N	Percentage of chemical P	Cost per kg
A	40%	60%	\$19.2
B	70%	30%	\$24.0

(a) Find graphically the number of kg of each type of fertilizer used by the farmer so that the total cost can be kept to a minimum.

◄ *Suggested scale for both axes:*
10 divisions (1 cm) = 5 units .

(b) What is this minimum cost?

12. A builder plans to build housing units on a plot of land with x units for couples and y units for single persons satisfying the following conditions:

(1) There must be at least 9 units.

(2) The number of units for single persons cannot exceed the number of units for couples by 7 or more.

(3) There is a maximum of 480 m^2 of floor area available. Each unit for couples takes 60 m^2 and each unit for single persons takes 30 m^2.

(a) Write down all the constraints on x and y for the above information.

(b) If the units are for hire and the rents on a unit for couples and a unit for single persons are $400 and $300 respectively, find graphically the values of x and y so that the total rent received will be a maximum.

◄ *Suggested scale for both axes:*
10 divisions (1 cm) = 2 units.

13. Wilma and Fred are preparing for their wedding. The price for the banquet is $3 000 per table (for 12 people) and they need to rent a flat for 12 months. It is known that the rent is $200 per m^2 each month. They have $84 000 cash in hand to cover both expenses. Wilma's mother insists to invite at least 72 people to the banquet. Wilma wants to live in a flat not smaller than 15 m^2. Fred's father advises them that the money spent on the banquet should not exceed the money for rent.

(a) Let the area of the flat be x m^2 and the number of tables they order be y. If everyone's wish is met, write down inequalities in x and y to represent all the constraints. Draw a suitable graph and shade the solution region.

◄ *Suggested scale for both axes:*
10 divisions (1 cm) = 5 units.

(b) Wilma and Fred expect to decorate their flat at a cost of $100 per m^2, and they want to provide wine for every table in the banquet. The wine will cost an additional amount of $240 per table. Let $C denote the sum of the decoration cost and the additional charge for the wine. What are the minimum and the maximum values of C?

*14. A manufacturer wanted to have at least 300 m^2 of floor area for his store room, so he decided to sell some of his machines at a loss to spare some space. He had two types of machines: type A and type B. The manufacturer lost \$100 on each machine of type A sold and \$200 on each machine of type B sold. Each machine of type A occupied 9 m^2 and each machine of type B occupied 13 m^2. It was necessary to sell at least 10 machines of type A.

(a) If x machines of type A and y machines of type B were sold, write down a set of inequalities in x and y.

(b) Graph the inequalities in **(a)**.

(c) How many machines of each type did he have to sell in order to keep his loss to a minimum? (*Two solutions*)

Part II | *Miscellaneous*

15. (a) Solve graphically the system of inequalities:
$$\begin{cases} y + 2x < 3 \\ 3y - 2x \geqslant -3 \end{cases}$$

◀ *Suggested scale for both axes:*
10 divisions (1 cm) = 1 unit.

(b) Hence, find all possible pairs of values of x and y satisfying the system of inequalities in **(a)**, if x and y are non-negative integers.

16.

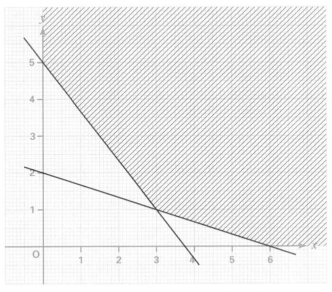

In the figure, the shaded region, including the boundary, is determined by a set of inequalities.

(a) Write down the set of inequalities.

(b) (x, y) is any point in the shaded region. Find the minimum value of $100 + 2x + 3y$.

17. In a day, a man can work x hours on gardening and y hours on woodcarving. He works at least 6 hours/day and at most 9 hours/day. His time spent on gardening is at least equal to the time spent on woodcarving. The wages for gardening and for woodcarving are $20/h and $30/h respectively.

(a) Set up a system of constraints on x and y, and show the solution region on a sheet of graph paper.

◄ *Suggested scale for both axes:*
10 divisions (1 cm) = 2 units .

(b) Find the time that he has to spend on each job to maximize his daily wages.

(c) If he works 8 hours/day on the jobs, how long should he spend on each job so that the daily wages are maximum?

*18. The angles of $\triangle$XYZ are denoted by $x°$, $y°$ and $z°$. Given that $x > 100$ and $y > z > 30$.

(a) Show that $x + y < 150$,
$$x + 2y > 180.$$

(b) On a sheet of graph paper, draw and shade the region represented by the three inequalities
$$x > 100,$$
$$x + y < 150,$$
$$x + 2y > 180.$$

(c) If x and y are both multiples of 5, write down the coordinates of the point which satisfies the above inequalities.

PART III | HKCEE Questions

(Section A Questions)

19.

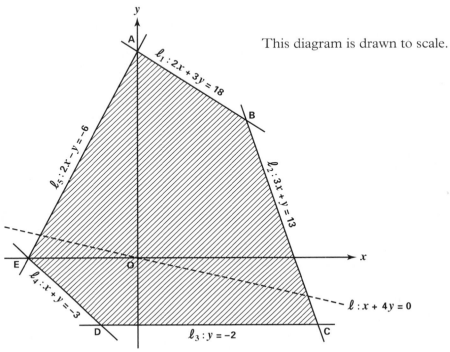

This diagram is drawn to scale.

In the figure, the shaded region ABCDE is bounded by the five given lines ℓ_1, ℓ_2, ℓ_3, ℓ_4 and ℓ_5. The line $\ell : x + 4y = 0$ passes through the origin O.

Let $P = x + 4y - 2$, where (x, y) is any point in the shaded region including the boundary. Find the greatest and the least values of P.   [HKCEE 90]

20.

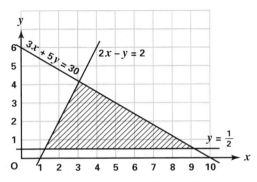

In the figure, the shaded region, including the boundary, is determined by three inequalities.

(a) Write down the three inequalities.

(b) How many points (x, y), where x and y are both integers, satisfy the three inequalities in **(a)**?

[HKCEE 92]

(Section B Questions) ━━━━━━━━━━━━━━━━━━━━━━━━━━━━━━━━━●

21. In the figure, $\ell_1 : 2y = 3$,

$\qquad \ell_2 : 3x - 2y = 0$.

The line ℓ_3 passes through $(0, 10)$ and $(10, 0)$.

(a) Find the equation of ℓ_3.

(b) Find the coordinates of the points A, B and C.

(c) In the figure, the shaded region, including the boundary, is determined by three inequalities. Write down these inequalities.

(d) (x, y) is any point in the shaded region, including the boundary, and $P = x + 2y - 5$. Find the maximum and minimum values of P.

[HKCEE 84]

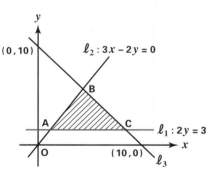

22. (a) (i)

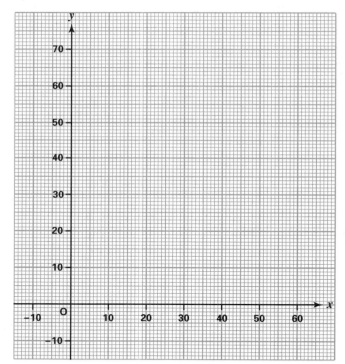

◀ *A duplicate of this graph paper is provided in the Student Handbook 5A.*

On the graph paper provided, draw the following straight lines:

$\qquad x + y = 40$,

$\qquad x + 3y = 60$,

$\qquad 7x + 2y = 140$.

(ii) On the same graph paper, shade the region that satisfies all the following constraints:

$\qquad x \geqslant 0$,

$\qquad y \geqslant 0$,

$\qquad x + y \geqslant 40$,

$\qquad x + 3y \geqslant 60$,

$\qquad 7x + 2y \geqslant 140$.

(b) A company has two workshops A and B. Workshop A produces 1 cabinet, 1 table and 7 chairs each day; Workshop B produces 1 cabinet, 3 tables and 2 chairs each day. The company gets an order for 40 cabinets, 60 tables and 140 chairs. The expenditures to operate Workshop A and Workshop B are respectively $1 000 and $2 000 each day. Use the result of **(a)(ii)** to find the number of days each workshop should operate to meet the order if the total expenditure in operating the workshops is to be kept to a minimum.

(*Denote the number of days that Workshops A and B should operate by x and y respectively.*)

[HKCEE 86]

23.

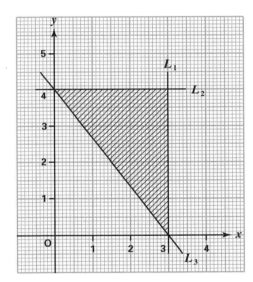

> ◄ A duplicate of this graph is provided in the <u>Student Handbook 5A</u>.

In the figure, L_1 is the line $x = 3$ and L_2 is the line $y = 4$. L_3 is the line passing through the points $(3, 0)$ and $(0, 4)$.

(a) Find the equation of L_3 in the form $ax + by = c$, where a, b and c are integers.

(b) Write down the three constraints which determine the shaded region, including the boundary.

(c) Let $P = x + 4y$. If (x, y) is any point satisfying all the constraints in **(b)**, find the greatest and the least values of P.

(d) If one more constraint $2x - 3y + 3 \leqslant 0$ is added, shade in the figure the new region satisfying all the four constraints.
For any point (x, y) lying in the new region, find the least value of P defined in **(c)**.

[HKCEE 88]

24. (a)

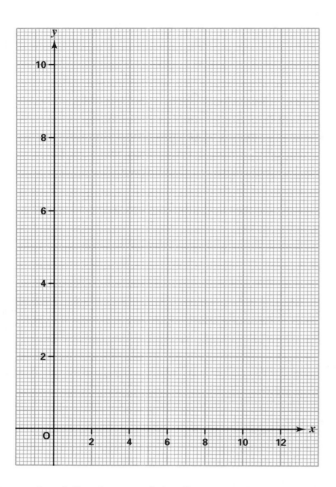

A duplicate of this graph paper is provided in the *Student Handbook 5A*.

Draw the following straight lines on the graph paper provided:

$$x + y = 10,$$
$$x + 2y = 12,$$
$$2x = 3y.$$

(b) Mr. Chan intends to employ a contractor to build a rectangular flower bed ABCD with length AB equal to x metres and width BC equal to y metres. This project includes building a wall of length x metres along the side AB and fences along the other three sides as shown in the figure.

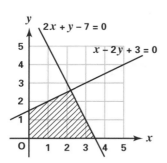

Mr. Chan wishes to have the total length of the four sides of the flower bed not less than 20 metres, and he also adds the condition that twice the length of the flower bed should not less than three times its width. However, no contractor will build the fences if their total length is less than 12 metres.

(i) Write down all the above constraints for x and y.

(ii) Mr. Chan has to pay the contractor $500 per metre for building the wall and $300 per metre for building the fences. Find the length and width of the flower bed so that the total payment for building the wall and fences is the minimum. Find also the minimum total payment.

[HKCEE 94]

(MC Questions) ————————————————————■

25.

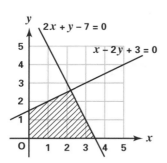

In the figure, (x,y) is a point in the shaded region (including the boundary) and x, y are integers. Find the greatest value of $3x+y$.

A. 7
B. 8
C. 9.2
D. 10
E. 10.5

[HKCEE 94]

The rise and fall of tides at different times of the day can be described by a curve related to the sine function. To find out the time that the sea surface is at a certain height, we need to solve the related trigonometric equation.

In this chapter, we are going to study a method to find the approximate solutions of similar equations with high accuracy.

CHAPTER

6

Approximate Solution of Equations

6.1   Graphical Solution of Equations

We can use algebraic methods to solve equations of the following types:

(1) $2x + 3 = 0$ ◀ *linear equation*

(2) $2x^2 + 3x - 2 = 0$ ◀ *quadratic equation*

(3) $x^3 + 4x^2 + x - 6 = 0$ ◀ *cubic equation*

(4) $6\cos x = 1$ ◀ *trigonometric equation*

(5) $\log x + \log(x - 3) = 1$ ◀ *logarithmic equation*

But we do NOT have any simple algebraic method to solve other equations such as:

(6) $x^3 + 2x^2 - 5x - 5 = 0$

(7) $\sin x = \dfrac{1}{2}x$

(8) $15\log(x + 1) = 5 - 3x$

◀ *To solve a logarithmic equation, normally we would make use of the definition and the properties of logarithm. But these do NOT work for this equation.*

However, we can find approximate solutions for equations **(6)**, **(7)** and **(8)** by plotting their graphs $y = f(x)$ on the rectangular coordinate plane. The solutions obtained in this way are called the graphical solutions of the equations, and these solutions are *approximations* only.

If we solve such equations graphically, there are basically TWO methods that we can use.

Method I: Finding the x-intercepts of *a graph*.

Method II: Finding the points of intersection of *two intersecting graphs*.

Both methods can help us locate the root(s) of the equation on the coordinate plane.

We had used **Methods** I and II before when we solved quadratic
equations of the form $ax^2 + bx + c = 0$ in Form 4.   ◄ $a \neq 0$.

Recall : **(i)** The x-intercepts of the graph $y = ax^2 + bx + c$ give the   ◄ This is **Method** I.
approximate values of the roots of the quadratic equation
$ax^2 + bx + c = 0$. [**Fig. 1**]

(ii) The equation $ax^2 + bx + c = 0$ is re-written in the form   ◄ This is **Method** II.
$x^2 = -\dfrac{b}{a}x - \dfrac{c}{a}$.

The graphs of $y = x^2$ and $y = -\dfrac{b}{a}x - \dfrac{c}{a}$ are drawn on the
same coordinate plane. The x-coordinates of the points of
intersection (if any) of the two graphs give the
approximate values of the roots of the given equation.
[**Fig. 2**]

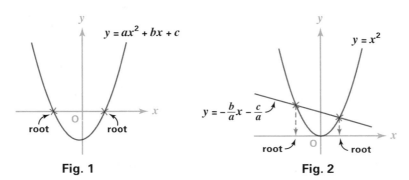

Fig. 1   **Fig. 2**

In the following examples, we shall use **Method** I to solve
equation **(6)**, **Method** II to solve equations **(7)** and **(8)** given on
P. 169.

Example **1** Draw the graph of $f(x) = x^3 + 2x^2 - 5x - 5$ for values | *Suggested scales:*
of x between -4 and 3 inclusive. Hence solve the | *x-axis, 10 divisions = 1 unit ;*
equation $x^3 + 2x^2 - 5x - 5 = 0$ for $-4 \leqslant x \leqslant 3$. | *y-axis, 10 divisions = 5 units .*

Solution   We first construct a table of values for x and $f(x)$
with the help of a calculator:

x	-4	-3	-2	-1	0	1	2	3
$f(x)$	-17	1	5	1	-5	-7	1	25

Then the graph of $y = x^3 + 2x^2 - 5x - 5$, i.e. $y = f(x)$, is plotted.

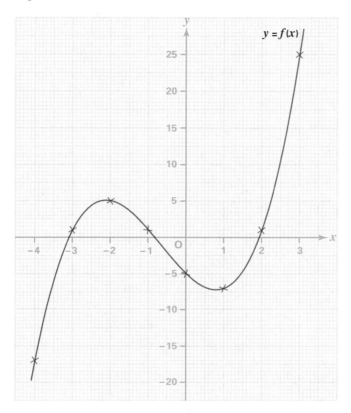

The graph cuts the x-axis at $x = -3.1$, $x = -0.8$ and $x = 1.9$ approximately. ◄ *The approximate x-intercepts are -3.1, -0.8 and 1.9 respectively.*

∴ The solutions of $x^3 + 2x^2 - 5x - 5 = 0$ are

$x = -3.1$, $x = -0.8$ and $x = 1.9$ for $-4 \leqslant x \leqslant 3$.

Note : **(i)** We learnt in Form 4 that the equation $x^3 + 2x^2 - 5x - 5 = 0$ is called a cubic equation or an equation of degree 3 since the highest power of x in the equation is $\underline{3}$. In a cubic equation, there are *at most $\underline{3}$* solutions. ◄ *Note:* *In general, an equation of degree n has at most n solutions.* Hence the three solutions obtained in **Example 1** above are ALL the solutions for the cubic equation $x^3 + 2x^2 - 5x - 5 = 0$.

　(ii) The specified range of values of x is particularly important in this kind of equations, since the range of values of x determines the number of solutions that the ◄ equation can have in that range. ┌*Question:* *What happens if the graph of $f(x) = x^3 + 2x^2 - 5x - 5$ is drawn for values of x between -4 and 0 instead? How many solutions are obtained for the same equation?*

Example 2 Solve graphically the equation $\sin x = \frac{1}{2}x$ for values of x from 0 to 3.

Suggested scales:
x-axis, 20 divisions = 0.5 unit ;
y-axis, 10 divisions = 0.1 unit .

Solution   Let $f(x) = \sin x$

and $g(x) = \frac{1}{2}x$.

Then draw the two graphs on the same rectangular coordinate plane.

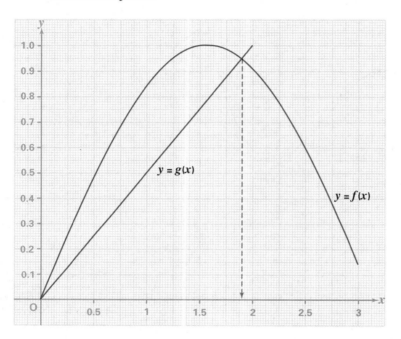

For $f(x) = \sin x$:

x	0	0.3	0.6	$\cdots$
$f(x)$	0	0.30	0.56	$\cdots$

For $g(x) = \frac{1}{2}x$:

x	0	0.5	1	$\cdots$
$g(x)$	0	0.25	0.5	$\cdots$

We see that the two graphs intersect at two points, where $x = 0$ and $x = 1.9$ approximately.

$\therefore$ The required solutions are $x = 0$ and $x = 1.9$.

Example 3 Solve graphically the equation $15 \log(x + 1) = 5 - 3x$ for values of x from 0 to 1.5.

Suggested scales:
x-axis, 10 *divisions* = 0.5 *unit ;*
y-axis, 5 *divisions* = 1 *unit .*

Solution Let $f(x) = 15 \log(x + 1)$
and $g(x) = 5 - 3x$.

Then draw the two graphs on the same rectangular coordinate plane.

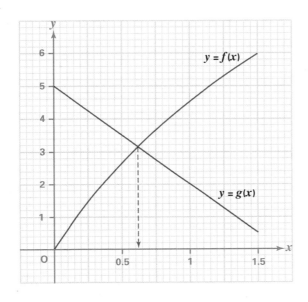

For $f(x) = 15 \log(x + 1)$:

x	0	0.2	0.4	$\cdots$
$f(x)$	0	1.2	2.2	$\cdots$

For $g(x) = 5 - 3x$:

x	0	0.4	0.8	$\cdots$
$g(x)$	5	3.8	2.6	$\cdots$

We see that the two graphs intersect at one point, where $x = 0.6$ approximately.

$\therefore$ The required solution is $x = 0.6$.

1. The figure shows the graph of the function $f(x) = x^3 + 2x - 2$ from $x = -0.5$ to $x = 1.5$.

   Estimate the root of the equation $x^3 + 2x - 2 = 0$ in the interval $-0.5 \leqslant x \leqslant 1.5$.

   Answer: _____

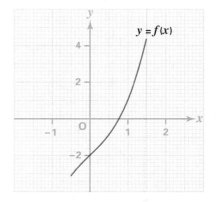

2. The figure shows the graph of the function $f(x) = \cos x + x$ from $x = -1.5$ to $x = 2.5$.

   Estimate the root of the equation $\cos x + x = 0$ in the interval $-1.5 \leqslant x \leqslant 2.5$.

   Answer: _____

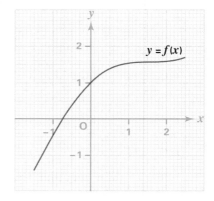

3. The figure shows the graph of the function $f(x) = x^3$ from $x = -1$ to $x = 1.5$. Using this graph and by adding a suitable straight line, estimate the root(s) of the equation $x^3 + 3x - 3 = 0$.

   Answer

   Equation of the straight line added : _____

   Root(s) : _____

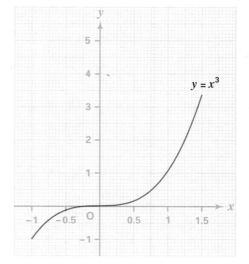

4. The figure shows the graph of the function $f(x) = 2\sin x$ from $x = 0$ to $x = 4$. Using this graph and by adding a suitable straight line, estimate the root(s) of the equation $4\sin x - x = 0$.

◄ *Recall:*
In radian measure, very often we skip the unit: 'radian'.

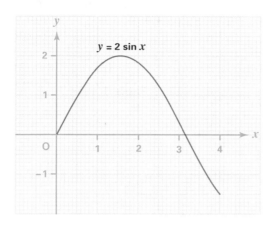

Answer

Equation of the straight line added: _____

Root(s): _____

6.2   Solving Equations by Method of Bisection

Although graphical methods work well for many equations, these methods have the disadvantage that answers cannot be given to a specified degree of accuracy.

In the following sections, we are going to introduce a simple method called the **method of bisection***, which we can use to improve the accuracy of the graphical solutions so that we can give the solutions to a prescribed degree of accuracy.

The method of bisection basically requires two steps in solving a given equation.

Step (1): 'Locating' intervals within which the roots may lie.

Step (2): 'Trapping' the roots within a range of desired accuracy.

_____

method of bisection 分半方法

A.   Locating Intervals of the Roots of Equations

Instead of finding the approximate roots of an equation graphically, as in **Example 1** on P. 170, we can *locate* the intervals within which the roots of the equation lie from **Table 1** below.

◄ *In* **Example 1** *on P.* 170, *we found that the roots of the equation* $x^3 + 2x^2 - 5x - 5 = 0$ *for* $-4 \leqslant x \leqslant 3$ *are* $x = -3.1$, $x = -0.8$ *and* $x = 1.9$ *approximately.*

x	-4	-3	-2	-1	0	1	2	3
$f(x)$	-17	1	5	1	-5	-7	1	25

Table 1

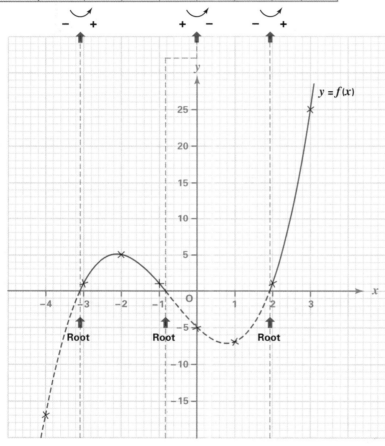

The graph of $y = f(x)$ *above the x-axis shows where the value of the function is positive (i.e. the black SOLID lines of the graph).*

The graph of $y = f(x)$ *below the x-axis shows where the value of the function is negative (i.e. the black DOTTED lines of the graph).*

Fig. 3

Hence there are roots of the equation $x^3 + 2x^2 - 5x - 5 = 0$ in the intervals: $-4 < x < -3$, $-1 < x < 0$ and $1 < x < 2$.

From **Table 1** and **Fig. 3**, obviously the values of $f(x)$ change signs (*either* from negative to positive *or* from positive to negative) at the roots of the given equation, i.e. the position where the graph crosses the x-axis.

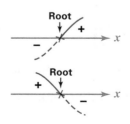

As a conclusion, we can locate the intervals within which the roots of an equation lie if we know the signs of the values of the corresponding function.

Note : **(i)** If the value of $f(x)$ has the same sign at both ends of an interval, we <u>cannot</u> be certain that there is <u>no</u> root in that interval.

e.g. The value of $f(x)$ is negative at both ends of the interval $-4 < x < 0$ but there are two roots in that interval.

(ii) If the graph of the function is NOT continuous in a certain interval, then it is impossible to use the signs of the values of the function to locate the root(s) of the equation in that interval.

Example 4 Show that each of the following equations has a root between $x = 0$ and $x = 1$.

(a) $x^3 - x^2 + 3x - 1 = 0$

(b) $-x^4 + x^3 + 5x - 1 = 0$

Solution **(a)** Let $f(x) = x^3 - x^2 + 3x - 1$.

$$f(0) = (0)^3 - (0)^2 + 3(0) - 1$$
$$= 0 - 0 + 0 - 1$$
$$= -1 \text{ , which is negative}$$

$$f(1) = (1)^3 - (1)^2 + 3(1) - 1$$
$$= 1 - 1 + 3 - 1$$
$$= 2 \text{ , which is positive}$$

Since $f(0)$ is negative and $f(1)$ is positive, there is a root between $x = 0$ and $x = 1$ for the given equation.

(b) Let $g(x) = -x^4 + x^3 + 5x - 1$.

$$g(0) = -(0)^4 + (0)^3 + 5(0) - 1$$
$$= -0 + 0 + 0 - 1$$
$$= -1 \text{ , which is negative}$$

$$g(1) = -(1)^4 + (1)^3 + 5(1) - 1$$
$$= -1 + 1 + 5 - 1$$
$$= 4 \text{ , which is positive}$$

Since $g(0)$ is negative and $g(1)$ is positive, there is a root between $x = 0$ and $x = 1$ for the given equation.

178   *Chapter 6*

CLASS PRACTICE

For each of the following equations in x, find correct to 3 significant figures when necessary, the values of the corresponding function for the given values of x. Hence determine whether it is certain that the equation has a root between the given values of x.

Answer

1. Given $x^3 + 7x - 7 = 0$.

   (a) For $f(x) = x^3 + 7x - 7$, find the values of $f(0)$ and $f(1)$. $f(0) =$ _____ $f(1) =$ _____

   (b) From the results of **(a)**, is it certain that $x^3 + 7x - 7 = 0$ has a root between $x = 0$ and $x = 1$?   Yes ☐   No ☐

2. Given $x^3 - 6x + 4 = 0$.

   (a) For $f(x) = x^3 - 6x + 4$, find the values of $f(-2)$ and $f(-3)$. $f(-2) =$ _____ $f(-3) =$ _____

   (b) From the results of **(a)**, is it certain that $x^3 - 6x + 4 = 0$ has a root between $x = -3$ and $x = -2$?   Yes ☐   No ☐

3. Given $2\log x + x^2 - 15 = 0$.

   (a) For $f(x) = 2\log x + x^2 - 15$, find the values of $f(3)$ and $f(4)$. $f(3) =$ _____ $f(4) =$ _____

   (b) From the results of **(a)**, is it certain that $2\log x + x^2 - 15 = 0$ has a root between $x = 3$ and $x = 4$?   Yes ☐   No ☐

4. Given $x^4 - x^2 + 2x + 1 = 0$.

   (a) For $f(x) = x^4 - x^2 + 2x + 1$, find the values of $f(0)$ and $f(1)$. $f(0) =$ _____ $f(1) =$ _____

   (b) From the results of **(a)**, is it certain that $x^4 - x^2 + 2x + 1 = 0$ has a root between $x = 0$ and $x = 1$?   Yes ☐   No ☐

5. Given $x - \cos x = 0$.

   (a) For $f(x) = x - \cos x$, find the values of $f(0)$ and $f(1)$. $f(0) =$ _____ $f(1) =$ _____

   (b) From the results of **(a)**, is it certain that $x - \cos x = 0$ has a root between $x = 0$ and $x = 1$?   Yes ☐   No ☐

6. Given $3\sin x = x^2 + 1$.

   (a) For $f(x) = 3\sin x - x^2 - 1$, find the values of $f(0)$ and $f(1)$. $f(0) =$ _____ $f(1) =$ _____

   (b) From the results of **(a)**, is it certain that $3\sin x - x^2 - 1 = 0$ has a root between $x = 0$ and $x = 1$?   Yes ☐   No ☐

B. *Trapping the Roots of an Equation within a Range of Desired Accuracy*

In the previous section, we learnt how to locate the interval within which a root of an equation lies.

In this section, we shall learn how to reduce the interval $x_1 < x_0 < x_2$, which we call the 'bracketing interval' successively by half, until the root x_0 is 'trapped' within an interval which is small enough to give the root its desired degree of accuracy.

This is illustrated in the diagrams below. [**Fig. 4(a)**, **4(b)** and **4(c)**]

In **Fig. 4(a)**, $\quad x_3 = \dfrac{x_1 + x_2}{2}$

$\qquad$ and $f(x_3) > 0$.

[*By halving the interval x_1 and x_2, we have trapped the root x_0 of $f(x) = 0$ within a small interval $x_1 < x_0 < x_3$.*]

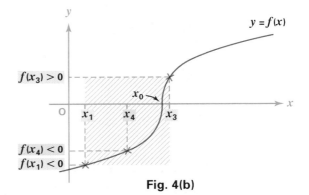

Fig. 4(a)

In **Fig. 4(b)**, $\quad x_4 = \dfrac{x_1 + x_3}{2}$

$\qquad$ and $f(x_4) < 0$.

[*By halving the interval x_1 and x_3, we have trapped the root x_0 of $f(x) = 0$ within a small interval $x_4 < x_0 < x_3$.*]

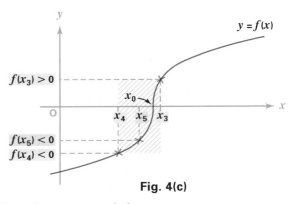

Fig. 4(b)

In **Fig. 4(c)**, $\quad x_5 = \dfrac{x_3 + x_4}{2}$

$\qquad$ and $f(x_5) < 0$.

[*By halving the interval x_3 and x_4, we have trapped the root x_0 of $f(x) = 0$ within a small interval $x_5 < x_0 < x_3$.*]

Fig. 4(c)

If we wish, we can continue the process until we have trapped the root x_0 of $f(x) = 0$ within a **very** small interval. In so doing, we can obtain x_0 to the desired degree of accuracy.

Example 5 Given that $f(x) = x^3 - 2x^2 + 7x - 5$.

(a) Complete the table for the values of $f(x)$ from $x = 0$ to $x = 3$.

x	0	1	2	3
$f(x)$				

(b) Hence find, by the method of bisection, the root of the equation $f(x) = 0$ correct to 1 decimal place.

Solution   (a)

x	0	1	2	3
$f(x)$	-5	1	9	25

(b) Let the root of the equation be x_0.

∵ $f(0) = -5$ ($-ve$)

and $f(1) = 1$ ($+ve$).

∴ x_0 lies between 0 and 1.

The *1st* bracketing interval is $0 < x_0 < 1$.

[*The mid-value of 0 and 1 is 0.5,*
  and $f(0.5) = -1.875$ ($-ve$).]
The *2nd* bracketing interval is $0.5 < x_0 < 1$.

[*The mid-value of 0.5 and 1 is 0.75,*
  and $f(0.75) = -0.453\ 1^†$ ($-ve$).]
The *3rd* bracketing interval is $0.75 < x_0 < 1$.

[*The mid-value of 0.75 and 1 is 0.875,*
  and $f(0.875) = 0.263\ 7$ ($+ve$).]
The *4th* bracketing interval is $0.75 < x_0 < 0.875$.

[*The mid-value of 0.75 and 0.875 is 0.812 5,*
  and $f(0.812\ 5) = -0.096\ 44$ ($-ve$).]
The *5th* bracketing interval is $0.812\ 5 < x_0 < 0.875$.

[*The mid-value of 0.812 5 and 0.875 is 0.843 75,*
  and $f(0.843\ 75) = 0.083\ 10$ ($+ve$).]
The *6th* bracketing interval is $0.812\ 5 < x_0 < 0.843\ 75$.

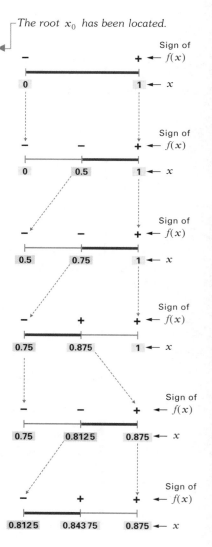

The root x_0 has been located.

† *For convenience, these values of* $f(x)$ *are often corrected to 4 sig. fig.*

$\because$ $0.812\ 5 = 0.8$, *cor. to 1 d.p.*

and $0.843\ 75 = 0.8$, *cor. to 1 d.p.*   ◀ *The root x_0 has now been trapped.*

$\therefore$ The root x_0 of the equation is 0.8, *cor. to 1 d.p.*

Note : Whenever we reach a stage such that the two end points of the bracketing interval give the SAME number when corrected to the required degree of accuracy (1 decimal place in the above example), we end the process of '*halving the intervals*'.

The solution in **Example 5(b)** can be presented neatly in a table form [**Table 2**] after we have found the first bracketing interval.

Bracketing interval $(x_1 < x_0 < x_2)$	$f(x_1)$	$f(x_2)$	Mid-value (x_m)	$f(x_m)$
$0 < x_0 < 1$	$-ve$	$+ve$	0.5	$-ve$
$0.5 < x_0 < 1$	$-ve$	$+ve$	0.75	$-ve$
$0.75 < x_0 < 1$	$-ve$	$+ve$	0.875	$+ve$
$0.75 < x_0 < 0.875$	$-ve$	$+ve$	0.812 5	$-ve$
$0.812\ 5 < x_0 < 0.875$	$-ve$	$+ve$	0.843 75	$+ve$
$0.812\ 5 < x_0 < 0.843\ 75$	$-ve$	$+ve$		

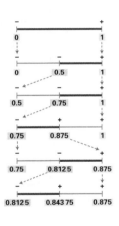

Table 2

Example 6 Given that $f(x) = 2x^4 - 3x - 5$.

(a) Complete the table for the values of $f(x)$ from $x = 0$ to $x = 3$.

x	0	1	2	3
$f(x)$				

(b) Hence find, by the method of bisection, the root x_0 of the equation $2x^4 - 3x - 5 = 0$ correct to 2 significant figures.

Solution   (a)

x	0	1	2	3
$f(x)$	-5	-6	21	148

(b) From the table in (a), we can see that the root x_0 of $2x^4 - 3x - 5 = 0$ lies between $x = 1$ and $x = 2$ because $f(1) = -6 < 0$ and $f(2) = 21 > 0$.

◀ $\therefore$ $1 < x_0 < 2$ is the first bracketing interval.

Using the method of bisection, we construct the following table:

Bracketing interval $(x_1 < x_0 < x_2)$	$f(x_1)$	$f(x_2)$	Mid-value (x_m)	$f(x_m)$	
$1 < x_0 < 2$	$-ve$	$+ve$	1.5	$+ve$	
$1 < x_0 < 1.5$	$-ve$	$+ve$	1.25	$-ve$	
$1.25 < x_0 < 1.5$	$-ve$	$+ve$	1.375	$-ve$	
$1.375 < x_0 < 1.5$	$-ve$	$+ve$	1.437\,5	$-ve$	
$1.437\,5 < x_0 < 1.5$	$-ve$	$+ve$	1.468\,75	$-ve$	
$1.468\,75 < x_0 < 1.5$	$-ve$	$+ve$			

$\therefore$ The root x_0 of the equation is 1.5, *cor. to 2 sig. fig.*

Example 7 The figure shows the graph of $y = 10 \log x$ for $x = 1$ to $x = 2$.

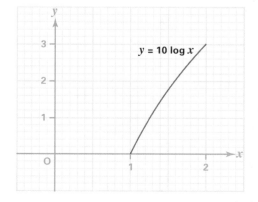

(a) By adding a suitable straight line to the graph, give an approximate solution of the equation $x = 10\log x$.

(b) Use the method of bisection to find the root x_0 of the equation $x = 10\log x$ correct to 2 decimal places.

Solution **(a)** [To solve the equation $x = 10\log x$, we draw the straight line $y = x$ which cuts the graph at A.]

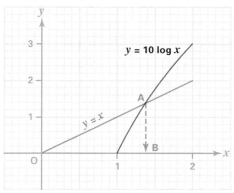

From the graph, an approximate solution of the given equation is $x = 1.4$.

(b) Let $f(x) = x - 10\log x$.

From the graph, we see that the root x_0 of $x = 10\log x$ lies between $x = 1.3$ and $x = 1.4$.

Here $f(1.3) = 0.160\,5\cdots > 0$
and $f(1.4) = -0.061\,2\cdots < 0$.

◀ ∴ $1.3 < x_0 < 1.4$ *is the first bracketing interval.*

Using the method of bisection, we construct the following table:

Bracketing interval $(x_1 < x_0 < x_2)$	$f(x_1)$	$f(x_2)$	Mid–value (x_m)	$f(x_m)$	
$1.3 < x_0 < 1.4$	+ ve	− ve	1.35	+ ve	
$1.35 < x_0 < 1.4$	+ ve	− ve	1.375	− ve	
$1.35 < x_0 < 1.375$	+ ve	− ve	1.362 5	+ ve	
$1.362\,5 < x_0 < 1.375$	+ ve	− ve	1.368 75	+ ve	
$1.368\,75 < x_0 < 1.375$	+ ve	− ve	1.371 875	− ve	
$1.368\,75 < x_0 < 1.371\,875$	+ ve	− ve			

∴ The root x_0 of the equation is 1.37, *cor. to 2 d.p.*

Example 8 **(a)** The figure shows a right square frustum of height *h* m. The side of the upper square is *a* m and that of the lower square is *b* m. Show that the volume $V \, \text{m}^3$ of the frustum is given by the formula

$$V = \frac{h(a^2 + ab + b^2)}{3}.$$

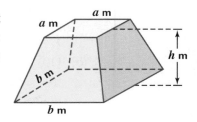
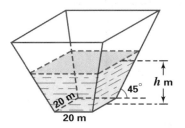

(b) A reservoir is in the shape of an inverted frustum with a square base of sides 20 m. The sides of the reservoir make an angle of 45° with the horizon as shown. When the depth of water is *h* m, show that the volume of water ($V \, \text{m}^3$) inside the reservoir is given by

$$V = \frac{4h^3}{3} + 40h^2 + 400h.$$

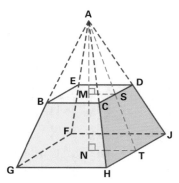

(c) When there are $25\,000 \, \text{m}^3$ of water in the reservoir, the depth of water lies between 15 m and 20 m. Find, by the method of bisection, the depth of water correct to 1 decimal place.

Solution **(a)** The frustum is formed by removing a small right pyramid ABCDE from the larger right pyramid AFGHJ.

$$\triangle \text{AMS} \sim \triangle \text{ANT}$$

$$\therefore \quad \frac{\text{AM}}{\text{AN}} = \frac{\text{MS}}{\text{NT}}$$

Let the length of AM be *x* m.

Then $\quad \dfrac{x}{x+h} = \dfrac{\frac{a}{2}}{\frac{b}{2}}$

$$bx = ax + ah$$

$$(b - a)x = ah$$

$$x = \frac{ah}{b - a}$$

Volume of the pyramid AFGHJ

$$= \left[\frac{1}{3} \times b \times b \times (x + h)\right] \text{m}^3$$

$$= \left[\frac{1}{3}b^2\left(\frac{ah}{b - a} + h\right)\right] \text{m}^3$$

$$= \frac{b^3 h}{3(b - a)} \text{m}^3$$

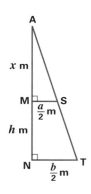

Volume of the pyramid ABCDE

$$= \left(\frac{1}{3} \times a \times a \times x\right) m^3$$

$$= \left[\frac{1}{3}a^2\left(\frac{ah}{b-a}\right)\right] m^3$$

$$= \frac{a^3 h}{3(b-a)} \ m^3$$

∴ Volume of the frustum $= \left[\frac{b^3 h}{3(b-a)} - \frac{a^3 h}{3(b-a)}\right] m^3$

$$= \frac{h(b^3 - a^3)}{3(b-a)} \ m^3$$

$$= \frac{h(b-a)(b^2 + ba + a^2)}{3(b-a)} \ m^3$$

$$= \frac{h(a^2 + ab + b^2)}{3} \ m^3$$

i.e. $\underline{V = \dfrac{h(a^2 + ab + b^2)}{3}}$

(b) The side of the water surface

$$= (20 + 2 \times h \tan 45°)\, m$$

$$= (20 + 2h)\, m$$

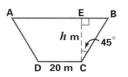

Using the result obtained in **(a)**, let $a = 20$ and $b = 20 + 2h$.

Then $V = \dfrac{h[(20)^2 + (20)(20 + 2h) + (20 + 2h)^2]}{3}$

$$= \frac{h[1\,200 + 120h + 4h^2]}{3}$$

∴ $\underline{V = \dfrac{4h^3}{3} + 40h^2 + 400h}$

(c) $V = 25\,000$, i.e. $\dfrac{4h^3}{3} + 40h^2 + 400h = 25\,000$.

Let $f(h) = \dfrac{4h^3}{3} + 40h^2 + 400h - 25\,000$ and the root of $f(h) = 0$ be h_0.

According to the question, the root h_0 lies between 15 and 20.

Here $f(15) = -5\,500 < 0$

and $f(20) = 9\,666\frac{2}{3} > 0$.

◀ ∴ $15 < h_0 < 20$ is the first bracketing interval.

Using the method of bisection, we construct the following table:

Bracketing interval $(h_1 < h_0 < h_2)$	$f(h_1)$	$f(h_2)$	Mid-value (h_m)	$f(h_m)$	
$15 < h_0 < 20$	$-ve$	$+ve$	17.5	$+ve$	
$15 < h_0 < 17.5$	$-ve$	$+ve$	16.25	$-ve$	
$16.25 < h_0 < 17.5$	$-ve$	$+ve$	16.875	$-ve$	
$16.875 < h_0 < 17.5$	$-ve$	$+ve$	$17.187\,5$	$+ve$	
$16.875 < h_0 < 17.187\,5$	$-ve$	$+ve$	$17.031\,25$	$+ve$	
$16.875 < h_0 < 17.031\,25$	$-ve$	$+ve$	$16.953\,125$	$-ve$	
$16.953\,125 < h_0 < 17.031\,25$	$-ve$	$+ve$			

$\therefore$ The depth of water is 17.0 m, *cor. to 1 d.p.*

C L A S S P R A C T I C E

It is given that $g(x) = x^3 + 2x - 2$.

(a) Complete the following table for the values of $g(x)$.

x	-2	-1	0	1	2
$g(x)$					

(b) State the bracketing interval in which the root x_0 of the equation $x^3 + 2x - 2 = 0$ lies.

Bracketing interval: _____ $< x_0 <$ _____

(c) Using the method of bisection, find the root x_0 of $x^3 + 2x - 2 = 0$ correct to 2 decimal places.

Bracketing interval $(x_1 < x_0 < x_2)$	$g(x_1)$	$g(x_2)$	Mid-value (x_m)	$g(x_m)$
$< x_0 <$				
$< x_0 <$				
$< x_0 <$				
$< x_0 <$				
$< x_0 <$				
$< x_0 <$				
$< x_0 <$				
$< x_0 <$				

$\therefore$ The root of the given equation is _____ , *cor. to 2 d.p.*

EXERCISE 6A

(*Level 1*)

1. Given $f(x) = x^3 + x - 3$.

   (a) Complete the following table.

x	0	1	2	3
$f(x)$				

   (b) Use the method of bisection to find a root of the equation $x^3 + x - 3 = 0$ correct to 1 decimal place.

2. (a) Show that the equation $\cos x + x = 0$ has a root between 0 and -1.

   (b) By the method of bisection, find the root in **(a)** correct to 1 decimal place.

3.

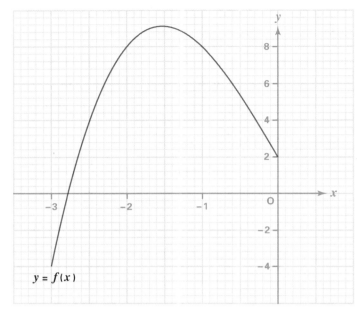

$$y = f(x)$$

The figure shows the graph of $f(x) = x^3 - 7x + 2$ for $-3 \leqslant x \leqslant 0$.

(a) From the graph, find an approximate root of the equation $x^3 - 7x + 2 = 0$.

(b) Using the method of bisection, find the root in **(a)** correct to 2 decimal places.

4.

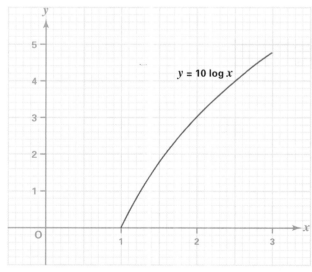

$$y = 10 \log x$$

◀ *A duplicate of this graph is provided in the Student Handbook 5A.*

The figure shows the graph of $y = 10 \log x$ where x takes values from 1 to 3.

(a) By adding a suitable straight line to this graph, find the approximate solution of the equation $10 \log x = 4$.

(b) Use the method of bisection to find the root in **(a)**, correct to 2 decimal places.

(*Level 2*)

5. **(a)** Show that a root of the equation $x^4 - 2x^3 - 5 = 0$ lies between 2.3 and 2.4.

   (b) Use the method of bisection to find the root in **(a)**, correct to 2 decimal places.

6.

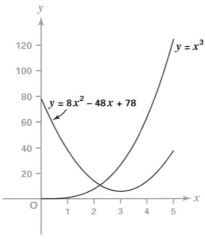

The figure shows the graphs of $y = x^3$ and $y = 8x^2 - 48x + 78$ for $0 \leqslant x \leqslant 5$.

   (a) Write down the interval, of width one unit, in which the root of the equation $x^3 - 8x^2 + 48x - 78 = 0$ lies.

   (b) Use the method of bisection to find the root of the equation $x^3 - 8x^2 + 48x - 78 = 0$, correct to 2 decimal places.

7. In the figure, VABC is a pyramid with a triangular base ABC. $BC = AC = x$ cm and $\angle ACB = 90°$. The height and the volume of the pyramid are $(x + 1)$ cm and 11 cm^3 respectively.

   (a) Show that $x^3 + x^2 = 66$ . . . . **(*)**.

   (b) Show that there is a root of **(*)** lying between 3.7 and 3.8.

   Hence use the method of bisection to find this root, correct to 3 significant figures.

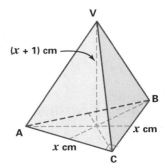

*8. The figure shows three lines

$$\ell_1 : y = kx$$
$$\ell_2 : ky = 2 - x$$
$$\ell_3 : x = 4$$

where $k > 0$.

The line ℓ_2 cuts the x-axis and ℓ_1 at A and B respectively while the line ℓ_3 cuts ℓ_1 and the x-axis at C and D respectively.

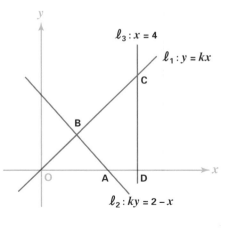

(a) Find, in terms of k,

    (i) the area of $\triangle OAB$,

    (ii) the area of the quadrilateral ABCD.

(b) Suppose the area of the quadrilateral ABCD $= 12$.

    (i) Show that $4k^3 - 6k^2 + 3k - 6 = 0$.

    (ii) Let $f(k) = 4k^3 - 6k^2 + 3k - 6$ where $k > 0$ and k_0 be the root of $f(k) = 0$. Show that k_0 lies between 1 and 2.

    (iii) Using the method of bisection, find the value of k_0 correct to 1 decimal place.

SUPPLEMENTARY EXERCISE 6

PART I | *Further Practice*

(Ex. 6A)

1. Given the equation $2^x - x^2 = 0$.

    (a) Show that there is a root lying between -1 and 0.

    (b) Use the method of bisection to find the root in **(a)**, correct to 1 decimal place.

2. (a) Let $f(x) = 2\cos^2 x + x - 1$.

Complete the following table.

x	-2	-1.5	-1	-0.5
$f(x)$				

(*Give the answers correct to 2 decimal places.*)

(b) State the interval of width 0.5 in which the root of the equation $2\cos^2 x + x - 1 = 0$ lies.

(c) Use the method of bisection to find the root in **(b)**, correct to 1 decimal place.

3.

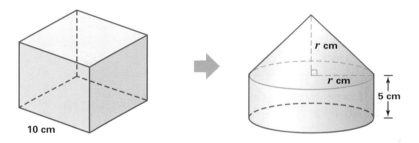

10 cm

A metal cube of side 10 cm is melted and recast into a solid consisting of a cylinder and a cone as shown in the figure. The height of the cylinder is 5 cm and its radius is r cm. The radius and the height of the cone are both r cm.

(a) Show that $r^3 + 15r^2 - \dfrac{3\,000}{\pi} = 0 \ldots\ldots\ldots$ **(*)**.

(b) Show that the root of **(*)** lies between 6.6 and 6.7.

(c) Using the method of bisection, find the value of r correct to 2 decimal places.

4. In the figure, AOBC is a semi-circle with centre O and radius r. A chord AC bisects the area of the semi-circle and $\angle CAB = x$ radians.

(a) Find the area of the sector OBC in terms of r and x.

(b) Find the area of $\triangle$OAC in terms of r and x.

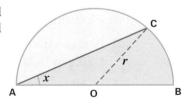

(c) Show that $\sin 2x + 2x = \dfrac{\pi}{2}$.

(d) Show that the value of x lies between 0.4 and 0.5.

(e) Use the method of bisection to find the value of x, correct to 2 decimal places.

*5.

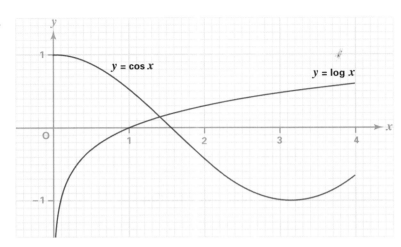

The figure shows the graphs of $y = \cos x$ and $y = \log x$ for $0 \leqslant x \leqslant 4$.

(a) From the graph, find a root of the equation $\cos x - \log x = 0$.

(b) Use the method of bisection to find the root in **(a)**, correct to 3 significant figures.

(c) Using the result of **(b)**, find one root of the equation $\frac{1}{2}\cos x^2 - \log x = 0$ correct to 2 significant figures.

*6. The first term of a geometric sequence is 2. The sum of the first 5 terms of the sequence is 6. Let R be the common ratio of the sequence.

(a) Show that $R^5 - 3R + 2 = 0$ . . . . **(*)**.

(b) The equation **(*)** has 3 roots. Show that the 3 roots lie between -1.5 and -1.4, 0.7 and 0.8, 0.9 and 1.1 respectively.

(c) Find the integral root of **(*)**.

(d) Use the method of bisection to find the other 2 roots.
(*Give the answers correct to 2 decimal places.*)

(e) If it is possible to sum the geometric sequence to infinity, find this sum.
(*Give the answer correct to 1 decimal place.*)

PART II | *HKCEE Questions*

(Section B Questions)

7.

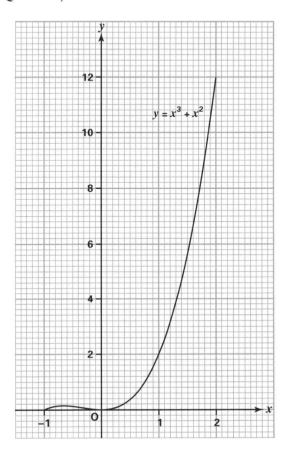

◄ A duplicate of this graph is provided in the *Student Handbook 5A*.

$y = x^3 + x^2$

(a) The figure shows the graph of $y = x^3 + x^2$ for $-1 \leqslant x \leqslant 2$.

    (i) Draw a suitable straight line in the figure and use it to find a root of the equation
$$x^3 + x^2 + x - 4 = 0.$$
    (Give your answer correct to 1 decimal place.)

    (ii) By the method of bisection, find the root obtained in **(i)** correct to 2 decimal places.

(b) A bank introduces the following savings scheme in which interest is compounded yearly:

    If a customer deposits $2 500 on the first day of each year for three successive years, he will receive $10 000 at the end of the third year.

    Assume that the interest rate is r % per annum.

    (i) Show that
$$(1 + r\%)^3 + (1 + r\%)^2 + (1 + r\%) = 4.$$

    (ii) Find, correct to 2 significant figures, the value of r, by using the results in **(a)(ii)** and **(b)(i)**.

[HKCEE 84 modified]

8.

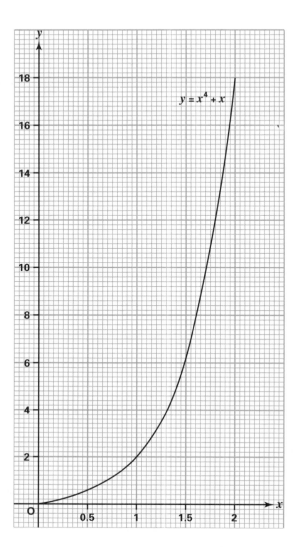

◀ *A duplicate of this graph is provided in the Student Handbook 5A.*

The figure shows the graph of $y = x^4 + x$ for $0 \leqslant x \leqslant 2$.

(a) Draw a suitable straight line on the figure and use it to find the approximate value of the root of the equation
$$x^4 - x - 1 = 0$$
in the interval $0 \leqslant x \leqslant 2$, correct to 1 decimal place.

(b) By the method of bisection, find the approximate value of the root in (a), correct to two decimal places.

(c) Use the result in (b) to find the approximate value of the root of the equation
$$(x-1)^4 = x$$
in the interval $1 \leqslant x \leqslant 3$, correct to two decimal places.

[*Hint: Put* $x = y + 1$]

[HKCEE 86 modified]

9.

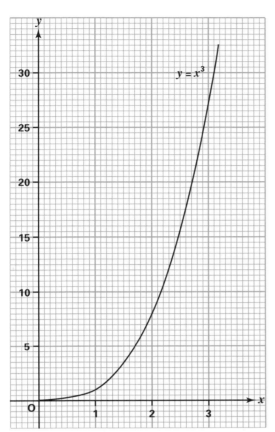

◀ A duplicate of this graph is provided in the <u>Student Handbook 5A</u>.

The figure shows the graph of $y = x^3$ for $x \geqslant 0$.

(a) Let r be the real root of the equation $x^3 - \frac{4}{3}x - 6 = 0$.

    (i) By adding a suitable straight line to the figure, find an interval of width 0.1 which contains r.

    (ii) Use the method of bisection to find the value of r correct to two decimal places. Show your working in the form of a table.

(b) Use **(a)** to find, correct to two decimal places, the real root of the equation $3(t+1)^3 - 4(t+1) - 18 = 0$.

[HKCEE 88]

10. A solid right circular cylinder has radius r and height h. The volume of the cylinder is V and the total surface area is S.

(a) **(i)** Express S in terms of r and h.

    (ii) Show that $S = 2\pi r^2 + \dfrac{2V}{r}$.

(b) Given that $V = 2\pi$ and $S = 6\pi$, show that $r^3 - 3r + 2 = 0$. Hence find the radius r by factorization.

(c) Given that $V = 3\pi$ and $S = 10\pi$, find the radius r $(1 < r < 2)$ by the method of bisection, correct to 1 decimal place.

[HKCEE 90]

11.

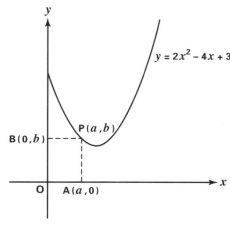

The figure shows the graph of $y = 2x^2 - 4x + 3$, where $x \geqslant 0$. $P(a, b)$ is a variable point on the graph. A rectangle OAPB is drawn with A and B lying on the x- and y-axes respectively.

(a) (i) Find the area of rectangle OAPB in terms of a.
   (ii) Find the two values of a for which OAPB is a square.

(b) Suppose the area of OAPB = $\frac{3}{2}$.

   (i) Show that $4a^3 - 8a^2 + 6a - 3 = 0 \ldots \ldots \ldots$ (∗).
   (ii) Show that there is a root of (∗) lying between 1.2 and 1.3.
       Hence use the method of bisection to find this root, correct to 2 decimal places.   [HKCEE 92]

12.

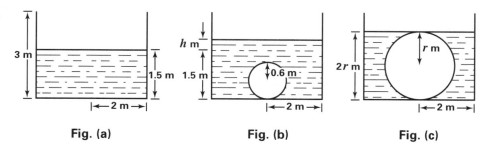

Fig. (a)   Fig. (b)   Fig. (c)

Fig. (a) shows the longitudinal section of a right cylindrical water tank of base radius 2 metres and height 3 metres. The tank is filled with water to a depth of 1.5 metres.

(a) Express the volume of water in the tank in terms of π.

(b) If a solid sphere of radius 0.6 metre is put into the tank and is completely submerged in water, the water level rises by h metres. Find h (see **Fig. (b)**).

(c) A solid sphere of radius r metres is put into the tank and is just submerged in water (see **Fig. (c)**).

(i) Show that $2r^3 - 12r + 9 = 0$.

(ii) Show that the equation in (i) has a root between 0.6 and 1, and find this root, correct to 2 decimal places, by the method of bisection.   [HKCEE 94]

(MC Questions) ———————————————————————■

13.

x	$f(x)$
1.22	+
1.23	+
1.24	+
1.25	−
1.245	+

From the table above, a root of $f(x) = 0$ must be

A. 1.20, *correct to 2 decimal places*
B. 1.24, *correct to 2 decimal places*
C. 1.25, *correct to 2 decimal places*
D. 1.245, *correct to 3 decimal places*
E. 1.247 5, *correct to 4 decimal places*

[HKCEE 90]

14. Which of the following intervals *must* contain a root of $2x^3 - x^2 - x - 3 = 0$?

I. $-1 < x < 1$
II. $0 < x < 2$
III. $1 < x < 3$

A. I only
B. II only
C. III only
D. I and II only
E. II and III only   [HKCEE 92]

15. From the table, which of the following intervals must contain a root of $f(x) - x = 0$?

x	$f(x)$
-2	1.2
-1	0.8
0	0.7
1	0.2
2	-0.1
3	0.8

A. $-2 < x < -1$
B. $-1 < x < 0$
C. $0 < x < 1$
D. $1 < x < 2$
E. $2 < x < 3$ [HKCEE 94]

Fine weathers or bad weathers can be predicted with the help of our knowledge in probability.

Probability

CHAPTER 7

7.1 The Theory of Probability – A Review

The theory of probability provides a means of evaluating the *likelihood of happenings* of things.

A. Basic Terms

When a die is rolled, one of its six faces: 1, 2, 3, 4, 5 or 6 will show up.

In the language of probability, we say:

(i)   When a die is rolled, there are <u>SIX</u> *possible outcomes*: 1, 2, 3, 4, 5 or 6.

◄ *The possible outcomes are ALL the possible results when a die is rolled.*

(ii) 'An even number shows up' is called an *event*.

◄ *There are many other events possible. Can you name one such possible event?*

(iii) For the event that an 'even number' shows up, there are <u>THREE</u> favourable outcomes: 2, 4 or 6.

◄ *Events are things that either happen or do NOT happen.*

(iv) The outcomes 2, 4 and 6 are *equally likely* to occur, i.e. each of them has an equal chance to show up when a die is rolled.

Favourable outcomes are outcomes that match the requirement(s) described in an event.

B. Definition of Probability

The probability of an event can be defined according to the basic terms that we have just mentioned above.

When all the possible outcomes under consideration are equally likely, the probability of the occurrence of an event E, often denoted by $P(E)$, is defined as:

$$P(\text{E}) = \frac{\text{Number of outcomes favourable to the event}}{\text{Total number of possible outcomes}}$$

Something More

Sometimes the probability of an event is expressed in percentage or in decimals.

Note : From the definition, we see that the probability of an event is a fraction.

Using the definition of probability, the probability of the event that an even number shows up when a die is rolled is given by

$$\frac{3}{6} \quad\begin{array}{l}\leftarrow \textit{THREE favourable outcomes}\\ \leftarrow \textit{SIX possible outcomes}\end{array}$$

Example 1 A bag contains 10 yellow balls and 7 red balls. One ball is drawn at random from the bag. Find the probability that

(a) the ball drawn is yellow,

(b) the ball drawn is red,

(c) the ball drawn is green,

(d) a coloured ball is drawn from the bag.

Solution   There are altogether $17\,(=10+7)$ possible outcomes.

(a) [For the event of drawing a yellow ball, there are 10 favourable outcomes.]

$$P(\text{yellow ball}) = \frac{10}{17}$$

◄ 10 *favourable outcomes.*
◄ 17 *possible outcomes.*

(b) [When looking for a red ball, there are 7 favourable outcomes.]

$$P(\text{red ball}) = \frac{7}{17}$$

◄ 7 *favourable outcomes.*
◄ 17 *possible outcomes.*

(c) [For the event of drawing a green ball, there are NO favourable outcomes.]

$$P(\text{green ball}) = \frac{0}{17}$$
$$= 0$$

◄ 0 *favourable outcome.*
◄ 17 *possible outcomes.*

(d) [For the event of drawing a coloured ball from the bag, there are 17 favourable outcomes.]

$$P(\text{coloured ball from the bag}) = \frac{17}{17}$$
$$= 1$$

┌ *Because all the balls in the*
◄ *bag are coloured, either*
└ *yellow or red.*

◄ 17 *favourable outcomes.*
◄ 17 *possible outcomes.*

Note : **(i)** In **Example 1(c)** above, we see that the event is *impossible* to happen and the probability of an impossible event is 'zero'.

(ii) In **Example 1(d)** above, we see that the event is *certain* to happen and the probability of an event of certainty is 'one'.

In fact,

> **the probability of an event that is certain to happen is 1;**
>
> **the probability of an event that is certain NOT to happen is 0.**

Thus the probability of any event E always lies between 0 and 1.

i.e.

$$0 \leqslant P(\text{E}) \leqslant 1$$

Example 2 A card is drawn at random from *a pack* 一副 of playing cards. What is the probability that the card drawn is

(a) a king?

(b) a diamond?

(c) a face card?

(d) either black or red?

Solution [There are 4 *suits* 同花色的一組牌 in a pack of playing cards, namely the spades ♠, the hearts ♥, the diamonds ♦ and the clubs ♣. Spades and clubs are black in colour while hearts and diamonds are red in colour. There are 13 cards in each suit, namely ace, king, queen, jack, 10, 9, 8, 7, 6, 5, 4, 3 and 2. Therefore, there are totally 52(= 4 × 13) cards.]

Note:
We can find the probability of an event by <u>*listing*</u> *the various kinds of possible outcomes. Depending on the requirement of an event, we can find the probability of its occurrence correspondingly.*

Total number of possible outcomes = 52

(a) There are 4 kings in the pack.

∴ Number of favourable outcomes = 4

i.e. $P(\text{king}) = \dfrac{4}{52} = \dfrac{1}{13}$

(b) There are 13 diamonds in the pack.

∴ Number of favourable outcomes = 13

i.e. $P(\text{diamond}) = \dfrac{13}{52} = \dfrac{1}{4}$

(c) [The kings, queens and jacks in a pack of cards are called the face cards of the pack.]

There are 12 face cards in the pack.

∴ Number of favourable outcomes = 12

i.e. $P(\text{face card}) = \dfrac{12}{52} = \dfrac{3}{13}$

(d) [The cards in the pack are either black or red, hence this is an event of certainty.]

i.e. $P(\textit{either} \text{ black } \textit{or} \text{ red}) = 1$

CLASS PRACTICE

In the table below, fill in the blanks of the following columns:

(i) Number of possible outcomes

(ii) Number of favourable outcomes

(iii) Probability of the event

	Experiment	Possible outcomes	Number of possible outcomes	Events	Favourable outcomes	Number of favourable outcomes	Probability of the event
1.	Tossing a coin	Head (H) and Tail (T)		The head shows up.	H		
				The tail shows up.	T		
2.	Throwing a die	1, 2, 3, 4, 5, 6		1 shows up.	1		
				An even number shows up.	2, 4, 6		
				The result is greater than 3.	4, 5, 6		
3.	Choosing a letter from the word 'APRIL'	A, P, R, I, L		The letter L is picked.	L		
				A vowel is picked.	A, I		
				A consonant is picked.	P, R, L		
4.	Drawing a ball from a bag of three red balls	Red ball (A), Red ball (B), Red ball (C)		A red ball is drawn.	A, B, C		
				A black ball is drawn.	(Nil)		

Table 1

C. The Concepts of Theoretical Probability and Experimental Probability

When a coin is tossed, we know that either the head or the tail will show up. Since the two outcomes are *equally likely*, we say that the probability of either outcome is *theoretically* equal to $\frac{1}{2}$.

For equally likely outcomes, the total number of possible outcomes and the number of favourable outcomes can be found by theory. The probability so obtained is called the **theoretical probability***.

Even though we can calculate and predict the probability of tossing a head to be $\frac{1}{2}$, it does not mean that whenever a coin is tossed twice, a head will show up one time and a tail will show up the other time.

Suppose we had tossed a coin 50 times and the results were recorded below:

No. of times the head shows up	*No. of times the tail shows up*
32	18

From the table, the chance that the head shows up in 50 trials is 32 out of 50. Hence the probability that a head shows up in our 50 trials is $\frac{32}{50}$ or 0.64, which is greater than the theoretical probability $\frac{1}{2}$ or 0.5.

> *Note:*
> *If we repeat the same experiment, i.e. toss the same coin for another 50 times, the results may be quite different.*

When the probability of an event is obtained from experimental results, we call this kind of probability the **experimental probability***.

> *We observe from our little experiment that theoretical probability only tells us what is likely to happen but it can NEVER tell us <u>exactly</u> what will happen.*

Experimental probability is defined as follows:

> $$\text{Experimental probability} = \frac{\text{Number of trials in which the event occurs}}{\text{Total number of trials}}$$

Note :   For a large number of trials, it is expected that experimental probability ≈ theoretical probability.

Something More

> *Another name for 'theoretical probability' is 'expected probability'. Another name for 'experimental probability' is 'empirical probability'.*

In our discussion above, we have seen how the probability of some equally likely outcomes can be obtained both theoretically and experimentally. However for some events, all the possible outcomes are NOT equally likely, hence we cannot use the definition of probability that we had on P. 199 to find the probabilities of these events. Instead the probabilities of such events must be found by experiment.

◄ *cf. the definition on P. 199.*

---

theoretical probability 理論概率
experimental probability 實驗概率

Here are some examples in which the outcomes are *not* **equally likely**:

(i) The probability of getting even numbers when a *loaded die* is rolled.

(ii) The probability that a person will catch a common cold.

(iii) The probability that a person chosen at random is left-handed.

◄ *A loaded die is a die loaded with some heavy material like lead, so that certain outcomes are more likely than others. These dice are also called unfair dice.*

Example 3 25 boxes of oranges are delivered to a market. The bad oranges in each box are counted and the following results are obtained.

No. of bad oranges	0	1	2	3	4	5
No. of boxes	3	10	5	4	2	1

A customer selects one box at random. What is the experimental probability that

(a) it contains 1 bad orange?

(b) it contains more than 3 bad oranges?

Solution **(a)** $P(1 \text{ bad orange}) = \dfrac{10}{25}$

$$= \frac{2}{5}$$

◄ *There are altogether 25 boxes of oranges and 10 of them contain 1 bad orange in each box.*

(b) [The box contains more than 3 bad oranges if it contains 4 or 5 bad oranges.]

$$P(\text{more than 3 bad oranges}) = \frac{2+1}{25}$$

$$= \frac{3}{25}$$

◄ *There are altogether 25 boxes of oranges. 2 of them contain 4 bad oranges in each box and 1 of them contains 5 bad oranges in each box.*

CLASS PRACTICE

1. A bag contains 2 red balls, 3 yellow balls and 4 blue balls. All the balls are of the same size and weight. If one ball is taken out at random, find the theoretical probability that it is

Answer

(a) red, _____

(b) yellow, _____

(c) white. _____

2. A traffic survey records the number of passengers per bus in 100 cross-harbour tunnel buses in one morning:

No. of passengers per bus	170	128	123	143	158
No. of buses	65	24	6	3	2

Basing on these results, find the experimental probability that a cross-harbour tunnel bus checked at random would have more than 200 passengers.

Answer: _____

Just for Fun

How would you obtain the probability that you will pick up a bag containing 1 million dollars on your way home from school? Would you find the probability from theory or from experiment?

Note : From now on, the words 'theoretical' and 'experimental' will not be shown in the questions. Students will have to decide on their own whether the question asks for theoretical probability or experimental probability.

EXERCISE 7A

(*Level 1*)

1. On a bookshelf, there are 3 Mathematics books, 4 Chinese books and 1 dictionary. If a book is taken at random from the bookshelf, find the probability that it is a

 (a) dictionary,

 (b) Mathematics book.

2. A letter is chosen from the word 'PROBABILITY'. Find the probability that the letter chosen is

 (a) the letter 'I',

 (b) a vowel.

3. One card is drawn at random from a pack of 52 cards. What is the probability that

 (a) the card is the ace of spades?

 (b) the card is a king?

(Level 2)

4. When a thumbtack is tossed, there are two possible ◄ outcomes: up and down.

   When a certain thumbtack is tossed 60 times, there are 24 times that the thumbtack points up. Find the probability that the thumbtack points down when it is tossed once.

   Up

   Down

5. Nine cards are marked 3, 0, 64, 7, 0, 0, 3, 6 and 2 respectively. One card is chosen at random. Find the probability that it shows

   (a) 0,

   (b) an even number,

   (c) a factor of 25,

   (d) a number less than 100.

6. Twenty cards are marked from 1 to 20, and one card is drawn at random. What is the probability that the number on the card drawn is a multiple of

   (a) 5?

   (b) 7?

   (c) either 5 or 7?

7. A die was rolled 600 times, and the frequency of each number shown was recorded as follows:

Number	1	2	3	4	5	6
Frequency	101	111	94	105	96	93

   What is the probability of getting

   (a) an odd number?

   (b) a number less than 3?

   (c) an even number?

   (*Give the answers correct to 3 decimal places if necessary.*)

8. A small box contains 27 clips of several colours. If a clip is ◄ picked at random from the box, the probability that it is pink is $\frac{7}{9}$. Find the number of pink clips in the box.

9. A farm keeps ducks and geese. There are 12 more ducks than geese. If one of them is picked at random, the probability of getting a goose is $\frac{9}{20}$. Find the total number of ducks and geese on the farm.

*10. A class has n students, of whom x are boys. If a student is chosen at random from the class, the probability that a girl is chosen is $\frac{2}{5}$.

    (a) Write down an equation connecting x and n.

    (b) If 4 boys and 6 girls leave the class, the probability of choosing a girl among the remaining students becomes $\frac{1}{3}$.

        (i) Write down another equation connecting x and n. Hence find the values of x and n.

        (ii) How many boys, in addition to those who have already left, must leave the class so that the probability of choosing a girl in the class is again $\frac{2}{5}$?

7.2   Addition of Probabilities

A. *Mutually Exclusive Events*

In our everyday life, we can easily find events such that when one occurs, the others cannot occur at the same time. Such events are called *mutually exclusive events* 互斥事件.

e.g. **(i)** When a coin is tossed, if the head turns up, then it is <u>not</u> possible for the tail to turn up *at the same time*. Therefore when a coin is tossed, the appearance of a head and the appearance of a tail are two mutually exclusive events.

    (ii) When a die is rolled, the event that the number '1' shows up and the event that any of the other numbers, i.e. 2, 3, 4, 5 or 6, shows up *at the same time* are also mutually exclusive.

In short, two events are said to be *mutually exclusive* when both *cannot* happen at the *same* time.

When two events E and F are **mutually exclusive**, the probability of the happening of either event E *or* event F is the **sum** of the probabilities of the happenings of the two events.

i.e. $\boxed{P(\mathbf{E}\ or\ \mathbf{F}) = P(\mathbf{E}) + P(\mathbf{F})}$

In general, when n events E_1, E_2, $\cdots$, E_n are mutually exclusive, the probability of the happening of E_1 *or* E_2 *or* E_3 *or* $\cdots$ *or* E_n is the sum of the probabilities of the happenings of the n events.

i.e.

$$P(E_1 \text{ or } E_2 \text{ or } \cdots E_n) = P(E_1) + P(E_2) + \cdots + P(E_n)$$

This is sometimes considered as the **addition law** of probability for mutually exclusive events.

Note : In fact, for any two events E and F, the **addition law of probability** states that the probability of the happening of event E *or* event F is given by

$$P(E \text{ or } F) = P(E) + P(F) - P(E \text{ and } F),$$

where $P(E \text{ and } F)$ stands for the probability that both events E and F happen.

When E and F are *mutually exclusive events*, then $P(E \text{ and } F) = 0$. Hence $P(E \text{ or } F) = P(E) + P(F)$.

Question:
Do you know why for mutually exclusive events, say E and F, $P(E \text{ and } F) = 0$?

Example 4 One card is drawn at random from a pack of playing cards. What is the probability that it is an ace or a jack?

Solution [The event of getting an ace and the event of getting a jack from a pack of cards are mutually exclusive.]

$$P(\text{ace or jack}) = P(\text{ace}) + P(\text{jack})$$
$$= \frac{4}{52} + \frac{4}{52}$$
$$= \frac{8}{52}$$
$$= \frac{2}{13}$$

◀ *There are 4 aces and 4 jacks in the pack of cards.*

Example 5 A loaded die is rolled and the probability that the number '1' shows up is found by experiment to be 0.05. The probability that the number '6' shows up on the same die is found by experiment to be 0.3. Find the probability that either the number '1' or the number '6' shows up when this loaded die is rolled.

The event '1' shows up and the event '6' shows up are mutually exclusive.

Solution $P(1 \text{ or } 6) = P(1) + P(6)$
$$= 0.05 + 0.3$$
$$= 0.35$$

B. Complementary Events

If E denotes an event, then the event that E does not happen is
called the *complementary event* 互補事件 of E, and is denoted by
E′. Since an event either happens or does not happen, the sum of
their probabilities is 1.

◀ **Question:**
*Do you agree that two
complementary events are
mutually exclusive events?*

*Is it true that two mutually
exclusive events must be
complementary events?*

i.e. $P(E) + P(E') = 1$

From this we have

$$P(E) = 1 - P(E')$$
$$or \quad P(E') = 1 - P(E)$$

Sometimes it is easier or more convenient to find the probability
of the complementary event of a particular event and then to
obtain the probability of the event itself by subtraction.

Example 6 One ball is drawn at random from a bag containing
10 white balls, 11 red balls, 6 green balls and
8 yellow balls. Find the probability that

(a) the ball drawn is neither white nor green,

(b) the ball drawn is white or red or green.

Solution   **(a)** [We consider the complementary event, i.e. the
event of drawing a white or a green ball.]

$P(\text{white } or \text{ green}) = P(\text{white}) + P(\text{green})$

$= \dfrac{10}{35} + \dfrac{6}{35}$

$= \dfrac{16}{35}$

◀ *The number of possible
outcomes
$= 10 + 11 + 6 + 8 = 35$*

∴ $P(neither \text{ white } nor \text{ green})$

$= 1 - P(\text{white } or \text{ green})$

◀ $P(E) = 1 - P(E')$

$= 1 - \dfrac{16}{35}$

$= \dfrac{19}{35}$

Alternative Method:

$$P(\textit{neither} \text{ white } \textit{nor} \text{ green}) = P(\text{red } \textit{or} \text{ yellow})$$
$$= P(\text{red}) + P(\text{yellow})$$
$$= \frac{11}{35} + \frac{8}{35}$$
$$= \frac{19}{35}$$

◀ *There are only four kinds of balls, i.e. white, red, green and yellow balls in the bag. If the ball drawn is neither white nor green, it must be either red or yellow.*

(b) [We consider the complementary event instead, i.e. the event of drawing a yellow ball.]

$$P(\text{yellow}) = \frac{8}{35}$$

$$P(\text{white } \textit{or} \text{ red } \textit{or} \text{ green}) = 1 - P(\text{yellow})$$
$$= 1 - \frac{8}{35}$$
$$= \frac{27}{35}$$

◀ $P(E) = 1 - P(E')$

EXERCISE 7B

(Level 1)

1. A card is drawn at random from a pack of 52 playing cards. Find the probability that it is either a black card or the diamond queen.

2. A loaded die is rolled 100 times, and the frequency of each number shown is recorded as follows:

Number	1	2	3	4	5	6
Frequency	5	12	10	27	18	28

Find the probability of obtaining '2' or a factor of 5 in a single throw.

3. If a letter is selected at random from the word PROFESSIONAL, find the probability that it is

   (a) a consonant,

   (b) not a consonant.

4. The probability that a *microchip* 微型晶片 works is 0.978. What is the probability that it does not work?

(Level 2)

5. In a bag there are 3 white marbles and 30 marbles of colours red, blue and green. The numbers of red, blue and green marbles are in the ratio $5 : 3 : 2$. If a marble is selected at random from the bag, find the probability that it is

   (a) white or green,

   (b) neither green nor blue.

6. In a school, there are 1 000 students, of whom 72% are boys. Half of the boys and 60% of the girls in that school are wearing glasses. A student is chosen at random from the school, find the probability that the student is

   (a) a boy wearing glasses,

   (b) a girl wearing glasses or a boy not wearing glasses.

7. Two dice are thrown. Find the probability that

   (a) the sum of the numbers is greater than 9,

   (b) the sum of the numbers is not greater than 9.

8. Among 4 500 calculators manufactured, 27 of them are found to be defective.

   (a) What is the probability that a calculator selected at random is
       (i) defective?
       (ii) not defective?

   (b) If 12 000 calculators are manufactured, how many of them would you expect to be defective?

9. Among a group of 1 000 men, the sizes of their shoes were recorded. The results are:

Shoe size	5	6	7	8	9	10	11	12
Number of men	22	83	125	309	245	126	50	40

If a man from the group is chosen at random, find the probability that he wears shoes of size

   (a) 7,

   (b) less than 8,

   (c) 10 or 12,

   (d) neither 9 nor 11.

7.3 Multiplication of Probabilities

A. Independent Events

When a coin is tossed *twice*, the outcome of the second toss is NOT affected by the outcome of the first toss. This means that an event concerning the *first toss only* and an event concerning the *second toss only* are **independent**.

When a coin is tossed **twice**, there are four equally likely outcomes:

H *and* H,   H *and* T,   T *and* H,   T *and* T.

↑   ↑

(means a head in the 1st toss and a tail in the 2nd toss)

◀ *Recall:*
The letter 'H' stands for head and the letter 'T' stands for tail.

The probability of tossing **two heads** is $P(\text{H } and \text{ H}) = \frac{1}{4}$.

Notice the probability that **a head** turns up in the *first toss* is $\frac{1}{2}$ $\left(\text{i.e. } P_1(\text{H}) = \frac{1}{2}\right)$, and that in the *second toss* is also $\frac{1}{2}$ $\left(\text{i.e. } P_2(\text{H}) = \frac{1}{2}\right)$.

It appears that $P(\text{H } and \text{ H})$ is *just* the **product** of $P_1(\text{H})$ and $P_2(\text{H})$.

i.e. $P(\text{H } and \text{ H}) = P_1(\text{H}) \times P_2(\text{H})$

$$= \frac{1}{2} \times \frac{1}{2}$$

$$= \frac{1}{4}$$

In fact, this result is generally true.

Hence for two independent events E and F,

$$\boxed{P(\text{E } and \text{ F}) = P(\text{E}) \times P(\text{F}).}$$

e.g. Getting a head when a coin is tossed and throwing the number '6' when a die is rolled are independent events.

The probability of getting a head is $P(\text{H}) = \frac{1}{2}$.

The probability of getting the number '6' is $P(6) = \frac{1}{6}$.

∴ The probability of getting a head followed by the number '6' is given by

$$P(\text{H } and \text{ } 6) = P(\text{H}) \times P(6)$$
$$= \frac{1}{2} \times \frac{1}{6}$$
$$= \frac{1}{12}$$

Example 7 Two cards are drawn, one after the other with replacement, from a pack of 52 well-shuffled playing cards. Find the probability that the first card drawn is black in colour and the second card drawn is a diamond.

Solution [Since the first card is replaced before the second card is drawn, the events are independent.]

The first card drawn is black means that the card is *either* a spade *or* a club.

∴ $P(\text{first black}) = P(\text{spade } or \text{ club})$

$\qquad = P(\text{spade}) + P(\text{club})$ ⟵ The two events are mutually exclusive.

$\qquad = \dfrac{13}{52} + \dfrac{13}{52}$ ◄ There are 13 spades and 13 clubs in the pack of cards.

$\qquad = \dfrac{26}{52}$

$\qquad = \dfrac{1}{2}$

$P(\text{second diamond}) = \dfrac{13}{52}$

$\qquad\qquad\qquad\quad = \dfrac{1}{4}$

∴ $P(\text{first black } and \text{ second diamond})$

$\qquad = P(\text{first black}) \times P(\text{second diamond})$

$\qquad = \dfrac{1}{2} \times \dfrac{1}{4}$

$\qquad = \dfrac{1}{8}$

Try This

When two cards are drawn, one after the other with replacement, from a pack of playing cards, what is the probability that the first card drawn is black in colour and the second card drawn is red?

Do not think that the probability is $\frac{1}{2} + \frac{1}{2} = 1$!

Note : The condition stated in the above example that '*two cards are drawn, one after the other with replacement*' meaning '*the first card is put back into the pack before the second card is drawn*' is very important. We shall see the reason why it is important in the following section.

Example 8 An electronic calculator manufacturer finds out by experiment the probability that any one of his calculators being defective after *assembling* 裝嵌 is 5%. He wishes to keep the percentage of defective calculators at that level, so he introduces the following scheme to encourage his workers.

(i) Every day a worker is chosen at random and the calculator that he has assembled is examined. If the calculator is found to be in good condition, i.e. not defective, then the worker has a chance to spin the company's 'Award Wheel'.

(ii) The 'Award Wheel' is a large circular board divided into 5 equal sectors. On each sector, there is a certain amount of 'award money', ranging from $60 to $100 as shown. The worker spins the wheel to determine the amount of his 'award money'.
(*Assume that the 'Award Wheel' pointer will NOT land on the lines that divide the sectors.*)

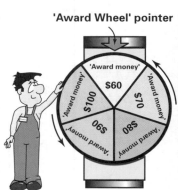

'Award Wheel' pointer

Find the probability that on any day, the chosen worker

(a) does not receive any 'award money',

(b) gets $100 as his 'award money'.

Solution **(a)** [The worker does not receive any 'award money' if the calculator he has assembled is defective.]

P(no 'award money') = P(examined calculator is defective)
$$= \underline{\underline{0.05}}$$

(b) The worker gets $100 as his 'award money' implies the occurrence of two events:

Event I: the calculator he assembles is in good condition,
Event II: he gets $100 as 'award money'.

P(Event I) = $1 - P$(examined calculator is defective)
$$= 1 - 0.05$$
$$= 0.95$$

◀ *Event I and the event that the examined calculator is defective are complementary events.*

$$P(\text{Event II}) = \frac{1}{5}$$
$$= 0.2$$

◀ *There is one favourable outcome ($100) and there are five equally likely possible outcomes ($60, $70, $80, $90 and $100).*

$\therefore$ P(gets $100 as 'award money')
$$= P(\text{Event I } and \text{ Event II})$$
$$= P(\text{Event I}) \times P(\text{Event II})$$
$$= 0.95 \times 0.2$$
$$= \underline{\underline{0.19}}$$

◀ *Event I and Event II are independent.*

B. *Dependent Events*

A bowl contains 2 red marbles and 1 green marble. Suppose two marbles are drawn from the bowl one after the other at random, *and* the first marble drawn is NOT replaced before the second marble is drawn. Then obviously the removal of the first marble affects the probability of drawing a specific second marble. This means that the two events are **dependent**.

◀ *We say that the two marbles are drawn 'without replacement'.*

Suppose that we label the two red marbles in the bowl as R_1 and R_2, and the green marble as G. When two marbles are drawn from the bowl, we list all the possible outcomes as shown in **Table 2** on the right.

The probability that both marbles drawn are red corresponds to the two indicated outcomes (R_1, R_2) and (R_2, R_1). Since there are six equally likely outcomes altogether,

1st marble	2nd marble	
R_1	R_2	◀ (R_1, R_2)
R_1	G	
R_2	R_1	◀ (R_2, R_1)
R_2	G	
G	R_1	
G	R_2	**Table 2**

$$P(\text{both red}) = \frac{2}{6} \leftarrow \textit{Two favourable outcomes} \atop \leftarrow \textit{Six possible outcomes}$$

$$= \frac{1}{3}$$

On the other hand, we can find the required probability as follows.

Since there are 2 red marbles and one green marble in the bowl, the probability that the *first marble* drawn is red is given by definition:

$$P(1\text{st red}) = \frac{2}{3}.$$

◀ *There are two red marbles in the bowl, hence 2 favourable outcomes. There are three marbles in the bowl altogether, hence 3 possible outcomes.*

Since the first red marble drawn is *not* returned to the bowl, there are now only two marbles left in the bowl: one red and one green, before the second marble is drawn. The probability that the *second marble* drawn is red is given by definition:

$$P(2\text{nd red}) = \frac{1}{2}.$$

Then $P(\text{both red})$ is just the **product** of $P(1\text{st red})$ and $P(2\text{nd red})$.

◀ *'1st red' and '2nd red' are two dependent events.*

i.e. $P(\text{both red}) = P(1\text{st red}) \times P(2\text{nd red}) = \frac{2}{3} \times \frac{1}{2} = \frac{1}{3}$

In fact, this result is generally true.

Hence for two dependent events A and B,

$$\boxed{P(\textbf{A \textit{and} B}) = P(\textbf{A}) \times P(\textbf{B}).}$$

Note :   For any two dependent events, the probability that the two events both happen is the product of the probability of the first event and the probability of the second event AFTER THE FIRST EVENT HAS OCCURRED. In short, we state that for two dependent events A and B,

$$P(A \ and \ B) = P(A) \times P(B \text{ after A has occurred}).$$

Example 9   Two cards are drawn, one after the other, from a pack of 52 playing cards. If the second card is drawn without replacement, find the probability that

(a) the first card is black and the second card is a diamond,

(b) the first card is black and the second card is a spade.

Solution   **(a)**   [Since the second card is drawn without replacement, the events are dependent.]

$$P(\text{first black}) = \frac{1}{2}$$ ◀ *By* **Example 7**.

$$P(\text{second diamond after first black}) = \frac{13}{51}$$ ◀ *There are* 13 *diamonds out of* 51 *cards left in the pack of cards since the first card is NOT replaced after it is taken out.*

∴ $P(\text{first black } and \text{ second diamond})$

$= P(\text{first black}) \times P(\text{second diamond after first black})$

$= \frac{1}{2} \times \frac{13}{51}$

$= \underline{\underline{\frac{13}{102}}}$

(b)   [The first card drawn is black means that the card is either a spade or a club.

∴ $P(\text{1st black } and \text{ 2nd spade})$

$= P(\text{'}1st \text{ } spade \text{ } and \text{ } 2nd \text{ } spade\text{'} \text{ or '}1st \text{ } club \text{ } and \text{ } 2nd \text{ } spade\text{'})$

$= P(\text{1st spade } and \text{ 2nd spade}) + P(\text{1st club } and \text{ 2nd spade})$

$= P(\text{1st spade}) \times P(\text{2nd spade after 1st spade}) +$

$\quad P(\text{1st club}) \times P(\text{2nd spade after 1st club})$]

$P(\text{first black } and \text{ second spade})$

$= \frac{13}{52} \times \frac{12}{51} + \frac{13}{52} \times \frac{13}{51}$

$= \frac{1}{17} + \frac{13}{204}$

$= \underline{\underline{\frac{25}{204}}}$

EXERCISE 7C

(Level 1)

1. A die is tossed twice, what is the probability that the die shows

   (a) a '6' in each toss?

   (b) an even number in each toss?

2. Two cards are drawn at random, one after another, from a pack of 52 cards with replacement. What is the probability that

   (a) the first card is a king and the second card is a queen?

   (b) none of the cards is a heart?

3. A bag contains 14 yellow marbles and 10 red marbles. Two marbles are taken out one by one from the bag and without replacement. What is the probability of drawing

   (a) two red marbles?

   (b) a red marble and then a yellow marble?

4. A basket contains 12 eggs and two of them are rotten. If two eggs are picked at random, one after the other, from the basket without replacement, find the probability that both eggs picked are

   (a) rotten,   **(b)** good.

5. Bill and ten other men are members of a men's club. Amy is one of the ten members of a women's club. If one person from each club is randomly selected to be members of a committee, calculate the probability that the selection will include

   (a) both Bill and Amy,

   (b) either Bill or Amy, but not both.

6. In a class, there are 15 girls and 25 boys. If two students are selected at random, what is the probability that one boy and one girl are selected?

(Level 2)

7. Two boys, John and Peter, attempt to solve a problem independently. The probability that John solves the problem is $\frac{4}{5}$ and the probability that Peter solves it is $\frac{3}{4}$. Find the probability that

   (a) both of them solve it,

   (b) John solves it but Peter does not.

8. The triangular spinner as shown in the figure is equally likely to give a score of 1, 2 or 3. It is spun two times. What is the probability that

    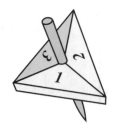

    (a) the sum of the scores obtained is six?

    (b) the first spin scores an odd number and the second spin scores an even number?

9. For simplicity, assume that every day can be described as either a cloudy day or a clear day. Given that the probability of having a cloudy day in a certain town is 0.56, what is the probability of having

    (a) a clear day?

    (b) two consecutive clear days?

10. In the figure, a mouse has to pass through a number of gates (labelled A, B, C, D, etc.) of a *maze* 迷宮 in order to reach a piece of cheese. If the mouse selects her route randomly, find the probability that she has passed through the following gates before she reaches the piece of cheese.

    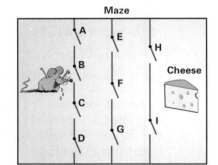

    (a) A, G and H,

    (b) B and I,

    (c) H.

    (*The gates can only be passed from left to right in the figure.*)

11. 8 men and 7 women applied for a temporary job. If 3 applicants from this group are randomly selected for an interview, find the probability that

    (a) all of them are women,

    (b) there is at least 1 woman.

12. A letter is taken at random from each of the two words CHOICE and CHANCE. What is the probability that the two letters picked are the same?

13. The figure shows a tree branch. A caterpillar wants to reach a leaf. If it selects the route randomly, what is the probability that it will

    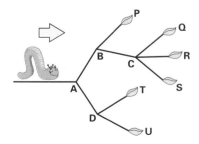

    (a) pass through junction C or junction D?

    (b) reach leaf S or leaf T?

14. It is found by experiment that, for a certain biased die, the probabilities of throwing 1, 2, 3, 4, 5 are $\frac{1}{12}, \frac{1}{8}, \frac{1}{8}, \frac{1}{6}, \frac{1}{4}$ respectively.

    (a) What is the probability of getting a 6?

    (b) Which is greater, the probability of getting an even number or the probability of getting an odd number?

    (c) If the die is thrown twice, what is the probability that the sum of the two scores is 4?

15. There are 25 boys and 12 girls in F.5C. 16% of the boys and 75% of the girls keep pets. If two students are selected at random from the class, find the probability that

    (a) none of them keeps pets,

    (b) exactly one of them keeps pets.

    (*Give the answers correct to 3 significant figures.*)

*16. George and Helen have taken examinations in Geography and History. The following table shows the probabilities that they will pass in each subject.

Subject⟍Candidate	Geography	History
George	$\frac{2}{3}$	$\frac{1}{2}$
Helen	$\frac{5}{12}$	$\frac{3}{4}$

    Find the probability that

    (a) they fail in both subjects,

    (b) at least one of them does not fail in both subjects.

*17.

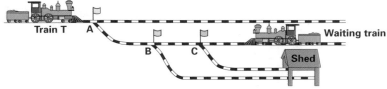

A, B and C are junctions on a toy train system as shown. At each junction, the probability of the toy train going straight ahead (without turning right) is $\frac{2}{3}$. Find the probability that

    (a) the train T hits the waiting train,

    (b) the train T goes into the shed.

*18. In a certain city, it is found that if today is rainy, then the probability that tomorrow will be rainy is $\frac{5}{7}$; whereas if today is not rainy, then the probability that tomorrow will not be rainy is $\frac{6}{7}$. Suppose a certain Monday is not rainy, what is the probability that the Wednesday of the same week is also not rainy?

7.4   The Tree Diagram

When two or more events take place, we have another method to find the probabilities of various events. This is by means of a tree diagram which can show all the possible events and their probabilities.

◄ *Recall:*
We learnt in lower Forms how to use the tree diagram to list all the possible outcomes of different events.

Example 10 Suppose that we toss a coin three times. Find the probability that in the 3 tosses we get

(a) 3 heads,

(b) 2 heads and 1 tail.

Solution   [There are <u>two</u> possible outcomes in the first toss, either a head turns up or a tail turns up. They are represented by <u>two</u> branches on a tree diagram.

1st toss

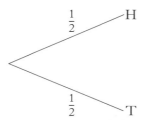

The end points of the branches are labelled with the possible outcomes, and the corresponding probabilities $\left(\frac{1}{2}\right)$ are written beside the branches. Now we continue and complete the tree diagram with the outcomes of the second toss and the third toss.

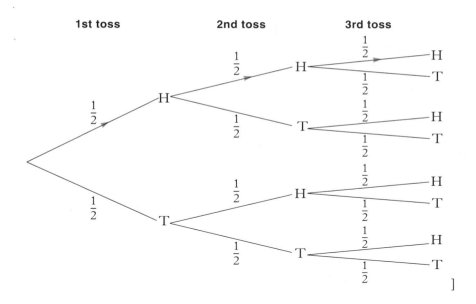

(a) [The top branches (indicated by single arrows) correspond to the event that heads are obtained in all the 3 tosses (i.e. HHH).]

The probability of getting a head in the 1st toss *and* the 2nd toss *and* the 3rd toss is given by:

$$P(\text{HHH}) = P(\text{H}) \times P(\text{H}) \times P(\text{H})$$
$$= \frac{1}{2} \times \frac{1}{2} \times \frac{1}{2}$$
$$= \frac{1}{8}$$

◀ *These are independent events. **P**(HHH) is obtained by multiplication of probabilities of individual events.*

(b) The probability of getting 2 heads and 1 tail in the 3 tosses (i.e. HHT, HTH or THH) is given by:

$$P(\text{HHT } or \text{ HTH } or \text{ THH})$$
$$= P(\text{HHT}) + P(\text{HTH}) + P(\text{THH})$$
$$= \frac{1}{8} + \frac{1}{8} + \frac{1}{8}$$
$$= \frac{3}{8}$$

◀ $P(\text{HHT}) = P(\text{HTH}) =$ $P(\text{THH})$ $= P(\text{H}) \times P(\text{H}) \times P(\text{T})$ $= \frac{1}{2} \times \frac{1}{2} \times \frac{1}{2}$ $= \frac{1}{8}$

Note :   Hence we can conclude as follows.

(i) The probability of any event represented by consecutive branches of the tree diagram is the *product* of the probabilities along these branches. [Example 10(a)]

(ii) The probability of any event which can occur in two or more ways is the *sum* of the probabilities at the end of the relevant branches. [Example 10(b)]

EXERCISE 7D

[Use the tree diagram in this exercise.]

(*Level 1*)

1. 3 coins are tossed. Find the probability of obtaining two tails and 1 head.

2. A 3-digit number is formed by one of the digits 1, 2 and 7. Find the probability that the number formed is divisible by 3.

3. In a short quiz there are 4 true or false questions. If each question is answered only by guessing, what is the probability that exactly 2 questions are answered correctly?

(*Level 2*)

4. It is found that, for patients with a certain disease, the probability of recovery within one year is 0.7. Find the probability that exactly two out of three patients currently under medical treatment will recover within one year.

5. Bag A contains 1 red ball, 3 blue balls and 2 green balls, bag B contains 2 red balls and 1 green ball. A ball is selected at random from bag A and put into bag B, then a ball is selected at random from bag B. Find the probability that the selected ball is green in colour.

6. Three balls are drawn in succession at random from a box containing 10 black balls, 8 white balls and 2 red balls with replacement. Find the probability that
   (a) all the balls drawn are black,
   (b) all the balls drawn are not white,
   (c) the first ball drawn is black, the second is white and the third is red,
   (d) all the balls drawn are of the same colour.

7. Three cards are drawn in succession without replacement from the heart suit in a pack of 52 playing cards. Find the probability that
   (a) all 3 cards drawn are face cards,
   (b) exactly 1 card drawn is a face card,
   (c) at least 2 cards drawn are face cards.

S U P P L E M E N T A R Y
E X E R C I S E 7

PART I | *Further Practice*

(*Ex. 7A*)

1. If all the red face cards are removed from a pack of 52 playing cards and then a card is drawn at random from the pack, find the probability of getting

    (a) a red ace,

    (b) a black king,

    (c) a heart.

2. What are the probabilities that a three-digit number chosen at random is

    (a) divisible by 5?

    (b) divisible by 2?

3. A dental survey is carried out in a primary school. The numbers of cavities found among the students are recorded as follows:

No. of cavities	0	1	2	3 or more
No. of students	142	112	31	15

    (a) Find the probability that a student chosen randomly from the school will have
    (i) no cavities,
    (ii) at least one cavity.

    (b) If the school has 1 200 students, estimate the number of students who have no cavities.

(*Ex. 7B*)

4. The table shows the *marital status* 婚姻狀況 of the employees of a company.

	Married	Single	Divorced
Male	14	7	1
Female	8	3	0

    If an employee is selected at random, find the probability that he/she is a married woman or a single man.

5. Team A is playing a football match against team B. If the probability that team A will win is twice the probability that team B will win, and the probability that the match will end with a draw is $\frac{5}{23}$, find the probability that team A will win.

6. In a large bucket there are umbrellas of colours yellow, blue and black. The numbers of yellow, blue and black umbrellas are in the ratio $7 : 15 : 20$. If an umbrella is picked at random from the bucket, what is the probability of getting a yellow or a black umbrella from the bucket?

7. In a certain Mathematics test, the results are classified into 6 grades: A, B, C, D, E and F. The percentage of candidates obtaining various grades are as follows:

A	4%
B or above	10%
C or above	28%
D or above	58%
E or above	72%
F or above	100%

If a candidate is chosen at random, find the probability that he obtains

(a) grade C,

(b) grade B or grade E,

(c) grade D or below.

(Ex. 7C)

8. Three different pairs of coloured socks are mixed together in a cabinet. If Mary takes out two socks at random in the dark, what is the probability that she obtains a matching pair of socks?

9. Three girls Joan, Jane and Jill plan to meet at a youth club one evening. The probabilities that Joan, Jane and Jill are unable to go are $\frac{1}{3}$, $\frac{1}{4}$ and $\frac{1}{5}$ respectively. Find the probability that

(a) none of them goes to the club,

(b) all of them go to the club.

10. A bag contains 6 red, 8 white and 10 blue marbles. If two marbles are drawn in succession from the bag without replacement, find the probability of each of the following events.

(a) Both marbles drawn are white.

(b) One marble is red and one marble is blue.

11. There are two bags A and B. Bag A contains 3 black balls, 4 white balls and 1 green ball. Bag B contains 5 white balls only. A ball is taken out at random from bag A and put into bag B. A ball is then taken out at random from bag B. What is the probability that the ball is

   (a) green in colour?

   (b) not white in colour?

12. The results of the final examination for a class of 40 students are such that 25 students pass in both English and Chinese, 8 students pass in Chinese only and 2 students pass in English only.

   (a) How many students fail in both subjects?

   (b) If 3 students are chosen at random from the class, what is the probability that
   (i) all of them fail in both subjects?
   (ii) all of them pass in English?
   (iii) all of them pass in at least one subject?
   (*Give the answers correct to 3 significant figures.*)

13. If two cards are drawn one after the other at random from a pack of 52 playing cards without replacement, find the probability that

   (a) both cards are black,

   (b) both cards are kings,

   (c) one card is a king and the other card is a queen,

   (d) both cards drawn are of the same suit.

14. Three men, A, B and C, shoot at a target. The probabilities of each hitting the target are $\frac{1}{3}$, $\frac{1}{4}$ and $\frac{1}{6}$ respectively. Find the probabilities that

   (a) none of them hits the target,

   (b) exactly one man hits the target.

15. There are two packs of playing cards. 4 aces are missing in the first pack and 4 kings are missing in the second pack. If a pack is chosen at random and then 2 cards are picked one after the other at random from the pack without replacement, find the probability of obtaining

   (a) two aces,

   (b) two queens,

   (c) one ace and one king.

*16. In the figure, there are 4 paths P_1, P_2, P_3 and P_4 joining towns A and B and there are 2 paths P_5 and P_6 joining towns B and C. Peter goes from A to C by choosing his paths at random.

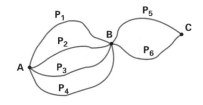

(a) Find the probability that Peter will choose the paths P_2 and P_5.

(b) If John goes from C to A by choosing his paths at random, find the probability that Peter and John will choose the same paths for their journeys.

(Ex. 7D)

[Use the tree diagram to solve **Questions 17** and **18**.]

*17. A sheet of paper goes through four unreliable printing machines.

(I) The first machine prints only the colour *cyan* 青色 and the probability that it fails to print this colour is $\frac{1}{4}$.

(II) The second machine prints only the colour *magenta* 紫紅色 and the probability that it fails to print this colour is $\frac{1}{6}$.

(III) The third machine prints only the colour yellow and the probability that it fails to print this colour is $\frac{1}{5}$.

(IV) The fourth machine prints only the colour black and the probability that it fails to print this colour is $\frac{2}{5}$.

Find the probability that

(a) only black is printed,

(b) only cyan and yellow are printed,

(c) all the four colours are printed,

(d) just one colour is printed.

*18. Bag A contains 3 red balls, 2 blue balls and 1 green ball. Bag B contains 2 red balls and 1 blue ball. A ball is taken out at random from A and put into B. Then a ball is taken out at random from B and put back into A. Find the probability that

(a) bag B contains 2 blue balls,

(b) the green ball is in bag A,

(c) bag B contains exactly 2 red balls.

PART II | *Miscellaneous*

19. In a pond, there are 20 red *carps* 鯉魚, 15 black carps and 7 white carps.

   (a) A carp is caught randomly from the pond. What is the probability that it is
   (i) red in colour?
   (ii) red or white in colour?
   (iii) not a white one?

   (b) If 8 of the carps died, among which 3 are white ones, what is the probability of catching a white carp from the remaining carps in the pond?

20. A glass bottle contains some stars folded from paper. There are 7 yellow stars, and the rest are either blue or pink. The ratio of the number of blue stars to the number of pink stars is $4 : 3$. Given that when two stars are picked at random from the bottle, the probability that they are both yellow is $\frac{1}{10}$, find the numbers of blue stars and pink stars in the bottle.

21. A bag contains 3 black marbles, 4 white marbles, 5 red marbles and 13 green marbles. If a marble is drawn at random, find the probability that

   (a) a green marble is drawn,

   (b) a black or white marble is drawn,

   (c) the marble drawn is neither red nor black.

22. Bag X contains 5 black balls, 4 white balls and 3 green balls. Bag Y contains 4 black balls and 3 white balls. A die is rolled, if '1' or '2' turns out, a ball is drawn from bag Y, otherwise, a ball is drawn from bag X. Find the probability that

   (a) a ball is drawn from bag X,

   (b) a ball is drawn from bag Y,

   (c) a green ball is drawn,

   (d) a black ball is drawn,

   (e) the ball drawn is not white.

*23. In a Mathematics examination, the probabilities that Paul gets grades A, B and F or below are $\frac{1}{5}$, $\frac{1}{4}$ and $\frac{1}{10}$ respectively. If it is equally likely for him to get grade C, D or E, find the probabilities that he will

   (a) get grade B or C,

   (b) get grade C or above,

   (c) not get grade B or above.

*24. A learner-driver, Carmen, is determined to pass the driving test. The probability that she will pass the driving test on any one occasion is $\frac{1}{3}$. Each time she takes the driving test, she has to pay $500. Find the probability that Carmen will

(a) fail the test in both her first and second attempts,

(b) fail the test in her first three attempts but pass the test in her fourth attempt,

(c) spend exactly $3 000 on driving tests,

(d) spend more than $1 000 on driving tests.

*25. In a group of 150 children, 74 are afraid of cockroaches and 60 are afraid of lizards. Among those children who are afraid of cockroaches or lizards, 24 of them are afraid of both.

(a) How many children are afraid of
  (i) cockroaches but not lizards?
  (ii) lizards but not cockroaches?
  (iii) neither cockroaches nor lizards?

(b) If 3 children are picked at random from the group, what is the probability that
  (i) all of them are afraid of cockroaches but not lizards?
  (ii) exactly one of them is afraid of lizards but not cockroaches?
  (*Give the answers correct to 3 significant figures.*)

PART III | *HKCEE Questions*

(*Section B Questions*)

26. (a) There are two bags. Each bag contains 1 red, 1 black and 1 white ball. One ball is drawn randomly from each bag. Find the probability that
  (i) the two balls drawn are both red;
  (ii) the two balls drawn are of the same colour;
  (iii) the two balls drawn are of different colours.

(b) A box contains 2 red, 2 black and 3 white balls. One ball is drawn randomly from the box. After putting the ball back into the box, one ball is again drawn randomly. Find the probability that
  (i) the two balls drawn are both red;
  (ii) the two balls drawn are of the same colour;
  (iii) the two balls drawn are of different colours.

[HKCEE 84]

27. A box contains wooden blocks of 5 different shapes A, B, C, D and E. For each shape, there are 5 different colours red, orange, yellow, green and blue. For each colour of each shape, there is one block of each of the sizes L, M and S.
[*Hint: There are altogether 75 blocks in the box.*]

(a) When a block is picked out randomly from the box, what is the probability that it is of
  (i) red colour?
  (ii) blue colour and shape C?
  (iii) size S, shape A or E but not yellow?

(b) Two blocks are drawn at random from the box, one after the other. The first block drawn is put back into the box before the second block is drawn. Find the probability that
  (i) the first block drawn is of size L and the second block is of size S,
  (ii) one of the blocks drawn is of size L and the other of size S,
  (iii) the two blocks drawn are of different sizes.

[HKCEE 86]

28.

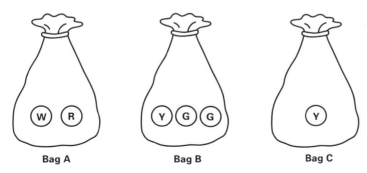

Bag A   Bag B   Bag C

The figure shows 3 bags A, B and C.

Bag A contains 1 white ball (W) and 1 red ball (R).
Bag B contains 1 yellow ball (Y) and 2 green balls (G).
Bag C contains only 1 yellow ball (Y).

(a) Peter chooses one bag at random and then randomly draws one ball from the bag. Find the probability that
  (i) the ball drawn is green;
  (ii) the ball drawn is yellow.

(b) After Peter had drawn a ball in the way described in **(a)**, he puts it back into the original bag. Next, Alice chooses one bag at random and then randomly draws one ball from the bag. Find the probability that
  (i) the balls drawn by Peter and Alice are both green;
  (ii) the balls drawn by Peter and Alice are both yellow and from the same bag.

[HKCEE 90]

29.

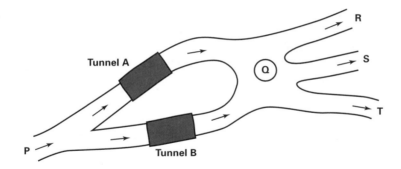

The figure shows a one-way road network system from Town P to Towns R, S and T. Any car leaving Town P will pass through either Tunnel A or Tunnel B and arrive at Towns R, S or T via the roundabout Q. A survey shows that $\frac{2}{5}$ of the cars leaving P will pass through Tunnel A. The survey also shows that $\frac{1}{7}$ of all the cars passing through the roundabout Q will arrive at R, $\frac{2}{7}$ at S, and $\frac{4}{7}$ at T.

(a) Find the probabilities that a car leaving P will
    (i) pass through Tunnel B,
    (ii) not arrive at T,
    (iii) arrive at R through Tunnel B,
    (iv) pass through Tunnel A but not arrive at R.
(b) Two cars leave P. Find the probabilities that
    (i) one of them arrives at R and the other one at S,
    (ii) both of them arrive at S, one through Tunnel A and the other one through Tunnel B.

[HKCEE 92]

30. Siu Ming lives in Tuen Mun. He travels to school either by LRT (Light Railway Transit) or on foot. The probability of being late for school is $\frac{1}{7}$ if he travels by LRT and $\frac{1}{10}$ if he travels on foot.

(a) In a certain week, Siu Ming travels to school by LRT on Monday, Tuesday and Wednesday. Find the probability that
    (i) he will be late on all these three days;
    (ii) he will not be late on all these three days.

(b) In the same week, Siu Ming travels to school on foot on Thursday, Friday and Saturday. Find the probability that

    (i) he will be late on Thursday and Friday only in these three days;

    (ii) he will be late on any two of these three days.

(c) On Sunday, Siu Ming goes to school to take part in a basketball match. If he is equally likely to travel by LRT or on foot, find the probability that he will be late on that day.

[HKCEE 94]

(MC Questions) ──────────────────────────────■

31. There are 7 bags, 3 of which are empty and the remaining 4 each contains a ball. An additional ball is now put into one of the bags at random. After that a bag is randomly selected. Find the probability of selecting an empty bag.

    A. $\dfrac{2}{7}$

    B. $\dfrac{3}{7}$

    C. $\dfrac{6}{49}$

    D. $\dfrac{12}{49}$

    E. $\dfrac{18}{49}$ [HKCEE 90]

32. Two cards are drawn randomly from five cards A, B, C, D and E. Find the probability that card A is drawn while card C is not.

    A. $\dfrac{3}{25}$

    B. $\dfrac{3}{20}$

    C. $\dfrac{4}{25}$

    D. $\dfrac{6}{25}$

    E. $\dfrac{3}{10}$ [HKCEE 92]

33. A box contains 5 eggs, 2 of which are rotten. If 2 eggs are chosen at random, find the probability that exactly one of them is rotten.

    A. $\dfrac{2}{5}$

    B. $\dfrac{3}{5}$

    C. $\dfrac{3}{10}$

    D. $\dfrac{6}{25}$

    E. $\dfrac{12}{25}$ [HKCEE 94]

To learn about the environment, biologists collect various kinds of data and analyze them. In Canada, biologists measure the widths of the leaves in a forest to study the impact of air pollution on these trees. When the collected data are presented with a frequency distribution curve, we will find that the curve has a nice bell shape.

CHAPTER

8

Statistics

8.1　Review

A.　*Frequency Distribution*

The data given below are the weights (in kg) of 20 *portable computers* 手提電腦 produced by different manufacturers.

1.9	2.0	2.1	2.4	2.4
2.8	3.2	2.3	1.5	2.6
2.6	1.9	2.4	2.2	1.6
1.7	1.7	1.8	1.8	3.0

Table 1

We can group the data into different class intervals and then organize the data in the form of a table with the corresponding frequencies. The result is the frequency distribution table below.

Something More

Data that have not been organized in any way are called raw data.

Weight (kg)	Tally	Class boundaries (kg)	Class mark (kg)	Frequency
1.5 – 1.9	̸̶̶̶ ///	*1.45 – 1.95*	*1.7*	8
2.0 – 2.4	̸̶̶̶ //	*1.95 – 2.45*	*2.2*	7
2.5 – 2.9	///	*2.45 – 2.95*	*2.7*	3
3.0 – 3.4	//	*2.95 – 3.45*	*3.2*	2

Table 2

B. *Graphical Representation of Frequency Distribution*

Various kinds of statistical diagrams can be used to represent the data in **Table 2** graphically.

(1) Histogram

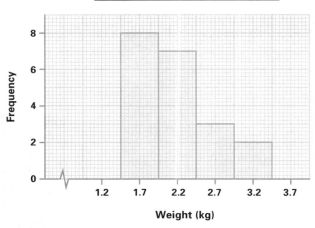

Fig. 1 Histogram for the weights of 20 portable computers

◄ *Recall:*
The symbol '⌁' shown on the horizontal axis is used to indicate that a portion of that axis has been omitted. The symbol can be used on the vertical axis as well.

(2) Frequency Polygon and Curve

Joining the mid-points of the tops of the rectangles in the histogram [**Fig. 1**] by straight lines, we obtain a frequency polygon (dotted line in **Fig. 2**). Smoothing the lines of a frequency polygon, we obtain a frequency curve (solid line in **Fig. 2**).

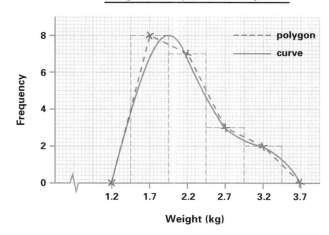

Fig. 2 Frequency polygon and curve for the weights of 20 portable computers

(3) Cumulative Frequency Polygon and Curve

In order to tell how many of the 20 computers are less than a certain weight, we construct a cumulative frequency table [**Table 3**] from the frequency distribution table [**Table 2**]. Making use of **Table 3**, we then draw the corresponding cumulative frequency polygon (dotted line in **Fig. 3**) or curve (solid line in **Fig. 3**).

Weight less than (kg)	*Cumulative frequency*
1.95	8
2.45	15 $(8 + 7)$
2.95	18 $(8 + 7 + 3)$
3.45	20 $(8 + 7 + 3 + 2)$

Table 3

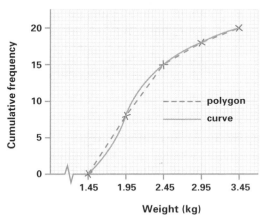

Fig. 3 Cumulative frequency polygon and curve for the weights of 20 portable computers

---

C. *Measures of Central Tendency: Mean, Median and Mode*

(1) Mean

(i) For ungrouped data:

$$\text{Mean}(\bar{x}) = \frac{\sum_{i=1}^{n} x_i}{n} \qquad \left(\text{or simply } \bar{x} = \frac{\Sigma x}{n}\right)$$

◄ $\sum_{i=1}^{n} x_i = x_1 + x_2 + \cdots + x_n$

Note : x_i stands for the data.

(ii) For grouped data:

$$\text{Mean}(\bar{x}) = \frac{\sum_{i=1}^{n} f_i x_i}{\sum_{i=1}^{n} f_i} \qquad \left(\text{or simply } \bar{x} = \frac{\Sigma f x}{\Sigma f}\right)$$

◄ $\sum_{i=1}^{n} f_i x_i = f_1 x_1 + f_2 x_2 + \cdots + f_n x_n$

and $\sum_{i=1}^{n} f_i = f_1 + f_2 + \cdots + f_n$.

Note : **(i)** x_i stands for the class mark of a class interval while f_i stands for the corresponding frequency in the interval.

(ii) The mean obtained from grouped data is an estimated mean only.

(2) Median

(i) For ungrouped data:

> The median is the middle value of a group of data when they are arranged in order of magnitude.

◄ *Note:*
(i) *For odd number of data, the median is the <u>middle</u> datum.*

(ii) *For even number of data, the median is the mean of the middle <u>two</u> data.*

(ii) For grouped data:

> When the frequency distribution is presented graphically with a cumulative frequency polygon (or curve), the median is an approximate value (read from the graph) which corresponds to the middle value of the cumulative frequency.

(3) Mode

(i) For ungrouped data:

> The mode is the datum that occurs most frequently in a set of data.

(ii) For grouped data:

> The modal class is the class of data with the highest frequency.

CLASS PRACTICE

For the weights of the portable computers given on P. 233, find

(i) the mean,   **(ii)** the median,   **(iii)** the mode / modal class,

when the data are

(a) NOT grouped into intervals,

(b) grouped into intervals.
(*Give the answers correct to 2 decimal places if necessary.*)

Answer:

(a) For ungrouped data:

  (i) Mean = _____

  (ii) Median = _____

  (iii) Mode = _____

(b) For grouped data:

  (i) Mean = _____

  (ii) Median = _____

  (iii) Modal class = _____

8.2   Weighted Mean

In the previous discussion on measures of central tendency, we assumed that each datum has the *same* importance in the determination of the central tendency of the set of data. But this may not always be the case. Sometimes, some data are more important than the other data in the same set. In such a case, we often need to adjust the way we calculate the measures of central tendency, i.e. the averages.

One way of adjusting is to use the **weighted mean*** as a measure of central tendency. This is explained as follows.

WEIGHTED MEAN OF UNGROUPED DATA

The Mathematics marks scored by a student in two tests, the mid-term examination and the final examination, are shown in the table below. [**Table 4**]

	Test 1	Mid-term exam.	Test 2	Final exam.
Marks	90	72	78	70

Table 4

If the two tests and the two examinations are considered as equally important, then according to the data in **Table 4**, the mean mark $(\bar{x})$ is

$$\frac{90 + 72 + 78 + 70}{4} = 77.5 \,.$$

However the teacher considers that the examinations should be more important than the tests. Therefore the teacher gives different *weights* to the examination marks and the test marks as shown in **Table 5** below.

	Test 1	Mid-term exam.	Test 2	Final exam.
Marks (x)	90	72	78	70
Weights (w)	10%	30%	20%	40%

Table 5

◄ *Note:*
    $10\% + 30\% + 20\% + 40\%$
    $= 100\%$

The new mean mark is then calculated as follows:

$$\frac{90 \times 0.1 + 72 \times 0.3 + 78 \times 0.2 + 70 \times 0.4}{0.1 + 0.3 + 0.2 + 0.4} = 74.2$$

◄ $10\% = 0.1$, $30\% = 0.3$,
    $20\% = 0.2$ *and* $40\% = 0.4$.

---

weighted mean 加權平均數

The mean obtained in this way is called the *weighted mean*. In general, for data x_1, x_2, x_3, $\cdots$, x_n and their weights w_1, w_2, w_3, $\cdots$, w_n respectively,

the weighted mean $= \dfrac{w_1 x_1 + w_2 x_2 + w_3 x_3 + \cdots + w_n x_n}{w_1 + w_2 + w_3 + \cdots + w_n}$,

or simply

$$\textbf{weighted mean} = \frac{\Sigma wx}{\Sigma w}.$$

Example 1 An English examination consists of four Papers: I, II, III and IV. The marks of two students A and B in the examination are shown in the table below.

Paper	Student A	Student B
I	75	70
II	68	55
III	50	72
IV	79	67

Find out which student did better in the examination

(a) if each paper carries equal weight;

(b) if Papers I, II, III and IV carry weights 3, 2, 4 and 1 respectively.

Solution (a) Mean mark of A $= \dfrac{75 + 68 + 50 + 79}{4}$

$\qquad\qquad\qquad = 68$

Mean mark of B $= \dfrac{70 + 55 + 72 + 67}{4}$

$\qquad\qquad\qquad = 66$

$\therefore$ Student A did better in the examination.

(b) Weighted mean of A's marks

$= \dfrac{3 \times 75 + 2 \times 68 + 4 \times 50 + 1 \times 79}{3 + 2 + 4 + 1}$

$= 64$

◄ *Weighted mean* $= \frac{\Sigma wx}{\Sigma w}$

Weighted mean of B's marks

$= \dfrac{3 \times 70 + 2 \times 55 + 4 \times 72 + 1 \times 67}{3 + 2 + 4 + 1}$

$= 67.5$

$\therefore$ Student B did better in the examination.

WEIGHTED MEAN OF GROUPED DATA

When we group data to form a frequency distribution, the frequency in each interval acts like a weight for the value in that interval.

◄ *Although individual data are equally important, when they are grouped, an interval with a high frequency is more important than an interval with a low frequency.*

Hence the weighted mean of the data grouped into a frequency distribution is given by

$$\text{weighted mean} = \frac{\Sigma f x}{\Sigma f}.$$

Note : **(i)** This is exactly the formula we had for calculating the mean of a set of grouped data on P. 235.

(ii) The weighted mean calculated for grouped data is an estimated mean. In fact, all measures of central tendency on grouped data are estimations only.

Example 2 For the weights (in kg) of the 20 portable computers given in **Table 2** on P. 233, the data within each interval are weighted by the corresponding frequency. Find the weighted mean of the distribution.

Solution Weighted mean

$$= \frac{1.7 \times 8 + 2.2 \times 7 + 2.7 \times 3 + 3.2 \times 2}{8 + 7 + 3 + 2} \text{ kg}$$

$$= \underline{2.175 \text{ kg}}$$

Weight (kg)	Class mark (kg)	Frequency
1.5–1.9	1.7	8
2.0–2.4	2.2	7
2.5–2.9	2.7	3
3.0–3.4	3.2	2

Table 2
(**Table 2** *is simplified and repeated here for easy reference.*)

EXERCISE 8A

(*Level 1*)

1. A teacher considers four tests to be equally important and considers the final examination to be as important as the four tests together. A student obtains the following marks in the tests: 61, 73, 67, 71 and he scores 76 in the final examination. Find the weighted mean mark of the student.

2. Below are the scores Mary obtained in the final examination and the weights assigned to the subjects:

Subject	English Language	Chinese Language	Mathematics	History	Geography
Score	55	60	75	50	70
Weight	3	3	3	2	2

Find her weighted mean mark.
(*Give the answer correct to the nearest integer.*)

3. The table gives the heights of 100 boys in a secondary school. If the data within each interval are weighted by the corresponding frequency, find the weighted mean height of the boys.

Height (cm)	Number of boys
158–160	5
161–163	22
164–166	44
167–169	25
170–172	4

(Level 2)

4. The number of pages of the books on a library shelf are checked and the result is shown below.

No. of pages per book	1–100	101–200	201–300	301–400	401–500	501–600	601–700
Frequency (no. of books)	2	13	5	8	7	4	1

When the data within each interval are weighted by the corresponding frequency, estimate the weighted mean of the number of pages for these books.

5. The table shows the weights assigned to the scores of a student in 4 Mathematics tests. If the arithmetic mean and the weighted mean are both equal to 65, find the values of a and b.

	Score	Weight
Test 1	70	3
Test 2	a	1
Test 3	50	1
Test 4	60	b

6. A Mathematics examination consists of 4 papers. The examination marks of a student and the weights of each paper are given in the table below.

Paper	I	II	III	IV
Marks	20	50	85	75
Weight	4	3	2	1

(a) Find the mean mark of the student.

(b) Find the weighted mean mark of the student.

(c) If a weighted mean mark of 50 is the pass mark of the examination, does the student pass the examination?

7. An advertising firm has a vacancy for the post of *copywriter* 廣告撰稿員. A test is given to the applicants to assess them on three qualities considered essential for the post. Weights are given to the three scores according to their relative importance. These weights and the scores obtained by three applicants: John, Joan and Joyce, are shown in the table below.

Qualities assessed	Assessment score			Weight
	John	Joan	Joyce	
Creativity	70	90	65	4
Language	40	75	50	3
General knowledge	80	35	60	1

Find the weighted average score for each applicant and hence suggest which of the three applicants should be selected for the post.

8.3   Dispersion

The mean, the median and the mode are measures of the central tendency of a set of data. But they cannot tell us how 'spread out' or how 'dispersed' the data are. Let us study **Example 3** below.

Example 3 For each of the following two sets of data, calculate
(i)   the mean, **(ii)** the median, **(iii)** the mode.

(a) 2, 8, 14, 23, 25, 35, 35, 48, 60, 65, 70
(b) 32, 33, 33, 34, 35, 35, 35, 35, 36, 37, 40

Solution   **(a)** **(i)** Mean $= \dfrac{2 + 8 + 14 + 23 + 25 + 35 + 35 + 48 + 60 + 65 + 70}{11}$

$= \underline{\underline{35}}$

(ii) 2, 8, 14, 23, 25, 35, 35, 48, 60, 65, 70
$\uparrow$
middle datum

∴ Median $= \underline{\underline{35}}$

(iii) Mode $= \underline{\underline{35}}$

(b) **(i)** Mean $= \dfrac{32 + 33 + 33 + 34 + 35 + 35 + 35 + 35 + 36 + 37 + 40}{11}$

$= \underline{\underline{35}}$

(ii) 32, 33, 33, 34, 35, 35, 35, 35, 36, 37, 40
$\uparrow$
middle datum

∴ Median $= \underline{\underline{35}}$

(iii) Mode $= \underline{\underline{35}}$

The two sets of data in **Example 3** have the *same* mean, the *same* median and the *same* mode but obviously these two sets of data are *spreading* out very differently. [**Fig. 4(a)** and **Fig. 4(b)**]

<u>On a number line</u>

For **Example 3(a)**:

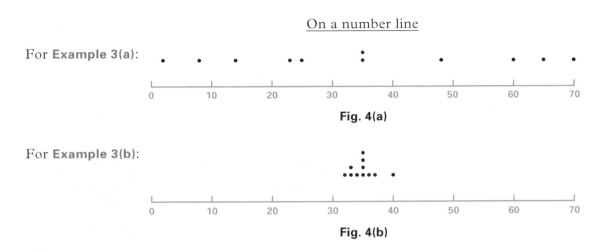

Fig. 4(a)

For **Example 3(b)**:

Fig. 4(b)

The data in **Example 3(b)** all lie within a narrow interval between 32 and 40, while the data in **Example 3(a)** can be as large as 70 and as small as 2. We say that the data in **Example 3(a)** are *more dispersed* than that in **Example 3(b)**.

We now see the need to explore and learn more statistical tools which we can use to study the '**dispersion***' of different sets of data.

The five common **measures of dispersion*** are:

(1) range*,

(2) inter-quartile range*,

(3) mean deviation*,

(4) variance*,

(5) standard deviation*.

---

dispersion 離差
range 分佈域
mean deviation 平均偏差
standard deviation 標準差

measure of dispersion 離差之量度
inter-quartile range 四分位數間距
variance 方差

8.4 Range and Inter-quartile Range

A. Range

One simple measure of dispersion is the *range* 分佈域, which is the difference between the *largest* datum and the *smallest* datum in the set.

For **Example 3(a)** on P. 242:   the range = $70 - 2 = 68$

For **Example 3(b)** on P. 242:   the range = $40 - 32 = 8$

The range in the first set of data is much larger than that of the second set, we say that the first set is 'more dispersed' than the second set.

Note : **(i)** One of the disadvantages of range:

Consider the following two sets of data:

$$8, 47, 48, 52, 74 \ \ldots\ldots\ldots \text{(i)}$$
$$45, 47, 48, 52, 74 \ \ldots\ldots\ldots \text{(ii)}$$

The range of **(i)** is $74 - 8 = 66$,
the range of **(ii)** is $74 - 45 = 29$.

Even though the two sets of data differ *only* in the first data, i.e. 8 in **(i)** and 45 in **(ii)**, their ranges suggest that their dispersion differ a great deal. Obviously this is not correct. In fact, one disadvantage of using range as a measure of dispersion is that the range is affected by extreme values.

(ii) For grouped data, the range of the frequency distribution is the difference between the highest class boundary and the lowest class boundary.

B. Inter-quartile Range

Consider a set of data arranged in order of magnitude. The **median** divides the data into *two* equal parts. Similarly, the **quartiles*** divide the data into *four* equal parts. [**Fig. 5**]

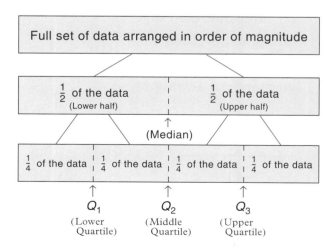

Fig. 5

_____

quartile 四分位數

Altogether there are three quartiles:

(i) The **first** or **lower quartile**, denoted by Q_1.
(*This is the **median** of the lower half of the data.*)

◀ $\frac{1}{4}$ *of the data are less than the lower quartile, Q_1.*

(ii) The **second** or **middle quartile**, denoted by Q_2.
(*This is the **median** of the whole set of data.*)

◀ $\frac{1}{2}$ *of the data are less than the middle quartile, Q_2.*

(iii) The **third** or **upper quartile**, denoted by Q_3.
(*This is the **median** of the upper half of the data.*)

◀ $\frac{3}{4}$ *of the data are less than the upper quartile, Q_3.*

The *inter-quartile range* 四分位數間距 is defined as the difference between the upper quartile and the lower quartile.

i.e.

$$\textbf{Inter-quartile range} = \boldsymbol{Q_3 - Q_1}$$

In general, a larger inter-quartile range indicates a greater dispersion while a smaller inter-quartile range indicates a smaller dispersion.

Example 4 Find the inter-quartile range for each of the following sets of data.

(a) 19, 20, 22, 24, 24, 26, 35

(b) 3, 4, 11, 17, 23, 48, 57, 69

Solution **(a)** $Q_1 = 20$

$Q_3 = 26$

∴ The inter-quartile range

$= Q_3 - Q_1$

$= 26 - 20$

$= \underline{\underline{6}}$

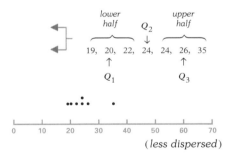

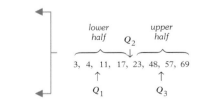

(*less dispersed*)

(b) $Q_1 = \dfrac{4 + 11}{2}$

$= 7.5$

$Q_3 = \dfrac{48 + 57}{2}$

$= 52.5$

∴ The inter-quartile range

$= Q_3 - Q_1$

$= 52.5 - 7.5$

$= \underline{\underline{45}}$

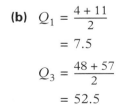

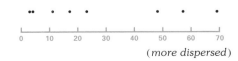

(*more dispersed*)

For a frequency distribution, the inter-quartile range is also the difference between the upper quartile and the lower quartile.

In order to find the upper quartile (Q_3) and the lower quartile (Q_1) of a set of grouped data, we make use of the fact that there are $\frac{1}{4}$ of the data below Q_1 while there are $\frac{3}{4}$ of the data below Q_3. The approximate values of Q_1 and Q_3 are usually obtained from the cumulative frequency polygon (or curve) of the corresponding frequency distribution.

Let us study **Example 5** below.

Example 5 The cumulative frequency curve of the weights (in g) of 100 Christmas cards is shown below. Find the inter-quartile range from the graph.

Weights of 100 Christmas cards

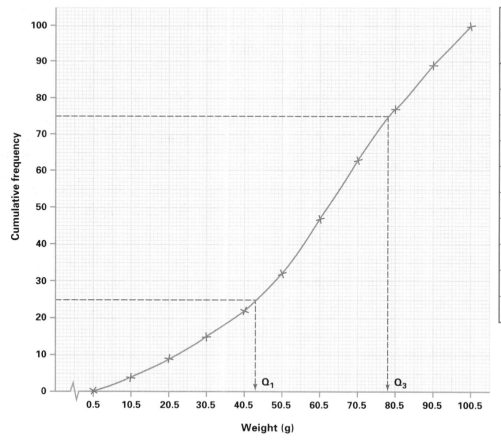

Weight less than (g)	Cumulative frequency
10.5	4
20.5	9
30.5	15
40.5	22
50.5	32
60.5	47
70.5	63
80.5	77
90.5	89
100.5	100

Solution   [The lower quartile (Q_1) corresponds to the $\left(100 \times \frac{1}{4}\right)$th value of the distribution, i.e. the 25th value. Similarly, the upper quartile (Q_3) corresponds to the $\left(100 \times \frac{3}{4}\right)$th value, i.e. the 75th value.]

From the graph, we have

$Q_1 = 43.5$ g

$Q_3 = 78.5$ g.

$\therefore$ The inter-quartile range $= Q_3 - Q_1$

$$= (78.5 - 43.5) \text{ g}$$
$$= 35 \text{ g}$$

Note : The inter-quartile range obtained in this way is an estimation. In fact, just like measures of central tendency for grouped data, the measures of dispersion for grouped data are all estimations.

CLASS PRACTICE

1. The scores of John and Mary in a bowling game are given below.

John's score	178	191	261	161	209	217
Mary's score	252	208	151	234	172	197

For John's score:

(i) range = _____ ,   **(ii)** inter-quartile range = _____ .

For Mary's score:

(i) range = _____ ,   **(ii)** inter-quartile range = _____ .

2. Given two sets of numbers A and B.
Set A: 1, 8, 10, 14, 15, 17, 38
Set B: 1, 8, 16, 21, 29, 37, 38

For the numbers in set A:

(i) range = _____ ,   **(ii)** inter-quartile range = _____ .

For the numbers in set B:

(i) range = _____ ,   **(ii)** inter-quartile range = _____ .

3. The cumulative frequency polygon of the lengths (in cm) of 60 video cameras of different models is shown below:

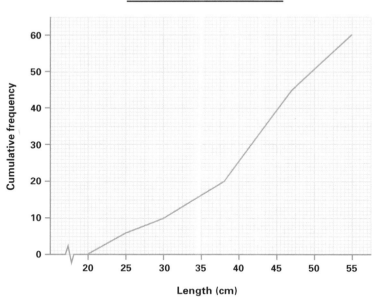

Lengths of 60 video cameras

From the cumulative frequency polygon,

the lower quartile = _____ ,

the upper quartile = _____ ,

the inter-quartile range = _____ .

EXERCISE 8B

(*Level 1*)

For each of the following sets of data, find **(a)** the range and **(b)** the inter-quartile range. **[Nos. 1–3]**

1. 2, 3, 4, 5, 7, 7, 9

2. 4 kg, 12 kg, 48 kg, 16 kg, 10 kg, 22 kg

3. 29, 22, 24, 27, 22, 0, 20, 20, 15, 24, 22, 34

4.

Time needed for solving a puzzle by 100 children

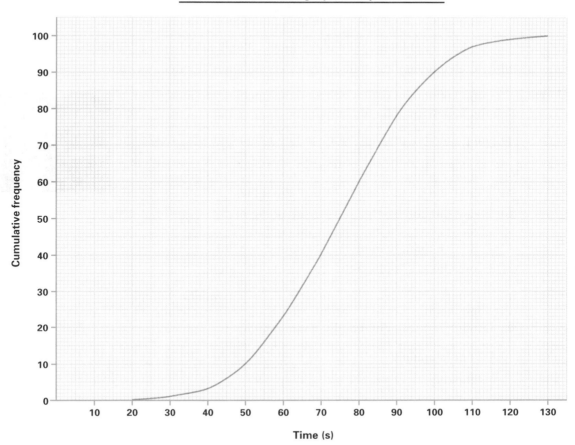

The figure shows the cumulative frequency curve for the time (in seconds) needed to solve a certain puzzle by 100 children, as recorded by a *child psychologist* 兒童心理學家. Find the inter-quartile range of the time from this figure.

(Level 2)

For each of the following sets of data, find **(a)** the range and **(b)** the inter-quartile range. **[Nos. 5–7]**

5. 5°C, 23°C, 0°C, −3°C, 5°C, −4°C, 32°C, 5°C, 14°C, 2°C, 7°C, −3°C

6. 1.5, 0.0, 2.0, 2.2, 2.9, 2.2, 2.4, 3.4, 2.7, 2.4, 2.2, 2.0

7. $\frac{1}{2}$, $\frac{3}{4}$, $\frac{5}{6}$, $\frac{4}{3}$, $\frac{7}{9}$

8. Eight students took part in a 100 m race, their time (in seconds) were recorded as below:

12.2, 11.9, 13.4, 16.5, 13.9, 14.4, 12.6, 14.4

Find

(a) the range, **(b)** the inter-quartile range.

9. **(a)** Given that x is a positive integer. Find, in terms of x, the range and the inter-quartile range of the following set of data:

$$10 - x, \quad 11 + x, \quad 21 + x, \quad 30 + x, \quad 35 + 2x, \quad 55 + 2x, \quad 90 + 2x.$$

   (b) If the range is twice the inter-quartile range, find x.

10. The heights of 100 plants of the same species are measured and the following data are obtained.

Height (cm)	0–2	3–5	6–8	9–11	12–14	15–17	18–20
No. of plants	0	4	10	25	27	18	16

   (a) Construct a cumulative frequency table.

   (b) Draw the cumulative frequency polygon.
   [*Scales: x-axis, 10 divisions (1 cm) = 1 unit;*
   y-axis, 10 divisions (1 cm) = 10 units.]

   (c) From the graph, find the inter-quartile range.

11. In February, the discipline master of a secondary school recorded, to the nearest minute, the time that the students are late for school. The results were as follows:

Time in minutes	1–3	4–6	7–9	10–12
Frequency	42	23	19	16

   (a) Complete the cumulative frequency table below:

Time less than (min)	3.5	6.5	9.5	12.5
Cumulative frequency				

   (b) Draw the cumulative frequency polygon.
   [*Scales: x-axis, 10 divisions (1 cm) = 1 unit;*
   y-axis, 10 divisions (1 cm) = 10 units.]

   (c) From the graph, find the inter-quartile range.

8.5   Mean Deviation

As measures of dispersion, both the range and the inter-quartile range depend on only a small number of values in the given set of data. In this section and the next, we shall introduce two other measures of dispersion: the *mean deviation* 平均偏差 and the *standard deviation* 標準差. Both of them involve all the values of a given set of data.

Let us illustrate with a simple example on how to calculate the mean deviation of a set of data.

Example 6 The marks in seven subjects that student A obtained in the HKCEE are 50, 58, 59, 60, 64, 65, 71. Find the mean deviation of his marks.

Solution   **Step (1):** [Find the mean $\bar{x}$ of the marks.]

$$\bar{x} = \frac{\Sigma x}{n} = \frac{50 + 58 + 59 + 60 + 64 + 65 + 71}{7}$$
$$= 61$$

Step (2): [Find $x - \bar{x}$, the deviation (difference) of each mark from the mean $\bar{x}$.

Mark (x)	50	58	59	60	64	65	71
Deviation from the mean ($x - \bar{x}$)	−11	−3	−2	−1	3	4	10

◄ *Note:*
The deviation can be either positive or negative.

The sum of the deviations from the mean
$$= (-11) + (-3) + (-2) + (-1) + 3 + 4 + 10$$
$$= 0$$

But this is not what we want to know. We want to find out, with the help of the mean deviation, the 'average *distance*' of the marks from the mean.

To do this, we take the **absolute values*** of the deviations from the mean, denoted by $|x - \bar{x}|$. The absolute value of a number is always positive.

◄ *e.g.* $|-7| = 7$
and $|5 - 7| = 2.$

Hence for the marks of student A in the HKCEE, we construct another table recording different values of $|x - \bar{x}|$.]

x	50	58	59	60	64	65	71
$|x - \bar{x}|$	11	3	2	1	3	4	10

Step (3): [Now we can find the 'average distance' of the marks from the mean, i.e. the mean of the values of $|x - \bar{x}|$.]

The mean deviation
$$= \frac{11 + 3 + 2 + 1 + 3 + 4 + 10}{7}$$
$$= \frac{34}{7}$$
$$= 4\frac{6}{7}$$

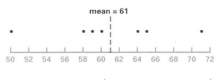

$$\left(mean\ deviation = 4\frac{6}{7}\right)$$

---

absolute value 絕對值

To conclude, given a set of *ungrouped* data x_1, x_2, $\cdots$, x_n, and let $\bar{x}$ denote the mean of the data, then the mean deviation of the data is defined by:

$$\text{mean deviation} = \frac{\Sigma|x - \bar{x}|}{n},$$

where n is the number of data.

Example 7   Find the mean deviation of the marks of student B in his seven HKCEE subjects given below.

$$57, \ 57, \ 58, \ 59, \ 60, \ 60, \ 62$$

Solution   The mean, $\bar{x} = \dfrac{57 + 57 + 58 + 59 + 60 + 60 + 62}{7}$

$$= 59$$

$$\Sigma|x - \bar{x}| = |57 - 59| + |57 - 59| + |58 - 59| + |59 - 59| +$$
$$|60 - 59| + |60 - 59| + |62 - 59|$$
$$= 2 + 2 + 1 + 0 + 1 + 1 + 3$$
$$= 10$$

$$\therefore \ \text{Mean deviation} = \frac{\Sigma|x - \bar{x}|}{n}$$

$$= \frac{10}{7}$$

$$= 1\frac{3}{7}$$

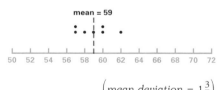

$$\left(mean\ deviation = 1\tfrac{3}{7}\right)$$

From **Example 6** and **Example 7** in this section, we note that a *small mean deviation* indicates a *small dispersion* while a *large mean deviation* indicates a *large dispersion*.

When we have a set of grouped data, the mean deviation of the frequency distribution is given by:

$$\text{mean deviation of grouped data} = \frac{\Sigma f_i|x_i - \bar{x}|}{\Sigma f_i}$$

Note : x_i stands for the class mark of a class interval while f_i stands for its corresponding frequency.

Example 8 Find the mean deviation of the weights (in kg) of 20 portable computers from the frequency distribution table given below.

Weight (kg)	Class mark (kg)	Frequency
1.5–1.9	1.7	8
2.0–2.4	2.2	7
2.5–2.9	2.7	3
3.0–3.4	3.2	2

Solution   The mean, $\bar{x} = \dfrac{\Sigma fx}{\Sigma f}$

$= 2.175$ kg   ◀ $\bar{x}$ *is obtained from* **Example 2** *on P. 239.*

$\Sigma f_i|x_i - \bar{x}| = [8 \times |1.7 - 2.175| + 7 \times |2.2 - 2.175| +$

$3 \times |2.7 - 2.175| + 2 \times |3.2 - 2.175|]$ kg

$= 7.6$ kg

∴ The mean deviation $= \dfrac{\Sigma f_i|x_i - \bar{x}|}{\Sigma f_i}$

$= \dfrac{7.6}{8 + 7 + 3 + 2}$ kg

$= \underline{\underline{0.38 \text{ kg}}}$

CLASS PRACTICE

1. Find the mean deviation of the following set of ungrouped data.

   4, 7, 9, 11, 14

   The mean, $\bar{x} = \dfrac{(\quad) + (\quad) + (\quad) + (\quad) + (\quad)}{5}$

   $= \underline{\quad}$

   $\Sigma|x - \bar{x}| = |4 - \underline{\quad}| + |7 - \underline{\quad}| + |9 - \underline{\quad}| + |11 - \underline{\quad}| + |14 - \underline{\quad}|$

   $= $

   ∴ The mean deviation $= \dfrac{\Sigma|x - \bar{x}|}{n}$

   $= $

2. Find the mean deviation of the following set of grouped data given in the frequency distribution table.

Height (cm)	Class mark (cm)	Frequency
150–154	152	1
155–159	157	3
160–164	162	4
165–169	167	7
170–174	172	5

The mean, $\bar{x}$ = _____

$\Sigma f_i |x_i - \bar{x}|$ = _____

$\therefore$ The mean deviation =

EXERCISE 8C

(*Level 1*)

For each of the following sets of data, find the mean deviation.
[Nos. 1–3]

1. 3, 5, 7, 9

2. 6, 7, 6, 5, 10, 20

3. $-5, -4, -3, -2, -1, 0, 1, 2, 3, 4, 5$
   (*Give the answer correct to 2 decimal places.*)

4. Find **(a)** the mean,
   (b) the mean deviation of the following distribution.

Data	15–19	20–24	25–29	30–34
Frequency	5	4	6	10

(*Give the answers correct to 1 decimal place if necessary.*)

(*Level 2*)

Find the mean deviation for each of the following sets of data.
[Nos. 5–6]

5. $2 + a, 4 + a, 6 + a, 8 + a, 10 + a$

6. $p + q, 2p + 3q, 3p + 5q, 4p + 7q, 5p + 9q$
   (*p and q are positive integers.*)

7. **(a)** Find, correct to 2 decimal places, the mean deviations of the following two sets of data.

  Set A: 0, 15, 20, 25, 30, 35, 40
  Set B: 45, 50, 60, 62, 65, 70, 85

  (b) Which set of data has a larger dispersion?

8. The duration of 40 telephone calls in a certain school office are as follows:

Time (min)	*1.0–1.4*	*1.5–1.9*	*2.0–2.4*	*2.5–2.9*	*3.0–3.4*
Frequency	12	10	11	5	2

  Find, correct to 2 decimal places,

  (a) the mean;

  (b) the mean deviation of the durations of the telephone calls.

*9. The mean and the mean deviation of 4 numbers a, b, c, d are m and k respectively.

  (a) Show that, for the 4 numbers $a+5$, $b+5$, $c+5$ and $d+5$, the mean is $m+5$ and the mean deviation is k.

  (b) Show that, for the 4 numbers $2a$, $2b$, $2c$ and $2d$, the mean is $2m$ and the mean deviation is $2k$.

8.6   Variance and Standard Deviation

A.   Variance

We can say that the mean deviation is a more accurate measure of dispersion than the range and the inter-quartile range, because all the data are used in calculating the mean deviation. But one major disadvantage of the mean deviation is that it involves the absolute values, which are difficult to use in further algebraic manipulation. One way of avoiding the use of absolute value is to use the square of the deviations: i.e. $(x-\bar{x})^2$ instead of $|x-\bar{x}|$.   ◀ $(x-\bar{x})^2$ *always give a positive value.*

The mean of the squares of the deviations, i.e. the mean of $(x-\bar{x})^2$ is called the *variance* 方差 which is another useful measure of dispersion. It is stated by the formula below.

$$\textbf{Variance} = \frac{\Sigma(x-\bar{x})^2}{n}$$

Example 9 Find the variance for each of the following two sets of data.

(a) 50, 58, 59, 60, 64, 65, 71

(b) 57, 57, 58, 59, 60, 60, 62

(*Give the answers correct to 1 decimal place.*)

Solution (a) The mean, $\bar{x} = 61$

◄ $\bar{x}$ *is obtained from* **Step (1)** *of* **Example 6** *on P. 251.*

$$\Sigma(x-\bar{x})^2 = (50-61)^2 + (58-61)^2 + (59-61)^2 +$$
$$(60-61)^2 + (64-61)^2 + (65-61)^2 + (71-61)^2$$
$$= 260$$

The variance $= \dfrac{260}{7}$

$$= \underline{\underline{37.1}} \text{ , } cor. \text{ to 1 d.p.}$$

(b) The mean, $\bar{x} = 59$

◄ $\bar{x}$ *is obtained from* **Example 7** *on P. 252.*

$$\Sigma(x-\bar{x})^2 = (57-59)^2 + (57-59)^2 + (58-59)^2 +$$
$$(59-59)^2 + (60-59)^2 + (60-59)^2 + (62-59)^2$$
$$= 20$$

The variance $= \dfrac{20}{7}$

$$= \underline{\underline{2.9}} \text{ , } cor. \text{ to 1 d.p.}$$

The results we get here agree with the conclusion we got from **Example 6** on P. 251 and **Example 7** on P. 252, i.e. the data in set **(a)** is more dispersed than the data in set **(b)**. Hence a larger variance indicates a larger dispersion while a smaller variance indicates a smaller dispersion.

Note : The formula for variance of a set of grouped data is given as:

$$\frac{\Sigma f_i (x_i - \bar{x})^2}{\Sigma f_i} \quad \text{or simply} \quad \frac{\Sigma f (x - \bar{x})^2}{\Sigma f} \text{ .}$$

◄ *As a practice on the use of this formula, students can try to find the variance for the set of grouped data given in* **Example 8** *on P. 253. The answer is* 0.24 *(cor. to 2 d.p.).*

B. *Standard Deviation*

One disadvantage of the variance as a measure of dispersion is that its dimension is higher than the dimension of the original set of data.

For instance, if the unit of the original data x is in cm, then $(x - \bar{x})^2$ will be in cm^2 and the variance of the set of data is also in cm^2.

To solve this problem, we simply take the *positive* square root of the variance and call the result the *standard deviation* 標準差 of the set of data. We normally denote the standard deviation by the Greek letter σ, pronounced as sigma.

> σ *is the small letter of Σ in Greek alphabets.*

STANDARD DEVIATION OF UNGROUPED DATA

For a set of ungrouped data,

> **the standard deviation,** $\sigma = \sqrt{\dfrac{\Sigma(x - \bar{x})^2}{n}}$.

> **Something More**
>
> Another formula for standard deviation is
>
> given by $\sigma = \sqrt{\dfrac{\Sigma x^2}{n} - \bar{x}^2}$.
>
> Both formulae will give the same standard deviation for the same set of data.

Like all other measures of dispersion previously learnt, a larger standard deviation indicates a larger dispersion; a smaller standard deviation indicates a smaller dispersion.

Consider the scores of two students in five school subjects as given below.

Scores of student A : 72, 78, 79, 85, 86

$\sigma = 5.1$, *cor. to 1 d.p.*

Scores of student B : 78, 78, 79, 82, 83

$\sigma = 2.1$, *cor. to 1 d.p.*

The scores of student A are more dispersed than those of student B.

Note : The calculation of the above two standard deviations is left to students as a class practice.

STANDARD DEVIATION OF GROUPED DATA

For a set of grouped data,

$$\textbf{the standard deviation, } \sigma = \sqrt{\frac{\Sigma f_i(x_i - \bar{x})^2}{\Sigma f_i}} \quad \left(\text{or simply } \sigma = \sqrt{\frac{\Sigma f (x - \bar{x})^2}{\Sigma f}} . \right)$$

Example 10 Find the standard deviation of the weights (in kg) of 20 portable computers from the frequency distribution table given below.

Weight (kg)	Class mark (kg)	Frequency
1.5–1.9	1.7	8
2.0–2.4	2.2	7
2.5–2.9	2.7	3
3.0–3.4	3.2	2

(*Give the answer correct to 3 decimal places.*)

Solution   The mean, $\bar{x} = 2.175$ kg

◀ $\bar{x}$ obtained from **Example 2** on P. 239.

$$\Sigma f(x - \bar{x})^2 = [8(1.7 - 2.175)^2 + 7(2.2 - 2.175)^2 + $$
$$3(2.7 - 2.175)^2 + 2(3.2 - 2.175)^2] \text{ kg}^2$$
$$= 4.737\ 5 \text{ kg}^2$$

The standard deviation, $\sigma = \sqrt{\dfrac{4.737\ 5}{8 + 7 + 3 + 2}}$ kg

$$= \underline{0.487 \text{ kg}} , \ \textit{cor. to 3 d.p.}$$

CLASS PRACTICE

1. Find the standard deviation, correct to 2 decimal places, of each of the following sets of ungrouped data.

   (a) 8, 9, 12, 15.   Standard deviation, $\sigma =$ _____

   (b) $x - 2$, x, $x + 6$, $x + 4$, $x - 3$.   Standard deviation, $\sigma =$ _____

2. Find the standard deviation of the following set of grouped data, correct to 2 decimal places.

Class interval	0–1	2–3	4–5	6–7	8–9
Frequency	15	5	57	43	25

Standard deviation, $\sigma =$ _____

EXERCISE 8D

(*Level 1*)

For each of the following sets of data, find **(a)** the variance,
(b) the standard deviation. **[Nos. 1–2]**

1. 8, 9, 6, 4   (*Give the answers correct to 2 decimal places.*)

2. 2, 6, 9, 2, 11, 12

3. Find **(a)** the mean,
          (b) the standard deviation of the following
                  temperature distribution.

Temperature (°C)	0–4	5–9	10–14	15–19
Frequency	4	6	5	10

(*Give the answers correct to 1 decimal place if necessary.*)

(*Level 2*)

For each of the following sets of data, find the standard deviation.
[Nos. 4–5]

4. −10, −15, 0, 3, 8, 12   (*Give the answer correct to 2 decimal places.*)

5. 2a, 6a, 9a, 2a, 11a, 12a   (*Give the answer in terms of a.*)

6. Mr. Kwok asked each of the ten students in his class to use
      a ruler to measure the length (in cm) of his/her own
      forearm, correct to the nearest 0.1 cm. The results are:

      29.3, 28.9, 29.6, 30.0, 30.5, 31.0, 29.7, 30.2, 30.8, 30.3

      Find the standard deviation correct to 2 decimal places.

7. The table shows the distribution of the monthly electric
      bills of 400 small factories:

Monthly electric bills ($)	Frequency
6 000– 6 999	80
7 000– 7 999	104
8 000– 8 999	120
9 000– 9 999	96

Find the standard deviation of this frequency distribution.

*8. The standard deviation of 4 numbers a, b, c and d is s.

   (a) Find the standard deviation of the 4 numbers: $a + 5$,
        $b + 5$, $c + 5$ and $d + 5$.

   (b) Find the standard deviation of the 4 numbers: $2a$, $2b$,
        $2c$ and $2d$.

8.7 Finding Standard Deviations Using a Calculator

Example 11 Using a calculator, find the mean and the standard deviation of the following data:

29, 39, 25, 43, 38, 22, 26, 32, 29

(*Give the answers correct to 2 decimal places.*)

Operation [First set the function mode to 'SD' (or the LR mode in some models of calculators). Then clear all the previous data in the SD mode prior to starting a calculation. In this book as well as in most calculators, the SD mode is referred to as the statistical data mode.]

◄ *In some calculators, to clear all the previous data in the SD mode, we press the keys* **INV** **KAC**.

Using 'SD' mode, press the following keys in sequence:

29 **DATA** 39 **DATA** 25 **DATA** 43 **DATA** 38 **DATA**
22 **DATA** 26 **DATA** 32 **DATA** 29 **DATA**

Press the $\bar{x}$ key to obtain the mean.　　　　　◄ [*Display*: 31.444⋯]
Press the σ_n key to obtain the standard deviation.　◄ [*Display*: 6.718⋯]

∴ The mean = 31.44 , *cor. to 2 d.p.*

The standard deviation = 6.72 , *cor. to 2 d.p.*

Example 12 Using a calculator, find the mean and the standard deviation of the distribution in **Example 10** (P. 258).
(*Give the answers correct to 3 significant figures.*)

Operation [For data of the same value, the $\times$ key enters the value and the **DATA** key enters the number of data (i.e. frequency).]

Using 'SD' mode, press the following keys in sequence:

1.7 $\times$ 8 **DATA** 2.2 $\times$ 7 **DATA**
2.7 $\times$ 3 **DATA** 3.2 $\times$ 2 **DATA**

Weight (kg)	Class mark (kg)	Frequency
1.5−1.9	1.7	8
2.0−2.4	2.2	7
2.5−2.9	2.7	3
3.0−3.4	3.2	2

Press the key $\bar{x}$.
Press the key σ_n.

The frequency distribution table in **Example 10** *is reproduced here for easy reference.*

∴ The mean = 2.18 kg , *cor. to 3 sig. fig.*

[*Display*: 2.175]

The standard deviation = 0.487 kg , *cor. to 3 sig. fig.*

[*Display*: 0.4866⋯]

Note : Some calculators use the formula $\sqrt{\frac{\Sigma(x-\bar{x})^2}{n-1}}$ to calculate the standard deviation when the $\boxed{\sigma_{n-1}}$ key is pressed. However, in this book the standard deviation is calculated using the formula $\sqrt{\frac{\Sigma(x-\bar{x})^2}{n}}$.

CLASS PRACTICE

In the following problems, the values of the mean and the standard deviation may be obtained directly using a calculator. (*Give the answers correct to 1 decimal place if necessary.*)

1. **(a)** Find the mean ($\bar{x}$) and the standard deviation (σ) of each set of numbers below.

Set A: 22, 24, 25, 27, 28, 30, 31 $\bar{x} =$ _____

$\sigma =$ _____

Set B: 5.6, 6.3, 7.5, 4.3, 6.9, 4.1 $\bar{x} =$ _____

$\sigma =$ _____

(b) By comparing the standard deviations of Set A data and Set B data, which set has a greater dispersion?

Answer: Set _____

2. The table shows the time taken (in min) by 200 students to finish a test.

Complete the table and compute the mean and the standard deviation of the distribution.

(*Give the answers correct to 1 decimal place if necessary.*)

Answer: $\bar{x} =$ _____

$\sigma =$ _____

Time (min)	Mid-value (min)	Number of students
30–39		2
40–49		5
50–59		28
60–69		46
70–79		55
80–89		41
90–99		23

3. (a) Find the standard deviations of the following distributions.
(*Give the answers correct to 1 decimal place.*)

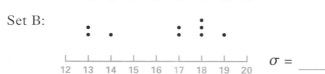

Set A:

$\sigma =$ _____

Set B:

$\sigma =$ _____

Set C:

$\sigma =$ _____

(b) Using the results of **(a)**, write down the set of distribution

(i) with the smallest dispersion,   **Answer:** _____

(ii) with the largest dispersion.   **Answer:** _____

Note : Students are encouraged to check the standard deviations that they obtained in **Exercise 8D** with a calculator as an additional exercise.

8.8   Applications of Standard Deviation

A. Simple Applications

Standard deviation can be used as an indication of precision or uniformity. The following examples illustrate this.

Example 13 Two instruments, A and B, are used to measure a quantity a number of times (30 times with each instrument, say). A gives a standard deviation of 1.2 units while B gives a standard deviation of 0.9 unit. Which instrument is less precise?

Solution [Since the standard deviation indicates how each measurement deviates from the mean, the larger the standard deviation, the larger the dispersion. The measurements taken by each instrument will be scattered around the mean. The more scattered the measurements, the less precise the instrument.]

∵ The standard deviation given by A (i.e. 1.2 units) is greater than that given by B (i.e. 0.9 unit),

∴ Instrument A is less precise.

Standard deviation can also be used to set up acceptable limits.

Example 14 Packets of rice are filled to the nominal weight of μ kg by a machine. The actual weights of the rice in the packets are thus not necessarily equal to μ kg, but can be somewhat heavier or somewhat lighter. If a packet of rice weighs much below its nominal weight, the customer may claim refund. Usually, the limit for underweight is expressed as the nominal weight minus a certain multiple of the standard deviation. If the nominal weight is 5 kg, the standard deviation is 80 g and the limit for underweight is expressed as $μ - 3σ$, find the weight of a packet of rice below which the customer may claim refund.

μ is a Greek letter pronounced as 'mu'.

Solution   When $μ = 5$, $σ = 0.08$,
then $μ - 3σ = 4.76$.

∴   The required weight is 4.76 kg.

◄ *80 g = 0.08 kg*

◄ *i.e. A customer may claim refund if the packet of rice he bought is less than 4.76 kg.*

CLASS PRACTICE

1. Two basketball teams, team A and team B, have the same number of members. The standard deviation of the heights of the members of team A is 10.2 cm and that of team B is 7.7 cm. Which team has a more uniform distribution in the heights of its members?

   Answer: _____

2. Two electronic balances A and B are checked for their precision by weighing an object of 15 g a number of times. The results are shown in the graph below:

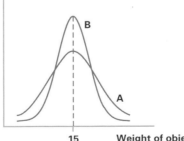

   By comparing the above two curves, answer the following questions.

   (a) Which curve indicates a larger standard deviation?

   (b) Hence which balance do you think is more reliable?

   Answer: **(a)** _____   **(b)** _____

3. The total seasonal rainfalls (in mm) of two cities A and B are given below:

	Rainfall (mm)	
	City A	*City B*
Spring	930	1 000
Summer	2 050	1 820
Autumn	680	750
Winter	270	510

(a) Calculate the standard deviations of the total seasonal rainfalls of the two cities.
(*Give the answers correct to 1 decimal place.*)

(b) Which city has more uniform seasonal rainfalls?

Answer: (a) Standard deviation of the total seasonal rainfalls of city A = _____

Standard deviation of the total seasonal rainfalls of city B = _____

(b) _____

B. *Standard Score*

The table [**Table 6**] below shows the examination marks of TEN students (A to J) in Mathematics and Chinese History. The table also shows the mean mark ($\bar{x}$) and the standard deviation (σ) of the marks in each subject.

Student	A	B	C	D	E	F	G	H	I	J	$\bar{x}$	σ
Mathematics	87	80	70	65	68	50	59	73	72	58	68.2	10.31
Chinese History	50	66	45	59	51	58	39	49	62	63	54.2	8.28

Table 6

Consider the marks of student D. He scores 65 in Mathematics and 59 in Chinese History. In appearance student D does better in Mathematics than in Chinese History. But if we consider the scores of the ten students together, and compare them with the mean mark, then we can obtain a better picture of student D's performance in the examination relative to his classmates. To compare the relative performance, we make use of the **standard score***.

———————————

standard score 標準分

Standard score is defined as follows:

Definition

The standard score (or z score) is the number of standard deviations that a given value is *above* or *below* the mean, and is given by

$$z = \frac{x - \bar{x}}{\sigma}.$$

Since $x - \bar{x}$ and σ have the same unit, the ratio $\frac{x - \bar{x}}{\sigma}$ is a number and has no units.

Hence we compare student D's performance in Mathematics and that in Chinese History by calculating his standard scores in the two subjects.

For Mathematics,

$\bar{x} = 68.2$, $\sigma = 10.31$ and student D's score, $x = 65$.

The standard score , $z = \dfrac{x - \bar{x}}{\sigma}$

$$= \frac{65 - 68.2}{10.31}$$

$$= -0.31 \text{ , } cor. \text{ to 2 d.p.}$$

The *negative* standard score (-0.31) for Mathematics indicates that student D's score in Mathematics is 0.31 times the standard deviation *below* the mean.

For Chinese History,

$\bar{x} = 54.2$, $\sigma = 8.28$ and student D's score, $x = 59$.

The standard score , $z = \dfrac{x - \bar{x}}{\sigma}$

$$= \frac{59 - 54.2}{8.28}$$

$$= 0.58 \text{ , } cor. \text{ to 2 d.p.}$$

The *positive* standard score (0.58) for Chinese History indicates that student D's score in Chinese History is 0.58 times the standard deviation *above* the mean.

By comparing the standard scores of the two subjects, we say that student D does better in Chinese History than in Mathematics because his standard score in Chinese History is higher than that in Mathematics.

Find the standard scores in Mathematics and Chinese History for students B and G as well by referring to **Table 6** on P. 264. By comparing the standard scores in each subject, determine in which subject the two students do better.

(*Give the answers correct to 2 decimal places.*)

For student B,

his standard score in Mathematics   = _____

his standard score in Chinese History = _____

Hence student B does better in _____ .

For student G,

his standard score in Mathematics   = _____

his standard score in Chinese History = _____

Hence student G does better in _____ .

EXERCISE 8E

(*Level 1*)

1. Find the standard scores for the following examination marks.

    (a) English: 89, standard deviation 36, mean 50.

    (b) Mathematics: 36, standard deviation 30, mean 46.

    (c) Chinese History: 62, standard deviation 16, mean 43.

    (*Give the answers correct to 2 decimal places.*)

2. John got a standard score of 2.5 in a test. If the mean and the standard deviation of the marks are 45 and 4 respectively, what are his marks?

3. A student obtained 54 marks and 60 marks in English and French respectively. For English the mean mark was 50 with a standard deviation of 20 while for French the mean mark was 62 with a standard deviation of 15. Find in which subject the student did better by comparing the standard scores.

(Level 2)

4. Cecilia and Bill are told that they received standard scores of 1.6 and −0.3 respectively in an I.Q. test. If their scores are 116 and 97 respectively, find the mean and the standard deviation of the test marks.

5. **(a)** In a Mathematics test given to a class, the mean and the standard deviation of the marks are 64 and 8 respectively. The table below shows the marks of some of the pupils. Complete the table.

Pupil	A	B	C	D	E	F
Marks	68	72	56	60	80	76
Standard score						

   (b) In another Mathematics test given to the same class a few weeks later, the mean is 49 and the standard deviation is 6. Complete the following table.

Pupil	A	B	C	D	E	F
Marks	58	52	43	49	64	52
Standard score						

   (c) **(i)** Who improved most?
   (ii) Who came down most?
   (iii) Who was the most consistent one in the two tests?

*6.

	$\bar{x}$	σ	Veronica's marks
Physics	54	6	70
Chemistry	63	10	83
Biology	58	7	78

   The above table shows the mean ($\bar{x}$) and the standard deviation (σ) of the marks of F.5B students for 3 science subjects in the Mock Examination. The marks of one of the students, Veronica, are also shown.

   (a) Determine the subject in which her performance is
   (i) the best,
   (ii) the worst.

   (b) Given that $\bar{x} = 64$ and $\sigma = 7$ for Mathematics. If Veronica's performance in Mathematics is better than her performance in the above 3 subjects, what is the least possible score she obtained in Mathematics?
   (*Assume the score is an integer.*)

C. *Normal Distribution*

THE NORMAL CURVE

Consider the following situations:

1. A large number of students take an I.Q. test and their results are recorded.

2. The widths of the leaves in a forest are measured and recorded.

If we organize the data collected in the above-mentioned surveys and present them with a frequency curve, then both curves will have a similar shape as shown below.

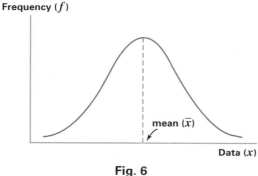

Fig. 6

The bell-shaped frequency curve is called the **normal curve***. The corresponding frequency distribution is called the **normal distribution***.

In fact in a normal distribution, the mean of the data lies at the centre of the distribution, and the frequency distribution is symmetrical about the mean, with fewer data found further away from the centre.

STANDARD DEVIATION OF NORMAL DISTRIBUTION

The following percentages relating the mean and the standard deviation of a normal distribution are important:

(I) About 68% of the data lie within one standard deviation from the mean. That is, 68% lie in the interval from $\bar{x} - \sigma$ to $\bar{x} + \sigma$. Because the curve is symmetrical, 34% lie between $\bar{x} - \sigma$ and $\bar{x}$ and 34% lie between $\bar{x}$ and $\bar{x} + \sigma$. [**Fig. 7**]

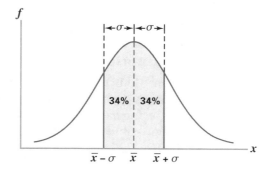

Fig. 7

normal curve 正態曲綫
normal distribution 正態分佈

(II) About 95% of the data lie within two standard deviations from the mean. That is, 95% lie in the interval from $\bar{x} - 2\sigma$ to $\bar{x} + 2\sigma$. Thus, 47.5% lie between $\bar{x} - 2\sigma$ and $\bar{x}$ and 47.5% lie between $\bar{x}$ and $\bar{x} + 2\sigma$. [**Fig. 8**]

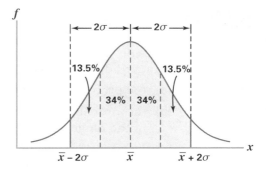

Fig. 8

(III) About 99.7% of the data lie within three standard deviations from the mean. That is, 99.7% lie in the interval from $\bar{x} - 3\sigma$ to $\bar{x} + 3\sigma$. Thus, 49.85% lie between $\bar{x} - 3\sigma$ and $\bar{x}$ and 49.85% lie between $\bar{x}$ and $\bar{x} + 3\sigma$. [**Fig. 9**]

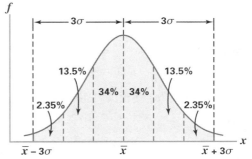

Fig. 9

Note : Students are NOT required to memorize all the above percentages since the percentages will be given in the questions.

Example 15 According to government statistics in a certain year, the mean weight of 4 000 firemen was 73 kg and the standard deviation was 3 kg.

Assuming the weights are normally distributed, find the percentage of the firemen who are

(a) heavier than 76 kg, **(b)** heavier than 70 kg.

(*Assume that 68% of the weights lie within one standard deviation from the mean weight.*)

Solution Here $\bar{x} = 73$ kg,

$\sigma = 3$ kg.

[Since 68% of the weights lie in the interval from $\bar{x} - \sigma$ to $\bar{x} + \sigma$, i.e. from 70 kg to 76 kg, then the remaining 32% will lie outside this range; of this remaining 32%, half (i.e. 16% of the whole) of the firemen are lighter than 70 kg and half are heavier than 76 kg.]

$\bar{x} - \sigma = (73 - 3)$ kg
$= 70$ kg
$\bar{x} + \sigma = (73 + 3)$ kg
$= 76$ kg

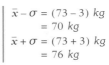

(a) Thus, the required percentage of the firemen who are heavier than 76 kg = <u>16%</u>

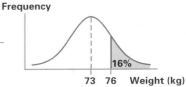

(b) The required percentage of the firemen who are heavier than 70 kg
$= 68\% + 16\% = \underline{\underline{84\%}}$

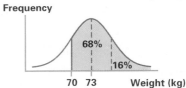

Example 16 The scores in an international English proficiency test of 20 000 candidates are approximately normally distributed. The mean score is 530 and the standard deviation is 40. Find

(a) the probable lowest and highest scores,

(b) the probable number of candidates with a score in the range 490 to 570.

(*Assume that 68% of the scores are within one standard deviation from the mean score and 100% of the scores are within three standard deviations from the mean score.*)

◄ **Question:**
We have assumed that 100% of the scores lie within three standard deviations from the mean score instead of the more accurate 99.7%. Do you know why?

Solution   Here $\bar{x} = 530,$

$\sigma = 40.$

(a) Since 100% of the scores lie in the interval from $\bar{x} - 3\sigma$ to $\bar{x} + 3\sigma$,

the probable lowest score $= 530 - 3(40) = \underline{\underline{410}}$

the probable highest score $= 530 + 3(40) = \underline{\underline{650}}$

(b) Since 68% of the scores are in the interval from $\bar{x} - \sigma$ to $\bar{x} + \sigma$, i.e. from $490\ (= 530 - 40)$ to $570\ (= 530 + 40)$,

the number of candidates with a score in this range $= 68\% \times 20\ 000$

$= \underline{\underline{13\ 600}}$

EXERCISE 8F

[In this exercise, unless otherwise stated, assume that in a normal distribution, 68%, 95% and 99.7% of the data lie within one, two and three standard deviations respectively from the mean.]

(*Level 1*)

1. The weights of some individuals are normally distributed with a mean of 80 kg and a variance of 49 kg^2. How many per cent of these individuals weigh more than 87 kg?

2. The frequency curve as shown in the figure represents a normal distribution with mean 10 and standard deviation 2. Find the percentage of the number of data that are

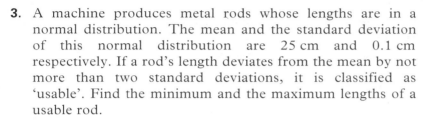

(a) less than 10,

(b) less than 8,

(c) between 8 and 14.

3. A machine produces metal rods whose lengths are in a normal distribution. The mean and the standard deviation of this normal distribution are 25 cm and 0.1 cm respectively. If a rod's length deviates from the mean by not more than two standard deviations, it is classified as 'usable'. Find the minimum and the maximum lengths of a usable rod.

4. The typing speeds of the employees in a publishing company are approximately normally distributed with a mean of 47 w.p.m. (words per minute) and a standard deviation of 4 w.p.m.

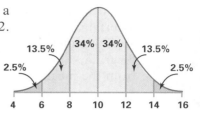

Find the typing speeds that are possibly

(a) the slowest,

(b) the fastest.

(*Assume that all these typing speeds lie within 3 standard deviations from the mean.*)

(*Level 2*)

5. A normal distribution of marks in a test has a mean of 60 and a standard deviation of 10. The passing mark is 50. Estimate

(a) the percentage of the candidates whose marks are over 80,

(b) the percentage of the candidates who pass the test.

6. The weights of 1 000 students are approximately normally distributed with a mean of 62 kg and a standard deviation of 5.8 kg. How many students are there in each of the ranges A to F illustrated in the diagram?

(*Assume that all the weights lie within 3 standard deviations from the mean.*)

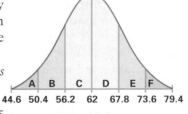

7. In the mid-term examination, the scores of 200 F.5 students in the subject Mathematics are approximately normally distributed with a mean of 55 and a standard deviation of 8.

(a) If 16% of the students fail in the examination, what is the passing mark?

(b) If a student obtains marks in the range 63 to 71, then he will be awarded grade B in the examination. Find the number of students who score grade B in the examination.

8. A statistician recorded the heights of 1 000 students in a certain school. The frequency curve of the heights is approximately a normal curve as shown. In the diagram, all the heights lie within 3 standard deviations from the mean.

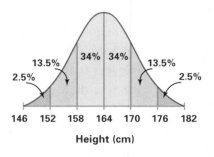

(a) What is the mean height of this group of students?

(b) What is the standard deviation?

(c) What percentage of the students were taller than 152 cm and shorter than 170 cm?

(d) How many students were shorter than 152 cm?

SUPPLEMENTARY
EXERCISE 8

[For problems concerning normal distributions in this exercise, unless otherwise stated, assume that 68%, 95% and 99.7% of the data lie within one, two and three standard deviations respectively from the mean.]

PART I | *Further Practice*

(Ex. 8A)

1. A pupil scores the following marks in an examination:
English 70, Mathematics 60, History 52.

Calculate the pupil's weighted mean mark if the weights used are English 4, Mathematics 3 and History 1.

2. A student's score for the subject of English in the final examination will be the weighted mean of his scores in 3 parts: comprehension, composition and oral. The table below shows John's scores in the 3 parts and the weights assigned to each part:

	Comprehension	*Composition*	*Oral*
Score	50	60	70
Weight	4	3	3

(a) John computed the arithmetic mean of the three scores and told his parents this score. What is it?

(b) What is John's actual score (i.e. the weighted mean)?

(c) If a weighted mean mark of 60 is the passing mark of the subject, does John pass the examination?

3. **(a)** A group of n numbers: x_1, x_2, x_3, $\cdots$, x_n carry weights w_1, w_2, w_3, $\cdots$, w_n respectively and the weighted mean is represented by $\overline{X}$. Another group of n numbers: $ax_1 + b$, $ax_2 + b$, $ax_3 + b$, $\cdots$, $ax_n + b$, (where a and b are real constants) carry weights w_1, w_2, w_3, $\cdots$, w_n respectively and the weighted mean is represented by $\overline{Y}$. Show that $\overline{Y} = a\overline{X} + b$.

   (b) Find the weighted mean of 1, 2, 3, 4, 5, 6 and 7 which carry weights 0.1, 0.2, 0.3, 0.4, 0.5, 0.6 and 0.7 respectively.

   (c) Using the results obtained in **(a)** and **(b)**, find the weighted mean of 1, 3, 5, 7, 9, 11 and 13 which carry weights 0.1, 0.2, 0.3, 0.4, 0.5, 0.6 and 0.7 respectively.

(*Ex. 8B*)

4. For each of the following two sets of data,
   Set A: 8, 8, 9, 12, 14, 15, 15, 18
   Set B: 7, 6, 4, 9, 10, 20, 27, 26, 25

   (a) find the range and the inter-quartile range,

   (b) hence determine which set of data is more dispersed.

5. Given a set of numbers: 0, 2, -4, 5, -8, 9, 11, 19, 30.

   (a) Find
   (i) the range,
   (ii) the inter-quartile range.

   (b) If 2 is subtracted from each number, find
   (i) the new range,
   (ii) the new inter-quartile range.

   (c) If each number is divided by 2, find
   (i) the new range,
   (ii) the new inter-quartile range.

6. Given two groups of numbers arranged in ascending order of magnitude as follows:

   Group A: 2, 2, 2, a, 7, 7, 8, 8, c, 12, 16, 22
   Group B: b, 8, 10, c, 12, 12, 14, 16, 16, $3a$, 28, $2c + b$

   (a) If the two groups have the same range, find the value of c. Hence deduce that $b = 8$.

   (b) If, in addition, the two groups have the same inter-quartile range, find the value of a.

7. The cumulative frequency curve shows the diameters (in mm) of a sample of 120 ball bearings. Find

    (a) the lower quartile,

    (b) the median,

    (c) the upper quartile,

    (d) the range,

    (e) the inter-quartile range.

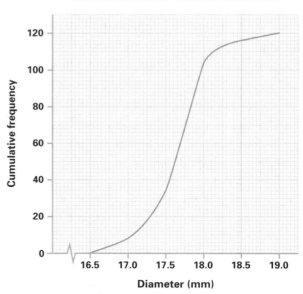

Diameters of a sample of ball bearings

*8. The cumulative frequency curves given below show the distribution of weights (in kg) of two groups of students: group A and group B.

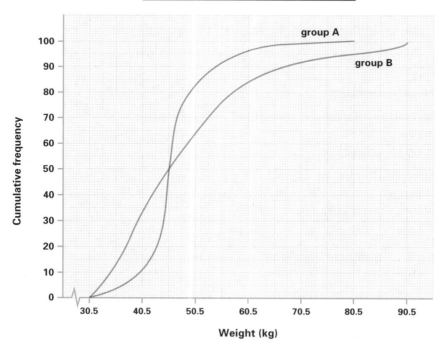

The weights of two groups of students

    (a) Determine the range of the weights for each group of students.

    (b) Estimate, for each group of students,
    (i) the median,
    (ii) the inter-quartile range.

(c) Now, the two groups merge together to form a new group C of 200 students. By using the information of the given curves,

    (i) draw a new cumulative frequency curve for group C,

    (ii) hence find the range and the inter-quartile range of group C.

(*Ex. 8C*)

9. Consider the following two groups of numbers A and B:

    Group A: 3, 2, 5, 3, 3, 1, 5, 3, 2
    Group B: 3, 2, 5, 3, 3, 3, 2, 3, 3

    (a) Express the mean deviation for each group of numbers as a fraction.

    (b) Which group of numbers is more dispersed?

10. Given two sets of numbers:

    Set A: $x+1$, $x+3$, $x+5$, $x+7$, $x+9$, $x+11$, $x+13$, $x+15$

    Set B: $x-2$, $x-4$, $x-6$, $x-8$, $x-10$, $x-12$, $x-14$, $x-16$

    Find the mean deviation of each set of numbers and hence determine which set has a larger dispersion.

11. The table shows the frequency distribution for the heights of 30 plants. Find

    (a) the mean,

    (b) the mean deviation.

Height (cm)	14–18	19–23	24–28	29–33
Frequency	13	3	9	5

12. Given three numbers x, y and 20, where $x < y$. Their mean is 20 and their mean deviation is 6.

    (a) Show that

      (i) $y+x = 40$,

      (ii) $y-x = 18$.

    (b) Hence find x and y.

(*Ex. 8D*)

13. Find the variance and the standard deviation of each of the following sets of data.

    (a) -1.8, -0.8, -0.4, 0, 0, 0.4, 0.8, 1.8

    (b) $x-2$, $x-1$, $x+1$, $x+2$

    (*Give the answers correct to 2 decimal places if necessary.*)

14. If the standard deviation of the numbers a, b, c, d, e is 10, find the standard deviation of the numbers

    $4a+3$, $4b+3$, $4c+3$, $4d+3$, $4e+3$.

15. The numbers a, b, c, d, e have a mean 7 and a standard deviation 2. If a, b, c, d also have a mean 7, find

(a) e,

(b) the standard deviation of a, b, c, d.
   (*Leave the answer in surd form.*)

*16. Given 5 integers: 75, 77, x, 78, 79, the standard deviation is 1.6.

(a) Show that $2x^2 - 309x + 11\,925 = 0$.

(b) Hence find x and the mean of the integers.

17. The table is a frequency distribution of the life time (in hours) of 100 electric lamps.

Calculate

(a) the mean life of the lamps,

(b) variance,

(c) the standard deviation, correct to 1 decimal place.

Life time (in hours)	Frequency
600–699	30
700–799	15
800–899	50
900–999	5

18. The following histograms represent the lengths (in cm) of two classes (class A and class B) of nails produced by a machine.

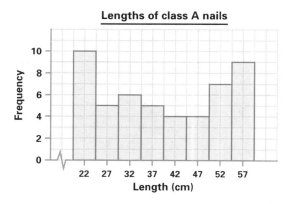
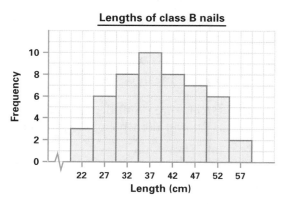

(a) Calculate the standard deviation of the lengths of nails for each class correct to 1 decimal place.

(b) Which class of nails is more dispersed?

(Ex. 8E)

19. A test is given to five students and the following marks: 60, 60, 85, 90, 95 are obtained.

(a) Find the mean mark.

(b) Find the standard deviation of these marks.

(c) Convert these marks into standard scores.
   (*Give the answers correct to 2 decimal places if necessary.*)

20. Tom received a mark of 85 in a Mathematics examination. The mean mark of the Mathematics examination was 65 and the standard deviation was 12.5. In an English examination Tom received a mark of 88 where the mean mark was 73 and the standard deviation was 10. By comparing Tom's standard score in each examination, find out which of his marks, in Mathematics or in English, was relatively higher.

(*Ex. 8F*)

21. A normal distribution of marks has a mean of 65 and a standard deviation of 7.5.

    (a) Estimate the percentage of students with marks over 80.

    (b) If the passing mark is 50, find the percentage of students who pass.

22. The figure below shows the distribution of weights of new-born babies in a certain month in Hong Kong. The weights are normally distributed with a mean of 3.50 kg and a standard deviation of 0.55 kg.

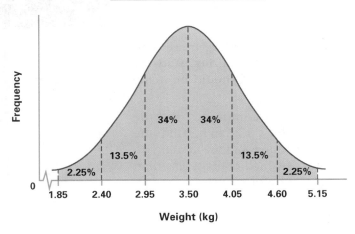

Weights of new-born babies

(a) Find the percentage of babies whose weights
    (i) lie between 2.95 kg and 5.15 kg,
    (ii) are less than 4.05 kg.

(b) If there are 8 000 new-born babies, find the number of babies whose weights
    (i) lie between 1.85 kg and 5.15 kg,
    (ii) are greater than 2.40 kg,
    (iii) are less than 4.60 kg.

*23. A factory produces machine components with an average length of 3.50 cm and a standard deviation of 0.01 cm. The tolerance limit for the lengths of the machine components is 3.50 ± 0.02 cm. Assuming that the lengths of the machine components are normally distributed.

    (a) Find the percentage of machine components whose lengths lie

        (i) between 3.48 cm and 3.51 cm,

        (ii) outside the tolerance limit.

    (b) If the factory workers make a mistake so that machine components with an average length of 3.51 cm and a standard deviation of 0.01 cm are produced, find the percentage of machine components whose lengths lie outside the tolerance limit.

*24. The Burned Twice Match Company makes boxes of wooden matches which are advertised to contain at least 40 matches in a box. The company knows that the number of matches in its boxes follow a normal distribution pattern with a mean of 44 matches per box and a standard deviation of 2 matches.

    (a) What percentage of the boxes of wooden matches made will contain less than 40 matches?

    (b) If 78 000 boxes of matches, each containing more than 40 matches, are planned to be made in a day, find the total number of boxes of matches that should be made in a day.

    (c) If the operations of the machines are improved and the standard deviation is decreased to 1 match, find the mean number of matches that a box should contain so that the percentage of the boxes which contain less than 40 matches remains the same as before.

PART II | *Miscellaneous*

25. Consider the following two groups of numbers:

        Group A: 1, 2, 3, 4, 4, 5, 5, 5, 6, 6, 7, 8, 9

        Group B: 1, 1, 4, 4, 4, 5, 5, 6, 6, 6, 8, 9, 9

    (a) Verify that they have the same range and the same inter-quartile range.

    (b) Express the mean deviation for each group of numbers as a fraction.

26. The ages at which people in a community got married were recorded and were found to be approximately normally distributed with a mean of 28 and a standard deviation of 2. Among them, Miss Yeung was the youngest while Mr. Lau was the oldest when married. Assuming that all the ages lie within 3 standard deviations from the mean, find the probable ages of Miss Yeung and Mr. Lau when married.

27. Given the following frequency distribution:

Length (*cm*)	*3 – 5*	*6 – 8*	*9 – 11*	*12 – 14*	*15 – 17*
Frequency	22	36	28	9	5

    (a) Construct a cumulative frequency table for this distribution.

    (b) Draw the cumulative frequency polygon.
    [*Scales: x-axis, 10 divisions (1 cm) = 1 unit;*
    y-axis, 10 divisions (1 cm) = 10 units.]

    (c) From the graph, find the inter-quartile range.

28. Show that the mean deviation and standard deviation of a set of data consisting of just two numbers are the same.
    [*Hint: Let the two numbers be x and y, where x is greater than or equal to y.*]

29. Given five integers: 45, 47, 48, 49, x. If the standard deviation is 1.6, find the value of x and the mean of all these five integers.

30. Given that the weights assigned to the numbers 1, 2, 3, 4 and 5 form an arithmetic sequence. Let a be the weight assigned to the number 1, and d be the common difference of the sequence of weights.

    (a) If the weighted mean is $\frac{7}{3}$, show that $a = -5d$.

    (b) If in addition, the weight assigned to the number 3 is 6, find the remaining weights.

31. A F.5 student obtained marks 60 and 55 for Biology and Mathematics respectively in the final examination. For Biology the mean mark was 50 with a standard deviation of 10 while for Mathematics the mean mark was 45 with a standard deviation of 7. The student decided that if she did better in Mathematics, she will choose the F.6 Mathematics stream, otherwise she will choose the F.6 Biology stream.

    (a) Find the standard scores of Biology and Mathematics.

    (b) Which stream should she choose?

32. A statistician recorded the I.Q.s of 2 000 children in a certain community. The frequency curve of the I.Q.s is approximately a normal curve which is shown in the diagram.

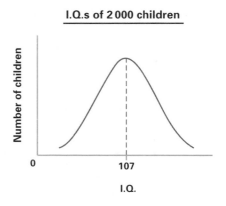

I.Q.s of 2 000 children

(a) What is the mean I.Q. of these 2 000 children?

(b) If 950 children have I.Q. between 107 and 129, what is the standard deviation of the I.Q.s?

(c) I.Q. values above 140 are classified as *genius* 天才 level intelligence. About how many children in the community possess genius level intelligence?

Part III | HKCEE Questions

(Section A Questions)

33. The table below shows the distribution of the marks of a group of students in a short test:

Marks	1	2	3	4	5
Number of Students	10	10	5	20	x

If the mean of the distribution is 3, find the value of x.

[HKCEE 84]

34. The table below shows the number of students in three classes of a school and their average marks in a test:

Class	No. of Students	Average Mark
F.5A	40	61
F.5B	x	70
F.5C	35	50

If the overall average mark of the three classes is 60, find x.

[HKCEE 86]

35. In a sports competition, the mean score of a team of m men and n women is 70.

(a) Find the total score of the team in terms of m and n.

(b) If the mean score of the men is 75 and the mean score of the women is 62, find the ratio $m : n$.

(c) If there are altogether 39 persons in the team, find the number of men.

[HKCEE 92]

36. The marks scored by eleven students in a mathematics quiz
are as follows:

10 20 30 45 50 60 65 65 65 70 70.

Find **(a)** the mean, **(b)** the mode and **(c)** the median of the above marks.
[HKCEE 94]

(Section B Questions)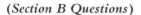

37.

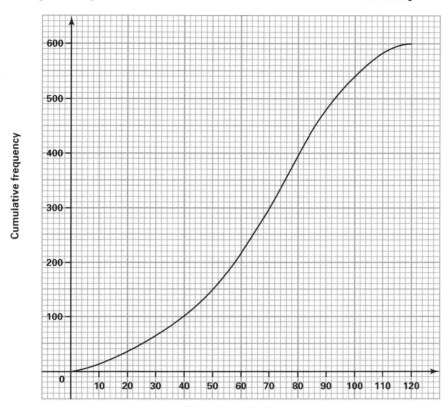

Marks (less than)

The figure shows the cumulative frequency curve of the
marks of 600 students in a mathematics contest.

(a) From the curve, find
(i) the median, and
(ii) the interquartile range of the distribution of marks.

(b) A student with marks greater than or equal to 100 will
be awarded a prize.
(i) Find the number of students who will be awarded
prizes.
(ii) If one student is chosen at random from the 600
students, find the probability that the student is a
prize-winner.
(iii) If two students are chosen at random, find the
probability that
(1) both of them are prize-winners,
(2) at least one of them is a prize-winner. [HKCEE 88]

38. (a) The distribution of the monthly salaries of 100 employees in a firm is shown in the histogram in the figure below.

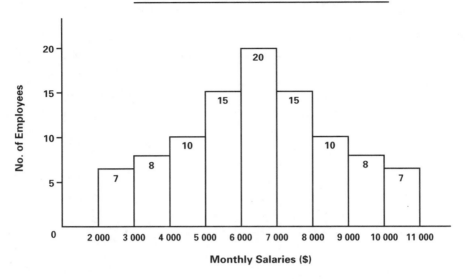

Distribution of monthly salaries of 100 employees

(i) Find the modal class, median, mean, interquartile range and mean deviation of the monthly salaries of the 100 employees.

(ii) Now the firm employs 10 more employees whose monthly salaries are all $6 500. Will the standard deviation of the monthly salaries of all the employees in the firm become greater, smaller or remain unchanged? Explain briefly.

(b) The mean of 7 numbers x_1, x_2, $\cdots$, x_7 is $\bar{x}$ and the *squares* of their deviations from $\bar{x}$ are 9, 4, 1, 0, 1, 4, 9 respectively.

Find the standard deviation of the 7 numbers.

[HKCEE 90]

39. If the mean of the numbers 3, 3, 3, 3, 4, 4, 5, 5, 6, *x* is also *x*, which of the following is/are true?

  I.   Mean = Median
  II. Mode = Range
  III. Median = Mode

  A. I and II only
  B. I and III only
  C. II and III only
  D. None of them
  E. All of them   [HKCEE 90]

40. Ten years ago, the mean age of a band of 11 musicians was 30. One of them is now leaving the band at the age of 40. What is the present mean age of the remaining 10 musicians?

  A. 40
  B. 39
  C. 37
  D. 30
  E. 29   [HKCEE 90]

41. The table shows the mean marks of two classes of students in a mathematics test.

	Number of students	Mean mark
Class A	38	72
Class B	42	54

A student in Class A has scored 91 marks. It is found that his score was wrongly recorded as 19 in the calculation of the mean mark for Class A in the above table. Find the correct mean mark of the 80 students in the two classes.

  A. 61.65
  B. 62.55
  C. 63
  D. 63.45
  E. 63.9   [HKCEE 92]

42.

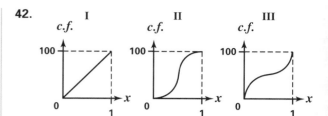

The figure shows the cumulative frequency curves of three distributions. Arrange the three distributions in the order of their standard deviations, from the smallest to the largest.

  A. I, II, III
  B. I, III, II
  C. II, I, III
  D. II, III, I
  E. III, I, II   [HKCEE 92]

43. Under which of the following conditions *must* the mean of *n* consecutive positive integers also be an integer?

  A. *n* is any positive integer
  B. *n* is any positive odd integer
  C. *n* is any positive even integer
  D. *n* is any multiple of 3
  E. *n* is the square of any positive integer
                        [HKCEE 92]

44. The mean, standard deviation and interquartile range of *n* numbers are *m*, *s* and *q* respectively. If 3 is added to each of the *n* numbers, what will be their new mean, standard deviation and interquartile range?

	Mean	Standard Deviation	Interquartile Range
A.	m	s	q
B.	m	$s + 3$	$q + 3$
C.	$m + 3$	s	q
D.	$m + 3$	s	$q + 3$
E.	$m + 3$	$s + 3$	$q + 3$

[HKCEE 94]

Preparatory Exercise for HKCEE

(Strand : Algebra)

A. Short Questions

(Group 1)

1. Solve the inequality $5x + 2 \geqslant 17$.

2. Find the values of x if $3 - 2x > 0$ *and* $10 - 7x > 2 - 9x$.

3. Solve the inequality $15x^2 + 29x < 14$.

4. Solve the inequality $(x + 3)(x + 2) \geqslant 2(x + 3)$.

5. Find the values of x if $3x - 2 \geqslant 1$ *or* $x^2 + 2x + 1 < 4$.

6. Solve the inequality $x^2 - x - 6 < 0$. Hence solve the inequality $(y - 200)^2 - (y - 200) - 6 < 0$.

7. In the figure, (x, y) is any point in the shaded region (including the boundary) and $P = 2x + 7y$. Find the maximum and the minimum values of P and the corresponding points to attain these values.

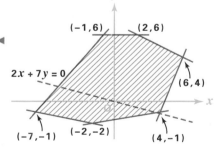

8. Four positive numbers a, x, b and c are in geometric sequence.

   (a) Express x in terms of a and b.

   (b) Express x in terms of b and c.

9. Consider $3x + 2 > \frac{1}{7}(x - 1)$.

   (a) Solve the inequality.

   (b) In addition, if $-1 \leqslant x \leqslant 1$, find the range of x.

10. **(a)** Find the sum of the first 15 terms of the arithmetic series $0 + (-2) + (-4) + (-6) + \cdots$.

    (b) Find the sum to infinity of the geometric series $1 + \left(-\dfrac{1}{2}\right) + \dfrac{1}{4} + \left(-\dfrac{1}{8}\right) + \cdots$.

11. From the table, find a root of $f(x) = 0$ correct to 3 significant figures.

x	2.54	2.55	2.56	2.57	2.565	2.562 5
$f(x)$	$-$	$-$	$-$	$+$	$+$	$-$

(Group 2)

12. Given that a, b and c are positive and $\log a$, $\log b$, $\log c$ are in arithmetic sequence, write an equation connecting a, b and c in its simplest form.

13. Let a, x_1, x_2, x_3, b and a, y_1, y_2, y_3, y_4, b be two arithmetic sequences where $a \neq b$. Find $\dfrac{x_3 - x_2}{y_2 - y_1}$.

14. If 4, x, y, z and 32 are in arithmetic sequence, find $x + y + z$.

15. Given that the sum to n terms of an arithmetic series is $2n^2 + 3n$, find the common difference of the corresponding arithmetic sequence.

16. Given that $a \neq 0$ and a, $-a$, $-5a^2$ are in geometric sequence, find a.

17. Find the $(2n)$th term of the geometric sequence $-\dfrac{1}{8}$, $\dfrac{1}{4}$, $-\dfrac{1}{2}$, 1, $\cdots$.

18. Let $p < q < 0$. If p and q are respectively the 1st and the 2nd terms of a geometric sequence, find the sum to infinity of the corresponding series in terms of p and q.

19. If the sum to infinity of a geometric series is $\dfrac{16}{3}$ and its second term is -4, find the common ratio of the corresponding geometric sequence.

20. If the quadratic equation $4ax^2 - 4bx + c = 0$ has two equal roots, where a, b and c are non-zero constants, which of the following is/are true?

    I. a, b and c form a geometric sequence.

    II. a, b and c form an arithmetic sequence.

    III. Both roots are $\dfrac{b}{2a}$.

21. If positive numbers a, b, c and d are in arithmetic sequence, which of the following <u>must</u> be true?

    I. ka, kb, kc and kd are in arithmetic sequence, where k is a non-zero constant.

    II. p^a, p^b, p^c and p^d are in geometric sequence, where p is a positive constant.

    III. $\log a$, $\log b$, $\log c$ and $\log d$ are in arithmetic sequence.

22. Solve $x(x+2) > 3(x+2)$.

23. Find the values of x which satisfy both $-x > 3$ *and* $\dfrac{2x-15}{3} < -1$.

24. If the solution of the inequality $x^2 - px + 12 \leqslant 0$ is $q \leqslant x \leqslant 4$, find p and q.

25. Find the greatest value of $2x + 3y$ if (x, y) is a point lying in the region OABCD (including the boundary).

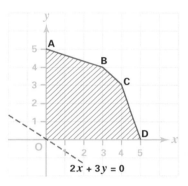

26. In the figure, (x, y) is a point in the shaded region (including the boundary). If x and y are integers, find the least value of $x - 3y$.

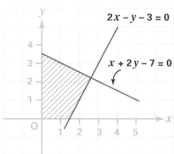

27. Show graphically the solution of the following inequalities:
$$\begin{cases} 1 \leqslant x + y \leqslant 3 \\ 0 \leqslant x \leqslant 2 \\ 0 \leqslant y \leqslant 2 \end{cases}$$

◀ *Suggested scale for both axes:*
10 divisions (1 cm) = 1 unit.

28. From the table, find an interval of width 0.1 which brackets a root of $x - f(x) = 0$.

x	-0.2	-0.1	0	0.1	0.2	0.3
$f(x)$	2.4	1.6	0.2	0	-0.1	-0.6

B. Long Questions

29. **(a)** Show that $\log 5$, $\log 5x$ and $\log 5x^2$, where $x > 0$, are in arithmetic sequence.

(b) **(i)** Write down the nth term of the arithmetic sequence
$\log 5$, $\log 5x$, $\log 5x^2$, $\cdots$.

(ii) Find the sum of the first n terms of the corresponding arithmetic series in terms of x and n.

(iii) If the sum of the first 20 terms of the corresponding arithmetic series is $19 + \log 5$, find the value of x.

30. $\dfrac{1}{3}$, 1, 3, $\cdots$ are in geometric sequence.

(a) Find

(i) the nth term,

(ii) the sum of the first n terms of the corresponding geometric series,

(iii) the sum of the corresponding geometric series from the 6th term to the 10th term.

(b) If the sum of the series from the 2nd term to the nth term is $1\,093$, find the value of n.

31. **(a)** Draw and shade the region represented by the following system of inequalities.

$$\begin{cases} y \leqslant 2 \\ x - 2y \leqslant 1 \\ x + y \leqslant 4 \\ 2x - y \geqslant -4 \end{cases}$$

(b) Given a linear function $P(x, y) = x - y - 2$.
Under the constraints given by the inequalities in **(a)**, find the maximum and the minimum values of P.

(c) Repeat **(b)** if there is an additional constraint $x \leqslant 2$.

◀ *Suggested scale for both axes:*
10 divisions (1 cm) = 1 unit.

32. In the figure, the three straight lines ℓ_1, ℓ_2 and ℓ_3 intersect at three points A, B and C. The equations of ℓ_1, ℓ_2 and ℓ_3 are given as follows:

$\ell_1 : y - kx = 0$, where $k > -\dfrac{3}{2}$

$\ell_2 : 3x + 2y + 3 = 0$

$\ell_3 : x - y - 4 = 0$

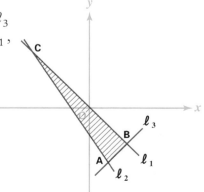

(a) Find the coordinates of A, B and C.
(*Give the answers in terms of k if necessary.*)

(b) Write the inequalities which determine the shaded region, including the boundary, in the given figure.
(*Give the answers in terms of k if necessary.*)

(c) If the minimum value of the linear function $P(x, y) = 2x + y$ subject to the constraints obtained in **(b)** is -3, find the value of k.

33.

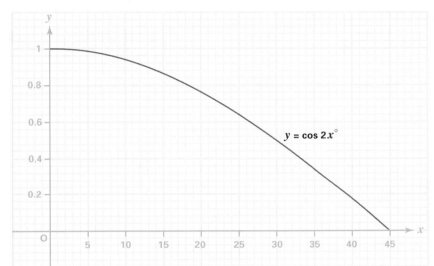

A duplicate of this graph is provided in the Student Handbook 5A.

The figure shows the graph of $y = \cos 2x°$ for $0 \leqslant x \leqslant 45$.

(a) By drawing a suitable straight line on the graph, solve the equation
$$30\cos 2x° - x = 0 \quad \text{for } 0 < x < 45.$$

(b) Using the method of bisection, improve the solution in part **(a)** correct to 3 significant figures.

34. The given figure shows the graph of
$$y = x^3 + ax + b \quad \text{for } 0 \leqslant x \leqslant 3.$$

(a) Find the values of a and b.

(b) By adding a suitable straight line on the graph, solve the equation
$$x^3 + 13x - 33 = 0.$$

(c) Use the method of bisection to find the solution of the equation given in **(b)** correct to 2 decimal places.

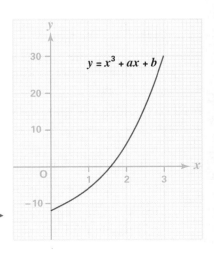

A duplicate of this graph is provided in the Student Handbook 5A.

End of Strand: Algebra

Preparatory Exercise for HKCEE

(Strand : Geometry)

A. Short Questions

(Group 1)

1. L_1 is the line passing through the point A($1, 1$) and parallel to the line $L_2 : 3x + 6y + 1 = 0$. Find the equation of L_1.

2. The equation of L_1 is $4x - y + 6 = 0$. L_2 is a straight line passing through the point A($-2, 1$) and its slope is half of the slope of L_1. Find the equation of L_2.

3. The equations of L_1, L_2 and L_3 are as follows:

   $L_1 : 5x - 2y = 4$

   $L_2 : 2x + 5y = 9$

   $L_3 : 5x + 2y = 1$

   (a) Find the slopes of L_1, L_2 and L_3.

   (b) Using the results of **(a)**, find which pair(s) of straight lines are perpendicular to each other.

4. Given two straight lines:

   $L_1 : x - 7y - 10 = 0$

   $L_2 : 5x - 3y - 18 = 0$

   (a) Find the point of intersection of L_1 and L_2.

   (b) Find the equation of the line perpendicular to L_1 and passing through the point of intersection of L_1 and L_2.

5. The equations of L_1, L_2 and L_3 are given below:

$$L_1 : y = 4$$
$$L_2 : x - 2y + 13 = 0$$
$$L_3 : 2x + y - 14 = 0$$

(a) Find the points of intersection of L_1, L_2 and L_3.

(b) Using the results of **(a)**, find the area bounded by L_1, L_2 and L_3.

6. In the figure, the equation of the circle $\mathcal{C}$ is $x^2 + y^2 + 4x - 6y + 9 = 0$.

(a) Find the coordinates of the centre and the radius of $\mathcal{C}$.

(b) If $\mathcal{C}$ touches the line $x = k$, find the value of k.

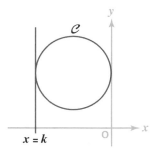

7. The figure shows a circle of radius 12 with centre at the origin O. The line AB touches the circle at A and cuts the x-axis at B.

(a) Find the equation of the circle.

(b) If $\tan \theta = \dfrac{4}{3}$, find the length of OB.

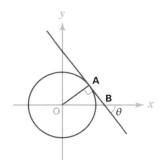

(Group 2)

8. Which of the following straight lines divide(s) the circle $(x + 1)^2 + (y - 1)^2 = 1$ into two equal parts?

I. $x - y + 2 = 0$
II. $x + y + 2 = 0$
III. $x + y - 2 = 0$

9. Given that the equation of a circle is $x^2 + y^2 - 2x + 4y + 1 = 0$. Which of the following statements is/are true?

I.   The centre is $(-1, 2)$.
II. The radius is 2 units.
III. The circle intersects the x-axis at two distinct points.

10. Two perpendicular lines $bx - y + 24 = 0$ and $x + 3y - 2 = 0$ intersect at the point (a, b). Find a and b.

11. In the figure, a circle intersects with the x-axis at two points four units apart. If the centre of the circle is $(3, 2)$, find the equation of the circle.

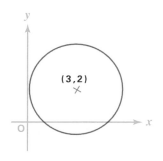

12. The circle $x^2 + y^2 - 12x + my + 47 = 0$ passes through the point $(2, 3)$. Find the radius of the circle.

13. Find the equation of the line parallel to $3x - 2y - 7 = 0$ and passing through the mid-point of the line segment joining $(3, -8)$ and $(-5, 4)$.

14. Find, in terms of π, the area of the circle $x^2 + y^2 - 8x + 14y + 40 = 0$.

B. Long Questions

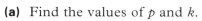

15. The equation of a circle $\mathcal{C}$ is $x^2 + y^2 = 20$ and the equation of a line L is $y = mx + 10$.

    (a) If L intersects $\mathcal{C}$, find the range of values of m.

    (b) If L is a tangent to $\mathcal{C}$, find the equation(s) of L.

    (c) Does the line $5y + 2x - 17 = 0$ intersect the circle $\mathcal{C}$?

16. In the figure, the straight line $L_1 : x - y = k$ intersects the circle $\mathcal{C}_1 : x^2 + y^2 + px = 0$ at two points P and Q, where p and k are real constants. S is the centre of the circle and the coordinates of P are $(4, 0)$.

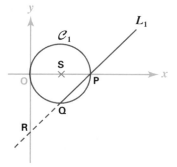

    (a) Find the values of p and k.

    (b) Find the coordinates of Q.

    (c) If L_1 cuts the y-axis at a point R, find the coordinates of R.

    (d) Find the equation of a circle $\mathcal{C}_2$ which passes through points P, R and S.

    (e) Find the equation of the straight line L_2 which touches the circle $\mathcal{C}_2$ at point R.

17. Given a circle $\mathcal{C} : x^2 + y^2 - 6x - 6y + 10 = 0$.

(a) Show that A(1 , 1) lies on the circle $\mathcal{C}$.

(b) L_1 is a tangent to the circle $\mathcal{C}$ at A.

(i) Find the equation of L_1.

(ii) If L_1 cuts the *x*- and *y*-axes at points P and Q respectively, find the coordinates of P and Q.

(c) From the point Q, another straight line L_2 tangent to the circle at a point B is drawn. Find the equation of L_2.

(d) Find the equation of the circle with AB as a diameter.

Preparatory Exercise for HKCEE

(Strand : Statistics)

A. Short Questions

(Group 1)

1. Andrew and Betty are two of the 32 young people joining a mass game. If two people are to be selected at random as group leaders, find the probability that both Andrew and Betty are selected. ·

2. Two cards are drawn at random from a pack of 52 cards. Find the probability that neither a king nor an ace is drawn.

3. In a secondary school, there are 200 Form 5 students. The following table shows the numbers of students having different total numbers of brothers and sisters.

Total number of brothers and sisters	Number of students
0	15
1	40
2	95
3	30
4	20
5 or more	0

What is the mean of the total numbers of brothers and sisters that the students have?

4. Two dice D_1 and D_2 are thrown. The numbers shown on the dice D_1 and D_2 are recorded in the form of an ordered pair (a, b). Find the probability that

   (a) the result is $(2, 5)$,

   (b) the sum of the numbers shown on the two dice is greater than 8.

5. The table shows the distribution of the daily wages of 100 staff in a company:

Daily wages($)	Number of staff
200–299	20
300–399	40
400–499	30
500–599	10

   (a) Find the mid-value of the class $400–$499.

   (b) Estimate the mean of the above distribution of daily wages.

6. Given five real numbers $r-2$, r, $r+1$, $r+2$ and $r+4$, find

   (a) the mean,

   (b) the standard deviation.

7. The weights of 800 people form a normal distribution with a mean of 56 kg and a standard deviation of 5 kg. If 32% of them lie outside one standard deviation of the mean and 5% lie outside two standard deviations of the mean, find

   (a) the number of people who weigh less than 66 kg,

   (b) the number of people whose weights lie between 46 kg and 61 kg.

8. Two dice are thrown at the same time. Find the probability that the sum of the numbers on the dice is

   (a) greater than 10,

   (b) equal to 10,

   (c) smaller than 10.

9. If three dice are thrown once, what is the probability that

   (a) all numbers on the dice are odd?

   (b) two of the numbers on the dice are odd and the other is even?

   (c) at most one of the numbers on the dice is even?

10.

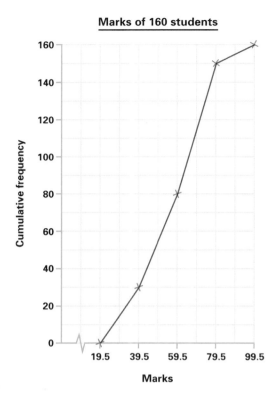

Marks of 160 students

The figure shows the cumulative frequency polygon of the marks obtained by 160 students in an English examination.

(a) What is the median of this distribution?

(b) (i) Copy and complete the following table.

Marks	Number of students
0 – 19	
20 – 39	
40 – 59	
60 – 79	
80 – 99	

(ii) What is the mean mark of the students in the examination?

11.

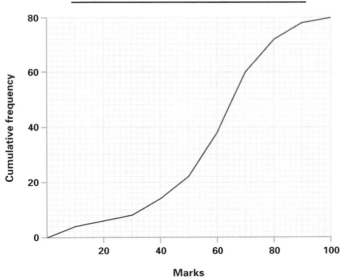

Marks of 80 students in a Mathematics test

In the figure, the cumulative frequency polygon shows the distribution of marks of 80 students in a Mathematics test.

(a) If 35% of the students fail the test, what is the pass mark, correct to the nearest integer?

(b) If the pass mark is 42, how many students pass the test?

(c) Find the inter-quartile range of the marks.

(Group 2)

12. One letter is taken from each of the names 'ERIC' and 'NICK' at random. Find the probability that the two letters are the same.

13. Abby, Bob, Chris and Dick sit randomly around a round table and are evenly spaced. Find the probability that Abby sits opposite to Bob.

14. Two cards are drawn randomly from five cards A, B, C, D and E. Find the probability that card C is drawn while card A or card E is not.

15. One red die and one blue die are thrown once. Find the probability that the number on the red die is smaller than that on the blue die.

16. Two fair dice are thrown. Find the probability of getting a total of 4 or 9.

17. A fair die is thrown 3 times. Find the probability that '3' occurs exactly twice.

18. A bag contains 7 coins, 3 of which are silver coins and the rest are gold coins. If 2 coins are chosen at random, find the probability that exactly one of them is a gold coin.

19. There are 8 bags. Three of the bags each contains a ball and the rest are empty. If a boy opens the bags at random, what is the probability that he can find all the three balls by opening three bags only?

20. There are 6 bottles. Four of them each contains 1 marble and each of the remaining 2 contains 2 marbles. A marble is taken from one of the bottles at random. Then a bottle is selected. Find the probability of selecting a bottle containing 1 marble.

21. In a certain game, the probability that Paul will lose is 0.6. If he plays the game 3 times, find the probability that he will win at most twice.

22. Given that the mean and the standard deviation of a distribution of test scores are m and s respectively. If each score of the distribution is multiplied by 1.2, find the mean and the standard deviation of the new distribution.

23. The mean, the standard deviation and the inter-quartile range of n numbers are m, s and q respectively. If 5 is subtracted from each of the n numbers, find the new mean, the new standard deviation and the new inter-quartile range.

24. Which of the following cannot be read directly from a frequency polygon?

    I. Mean
    II. Median
    III. Mode

25.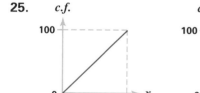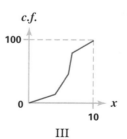

    The figures above show the cumulative frequency polygons of three frequency distributions. Arrange the three distributions in the ascending order of magnitude of their standard deviations.

26. The following figures show the histograms of three frequency distributions. Arrange their standard deviations in ascending order of magnitude.

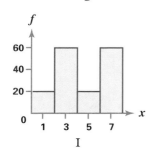 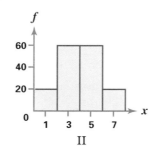 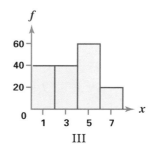

I II III

27. The figure shows the frequency curves of two symmetric frequency distributions A and B with the same mean. Which of the following is/are true?

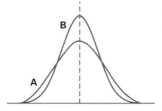

I.   Median of A < median of B

II. Mode of A < mode of B

III. Standard deviation of A > standard deviation of B

28. The graph shows the frequency curves of two symmetric frequency distributions P and Q.
Which of the following is/are true?

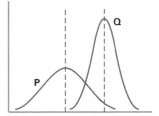

I.   Mean of P > mean of Q

II. Standard deviation of P > standard deviation of Q

III. Inter-quartile range of P > inter-quartile range of Q

B. Long Questions

29. There are three bags A, B and C. Bag A contains 7 red balls and 2 white balls while bag B contains 3 red balls and 4 white balls. One of the red balls in bag A is marked R and one of the white balls in bag B is marked W.

The changes take place according to the following steps:

(I) A ball is drawn from bag A at random and put into bag B.

(II) A red ball and a white ball are drawn from bag B at random and put into bag C.

(III) A ball is drawn from bag A at random and put into bag C.

Calculate the probability, after the above changes have taken place, that

(a) ball R is in bag B,

(b) both ball R and ball W are in bag B,

(c) both ball R and ball W are in bag C.

30. In a bookstore, the marked prices of some books are recorded in the table below:

Marked price ($)	40–59	60–79	80–99	100–119	120–139	140–159	160–179	180–199
Frequency	2	18	20	26	18	10	4	2

(a) Calculate the mean.

(b) Calculate the standard deviation correct to the nearest integer.

(c) Using the data given in the table, draw a cumulative frequency polygon. Hence, estimate the percentage of books with marked prices lying within one standard deviation from the mean.

(d) Books with marked prices higher than two standard deviations above the mean will be catagorized as 'expensive'.

(i) What is the highest price a book can be marked so that it is not catagorized as 'expensive'?
(*Give the answer correct to the nearest integer.*)

(ii) Estimate the percentage of the books which are 'expensive'.

31.

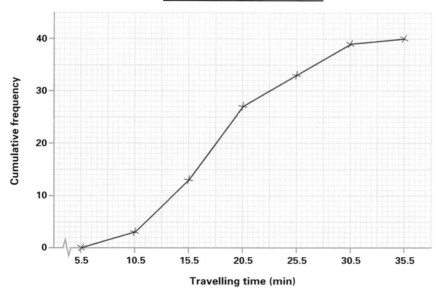

Travelling time of 40 students

The cumulative frequency polygon shows the time spent on travelling to school by 40 students.

(a) From the cumulative frequency polygon, find
    (i) the median,
    (ii) the inter-quartile range of the distribution of travelling time.

(b) **(i)** Complete the following corresponding frequency distribution table:

Travelling time (min)	*Frequency*
6–10	
11–15	
16–20	
21–25	
26–30	
31–35	

    (ii) Find the mean travelling time.
    (iii) Find the standard deviation, correct to 2 decimal places.

(c) If two students are chosen at random, find the probability that
    (i) both of them spend less than 13 minutes on travelling,
    (ii) at least one of them spends less than 13 minutes on travelling.

End of Strand: Statistics

APPENDIX:

Calculator Programs

APPENDIX
Calculator Programs

[A general introduction to calculator programming is given in **Book 4A** of this series.]

Program I. *FIND THE CENTRE AND THE RADIUS OF A CIRCLE IN THE GENERAL FORM*

Let the equation of the circle be $x^2 + y^2 + Dx + Ey + F = 0$.

Program

Steps	1	2	3	4	5	6	7	8
Program Keys	ENT	K in 1	ENT	K in 2	ENT	K in 3	2	+/−

Steps	9	10	11	12	13	14	15
Program Keys	K in ÷ 1	K in ÷ 2	K out 1	HLT	x^2	+	K out 2

Steps	16	17	18	19	20	21	22	23
Program Keys	HLT	x^2	−	K out 3	=	√	K in 3	RTN

Explanation: (i) This program consists of 23 steps.

(ii) After entering the values of D, E and F in sequence, the x-coordinate of the centre is displayed immediately. The y-coordinate of the centre is then displayed by pressing **RUN**. By pressing **RUN** again, the radius of the circle is displayed.

(iii) At last, the x-coordinate of the centre is stored in **K1**, the y-coordinate of the centre is stored in **K2** and the radius of the circle is stored in **K3**. We can recall each of them by pressing Kout 1, Kout 2 and Kout 3 respectively.

EXAMPLE 1 | Find the centre and the radius of the circle $x^2 + y^2 + 8x - 6y - 11 = 0$.

SOLUTION

Keying sequence	Display	Remark
P1 (or **I**)		
8 **RUN** 6 **+/−** **RUN** 11 **+/−** **RUN**	-4.	(*x-coordinate of the centre*)
RUN	3.	(*y-coordinate of the centre*)
RUN	6.	(*Radius of the circle*)
AC		*Stop the program. This step may be omitted if we continue to do* **Example 2.**

∴   The centre is $(-4, 3)$ and the radius is 6.

EXAMPLE 2 |

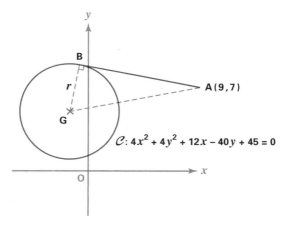

In the figure, $A(9, 7)$ is a point lying outside the circle $\mathcal{C} : 4x^2 + 4y^2 + 12x - 40y + 45 = 0$ with centre G and radius r. Find the length of a tangent segment AB drawn from A to the circle $\mathcal{C}$.

(*Give the answer correct to 3 significant figures.*)

SOLUTION We first divide the given equation by 4, then we have $x^2 + y^2 + 3x - 10y + \frac{45}{4} = 0$.

Keying sequence	Display	Remark
P1 (or I)		*This step may be omitted if we do not stop the program after doing* **Example 1**.
3 **RUN** 10 +/− **RUN** 45 ÷ 4 = **RUN**	-1.5	(*x-coordinate of the centre*) *Stored in* **K1**.
RUN	5.	(*y-coordinate of the centre*) *Stored in* **K2**.
RUN	4.	(*Radius of the circle*) *Stored in* **K3**.
MODE 8 3		*Round off the answer to 3 significant figures.*
[(--- 9 − Kout 1 ---)] x^2 + [(--- 7 − Kout 2 ---)] x^2 − Kout 3 x^2 = √	9.91^{00}	*Note that* $AB = \sqrt{AG^2 - r^2}$. (*The value of AB.*)
MODE 9	9.9121138	*Release the 'scientific' assignment.*
AC		*Stop the program.*

Thus the length of the tangent segment AB = <u>9.91</u> , *cor. to 3 sig. fig.*

Program II. *Locate the Root(s) of an Equation by Using the Method of Bisection*

We first write the following main program in **P1** (or **I**).

Program

Steps	1	2	3	4	5	6	7	8
Program Keys	Min	Kout 2	HLT	X↔K 3	K in 4	Kout 1	K in + 2	2

Steps	9	10	11	12	13	14	15
Program Keys	K in ÷ 2	MR	x>0	Kout 4	K in 2	X↔K 3	K in 1

Steps	16	17	18	19
Program Keys	K in + 2	2	K in ÷ 2	Kout 2

Explanation: (i) This program consists of 19 steps.

(ii) This program is used to decide the mid-value of the bracketing interval.

EXAMPLE 3 Solve $x^3 - 7x + 2 = 0$ for $-3 < x < 0$, correct to 1 decimal place.

SOLUTION Let $f(x) = x^3 - 7x + 2$ and write it on the program area **P2** (or **II**) as follows:

Program

Steps	1	2	3	4	5	6	7
Program Keys	Kout 2	x^y	3	−	7	×	Kout 2

Steps	8	9	10
Program Keys	+	2	=

(*Note :* The value of x is stored in **K2**.)

Before executing the programs, we first store the values of a and b (the end points of the first bracketing interval) in **K1** and **K2** respectively such that $f(a) < 0$ and $f(b) > 0$. Then, we press a positive number (e.g. 1) just before recalling the program in **P1** (or **I**).

$\therefore\ f(-3) = (-3)^3 - 7(-3) + 2 = -4 < 0$ and

$\qquad f(0) = 0^3 - 7(0) + 2 = 2 > 0,$

$\therefore\quad f(x) = 0$ has a real root x_0 between -3 and 0.

(We have $a = -3$, $b = 0$ in this case.)

Also, we key in MODE 7 4 to specify that the values on display are correct to 4 decimal places.[†]

Keying sequence	Display	Remark
3 +/− K in 1	-3.	-3 is stored in **K1** since $f(-3) < 0$.
0 K in 2	0.	0 is stored in **K2** since $f(0) > 0$.
1	1.	Press a positive number.
MODE 7 4	1.0000	Specify that the values displayed are correct to 4 decimal places.
P1 (or I) RUN	-1.5000	
P2 (or II)	9.1250	
P1 RUN	-2.2500	
P2	6.3594	
P1 RUN	-2.6250	
P2	2.2871	' P1 RUN ' gives the mid-value of the previous bracketing interval, then ' P2 ' evaluates the corresponding value of $f(x)$.
P1 RUN	-2.8125	
P2	-0.5598	
P1 RUN	-2.7188	
P2	0.9353	
P1 RUN	-2.7656	
P2	0.2060	

[†] We have chosen to display our calculated values to 4 decimal places. This is sufficiently accurate since we are required to find a root of $f(x) = 0$ correct to 1 decimal place only. In normal practice, if we are required to find a root correct to n decimal places, where n is a positive integer, then we would choose to display all our calculated values, concerning the question, to at least $n + 2$ decimal places as long as the number of digits displayed on our calculators allow us. For example, if the required root is to be correct to 3 decimal places, then we would choose MODE 7 5 or MODE 7 6, etc.

We can tabulate the results as follows:

Bracketing interval	Mid-value x	$f(x) = x^3 - 7x + 2$
$-3 < x_0 < 0$	-1.5	$9.125\ 0$
$-3 < x_0 < -1.5$	-2.25	$6.359\ 4$
$-3 < x_0 < -2.25$	-2.625	$2.287\ 1$
$-3 < x_0 < -2.625$	$-2.812\ 5$	$-0.559\ 8$
$-2.812\ 5 < x_0 < -2.625$	$-2.718\ 8$	$0.935\ 3$
$-2.812\ 5 < x_0 < -2.718\ 8$	$-2.765\ 6$	$0.206\ 0$
$-2.812\ 5 < x_0 < -2.765\ 6$		

$$\therefore \quad x_0 = \underline{\underline{-2.8}}, \quad cor.\ to\ 1\ d.p.$$

EXAMPLE 4 | Solve $\sin x - 2x + 1 = 0$ for $0.7 < x < 1$ where x is in radian measure, correct to 3 significant figures.

SOLUTION   Let $f(x) = \sin x - 2x + 1$ and write it on the program area **P2** (or **II**) as follows:

Program

Steps	1	2	3	4	5	6	7	8	9
Program Keys	Kout 2	sin	−	2	×	Kout 2	+	1	=

Before executing the programs, we press **MODE** 5 to set the calculator in 'radian' mode.

$\because \quad f(1) \approx -0.158\ 5 < 0$ and $f(0.7) \approx 0.244\ 2 > 0$,

$\therefore \quad f(x) = 0$ has a real root x_0 between 0.7 and 1.

Keying sequence	Display	Remark
MODE 5		*Set the calculator in radian mode.*
1 **K in** 1	1.	*1 is stored in* **K1** *since* $f(1) < 0$.
0.7 **K in** 2	0.7	*0.7 is stored in* **K2** *since* $f(0.7) > 0$.
1	1.	*This step may be omitted since 0.7 is a positive number.*
MODE 7 5	1.00000	*Specify that the values displayed are correct to 5 decimal places.*
P1 (or **I**) **RUN**	0.85000	(*Mid-value x*)
P2 (or **II**)	0.05128	(*Value of* $f(x)$)
P1 **RUN**	0.92500	
P2	-0.05138	
P1 **RUN**	0.88750	
P2	0.00050	
P1 **RUN**	0.90625	
P2	-0.02530	
P1 **RUN**	0.89688	
P2	-0.01237	
P1 **RUN**	0.89219	
P2	-0.00593	
P1 **RUN**	0.88984	
P2	-0.00271	
P1 **RUN**	0.88867	
P2	-0.00111	
P1 **RUN**	0.88809	
P2	-0.00031	

We may tabulate the results as follows:

Bracketing interval	Mid-value x	$f(x) = \sin x - 2x + 1$
$0.7 < x_0 < 1$	0.85	0.051 28
$0.85 < x_0 < 1$	0.925	$-0.051\ 38$
$0.85 < x_0 < 0.925$	0.887 5	0.000 50
$0.887\ 5 < x_0 < 0.925$	0.906 25	$-0.025\ 30$
$0.887\ 5 < x_0 < 0.906\ 25$	0.896 88	$-0.012\ 37$
$0.887\ 5 < x_0 < 0.896\ 88$	0.892 19	$-0.005\ 93$
$0.887\ 5 < x_0 < 0.892\ 19$	0.889 84	$-0.002\ 71$
$0.887\ 5 < x_0 < 0.889\ 84$	0.888 67	$-0.001\ 11$
$0.887\ 5 < x_0 < 0.888\ 67$	0.888 09	$-0.000\ 31$
$0.887\ 5 < x_0 < 0.888\ 09$		

$\therefore \quad x_0 = \underline{\underline{0.888}}$, *cor. to 3 sig. fig.*

A N S W E R S

EXERCISE 1A (P. 5)

(Level 1)

1. (a) 14 , 17 **(b)** 48 , 96 **(c)** 1 , −1

2. (a) 3 , 5 , 7 , 9 **(b)** 3 , 9 , 27 , 81
(c) 2 , 5 , 9 , 14

3. (a) (i) −1 **(ii)** 7
(iii) 37
(b) (i) 2 **(ii)** $\frac{8}{7}$
(iii) $\frac{61}{59}$
(c) (i) −1 **(ii)** 23
(iii) 398

4. (a) $n+1$ **(b)** $3n$ **(c)** $\frac{1}{3^n}$
(d) n^3

5. yes

(Level 2)

6. (a) 0 , 4 , 0 **(b)** 5 040 , 40 320 , 362 880
(c) 30 , 55 , 91

7. (a) $\frac{1}{256}$, $\frac{1}{128}$, $\frac{1}{64}$, $\frac{1}{32}$, $\frac{1}{16}$
(b) 2 , 3 , 5 , 7 , 11 **(c)** 0 , 0 , 2 , 2 , 0

8. (a) 10^n+1 **(b)** $3^{n-2} \cdot 4^{1-n}$

9. (a) $a=1$, $b=-1$ **(b)** 21

10. (a) 315 m **(b)** 3 s

EXERCISE 1B (P. 10)

(Level 1)

1. (a) (i) 3 **(ii)** $3n+3$
(b) (i) 4 **(ii)** $4n-8$
(c) (i) −15 **(ii)** $35-15n$

2. (a) (i) 5 **(ii)** 2
(b) (i) −3 **(ii)** −7
(c) (i) 0 **(ii)** $\frac{1}{2}$

3. (a) (i) $2n$ **(ii)** 20
(b) (i) $3n-10$ **(ii)** 20
(c) (i) $\frac{7-n}{2}$ **(ii)** $-\frac{3}{2}$

4. −4 **5.** 95

6. (a) 26 **(b)** 11

7. (a) yes **(b)** yes

8. (a) $10 900 **(b)** $(13\ 100-1\ 100n)$

(Level 2)

9. (a) (i) 7 **(ii)** $x+7n-4$
(b) (i) $a+2b$ **(ii)** $na+(2n-1)b$

10. 8 **11. (a)** 0 **(b)** −90

12. (a) 20 **(b)** 1 **13.** 34

14. (a) 2072 **(b)** no

15. (a) 7 cm **(b)** 4 cm
(c) AB = 3 cm , CD = 11 cm

EXERCISE 1C (P. 14)

(Level 1)

1. (a) 5 **(b)** −2.5 **(c)** −9

2. 30 **3.** 11 , 17 , 23

4. $p=-14$, $q=-10$, $r=-6$, $s=-2$

(Level 2)

5. 3

6. (a) $\frac{n+3}{4}$, $\frac{n+1}{2}$, $\frac{3n+1}{4}$
(b) $a=28$, $b=55$, $c=82$

7. (b) 20^2 **8.** $a=\frac{4}{3}\log 4$, $b=\frac{5}{3}\log 4$

9. (a) 750
(b) 1991: $12 150 , 1992: $12 900 ,
1993: $13 650 , 1994: $14 400 ,
1995: $15 150

EXERCISE 1D (P. 19)

(*Level 1*)

1. (a) $r = 2$, $T(n) = 2^n$
  (b) $r = -5$, $T(n) = 2(-5)^{n-1}$
  (c) $r = 3$, $T(n) = -4(3)^{n-1}$

2. (a) (i) 4^{n-1} **(ii)** 256
  (b) (i) $(-1)^{n-1} \cdot 2^n$ **(ii)** 32
  (c) (i) -2^{4-2n} **(ii)** $-\dfrac{1}{64}$

3. (a) (i) 4 **(ii)** 5
  (b) (i) 6 **(ii)** 2
  (c) (i) 9 **(ii)** 9
  (d) (i) $\dfrac{1}{2}$ **(ii)** $\dfrac{1}{2}$

4. $\dfrac{1}{27}$ **5. (a)** 21 **(b)** 6

6. (a) no **(b)** yes

(*Level 2*)

7. $r = \dfrac{1}{3}$, $T(n) = 7\left(\dfrac{1}{3}\right)^{n-1}$

8. (a) -3 **(b)** $\dfrac{1}{3}$ **(c)** -729

9. $\dfrac{1}{2}$ **10. (a)** 10 **(b)** 16

11. (a) $1\,968\,300$ **(b)** 9 a.m. , 2nd January

12. (a) $320 **(b)** 42 months

13. (a) Alan : $10\,000(1.1)^{n-1}$,
  Philip : $8\,000(1.13)^{n-1}$
  (b) 9 years **(c)** 35 years

EXERCISE 1E (P. 23)

(*Level 1*)

1. 21 **2.** $-\dfrac{1}{105}$ **3.** 6 , 12

4. 36 , 108 , 324

(*Level 2*)

5. 21 , 63 , 189 , 567 , $1\,701$ *or* -21 , 63 , -189 ,
  567 , $-1\,701$

6. 24 , 6 , $\dfrac{3}{2}$ *or* -24 , 6 , $-\dfrac{3}{2}$

7. (a) 3 , $-\dfrac{18}{5}$ **(b)** $\dfrac{27}{5}$, $\dfrac{48}{5}$

8. (a) $\dfrac{1}{x}$, $\dfrac{1}{3}$ **(b)** $\dfrac{4}{9}$

9. (a) 4 **(b)** 3 , 12 , 48

10. (a) 1.2
  (b) (i) $5\,000$ **(ii)** $8\,640$
  (c) $17\,900$

SUPPLEMENTARY EXERCISE 1 (P. 24)

1. (a) -1 , -3 , -5 , -7 **(b)** -1 , 1 , -1 , 1
  (c) -1 , 1 , -1 , 1 **(d)** 1 , 4 , 27 , 256

2. (a) $\dfrac{1}{2n-1}$ **(b)** 10^{-n}
  (c) $n(10)^n$ **(d)** $\sin\left(\dfrac{n\pi}{n+2}\right)$

3. (a) 4 **(c)** no

4. (a) (i) $n(n+2)$ **(ii)** $2n+1$
  (b) (i) 9 **(ii)** $3\,407$
  (iii) $-1\,997$

5. (a) first term $= -80$, common difference $= 28$
  (b) first term $= -4$, common difference $= -2$

6. (a) $a - b$ **(b)** $a + b$

7. (b) yes **8. (a)** $\dfrac{a}{4}$ cm **(b)** 12 cm , 9 cm

9. (a) 13 **(b)** 2 **(c)** -1

11. (a) 6 **(b)** $-\dfrac{5}{16}$

12. $4\sqrt{3}$, $5\sqrt{3}$, $6\sqrt{3}$

13. (a) $a = \dfrac{2x+y}{3}$, $b = \dfrac{x+2y}{3}$ **(b)** $-\dfrac{\sqrt{3}}{3}$, $\dfrac{\sqrt{3}}{3}$

14. (a) $\dfrac{b-a}{n+1}$ **(c)** 525

15. (a) (i) $\dfrac{1}{7}$ **(ii)** 7^{6-n}
  (iii) 8
  (b) (i) $\sqrt{3}$ **(ii)** $(\sqrt{3})^{n+1}$
  (iii) 5

16. (a) $3(2)^{n-2}$ **17. (a)** 3 , $\dfrac{22}{7}$ **(b)** 1 , -1 , 1

18. (b) $a = \dfrac{25}{4}$, $r = -\dfrac{3}{5}$ *or* $a = 1$, $r = \dfrac{3}{2}$

19. (a) car A : $120\,000(0.9)^{n-1}$,
  car B : $230\,000(0.8)^{n-1}$
  (b) 7 **20.** $\dfrac{\sqrt{2}}{25}$, $\dfrac{1}{10}$, $\dfrac{\sqrt{2}}{8}$

21. (a) -3 **(b)** -1

22. (a) $\frac{a-b}{a+b}$ **(c)** $\frac{9}{4}$, $\frac{3}{2}$, 1 , $\frac{2}{3}$

23. (a) (i) 14 802 000   **(ii)** 547 000
(b) 8.16%

24. (a) 4   **(b)** 3   **(c)** 47

26. (a) 4   **(b)** 256

27. (a) $5
(b) seventh: $90 , eighth: $85 , ninth: $80
(c) $120

28. (b) ±12   **29. (b)** 4

30. (a) (i) $\sqrt{5}a$ cm   **(ii)** $\frac{5}{3}a$ cm
(iii) $\frac{5\sqrt{5}}{9}a$ cm
(b) $\frac{5^n}{9^{n-1}}a^2$ cm^2 **(c)** 0.10 cm^2

(MC)

31. B   **32.** E   **33.** D

EXERCISE 2A (P. 35)

(Level 1)

1. (a) 1 800   **(b)** 690   **(c)** 100
2. (a) 345   **(b)** $71\frac{1}{4}$
3. (a) 20   **(b)** 1 660
4. (a) 40   **(b)** $-\frac{1}{3}$
5. 120

(Level 2)

6. (a) 10   **(b)** $\frac{55}{6}$
7. (a) 9   **(b)** 7 , 14
8. (a) -8 **(b)** 3
9. (a) (i) $\frac{n}{2}(1+3n)$ **(ii)** $n(48-n)$
(b) 19
10. (a) $\frac{3}{2}(11-n)$ **(b)** 10
(c) $82\frac{1}{2}$
11. (a) 45 m   **(b)** 500 m
12. (a) 12 months
(b) (i) $12 200   **(ii)** $70 200

13. (a) 2 450   **(b)** 1 683
(c) 816   **(d)** 3 317
14. (a) 20   **(b)** 25.5 m
(c) (i) 1 m   **(ii)** 25.5 m^2

EXERCISE 2B (P. 41)

(Level 1)

1. (a) 16 383   **(b)** -5 208   **(c)** $72\left[1-\left(\frac{1}{2}\right)^{20}\right]$
2. (a) 8   **(b)** 9
3. (a) $n = 8$, $S(8) = 1$ 020
(b) $n = 8$, $S(8) = 9$ 840
4. 729   **5.** $634 199

(Level 2)

6. (a) 7   **(b)** -9 **(c)** 478 297
7. (a) 5   **(b)** 121
8. (a) first term $= \frac{1}{3}$, common ratio $= 3$
(b) 3 $280\frac{1}{3}$
9. (a) $2(2^n-1)$
(b) (i) 8   **(ii)** 9
10. (a) 6 years   **(b)** $4 629 400
11. (a) 126 cm   **(b)** 2
12. (a) (i) $1.16x   **(ii)** $2.505 6x
(c) 37 600
13. (a) 173.2 cm^2 **(b)** 43.3 cm^2 **(c)** 230.9 cm^2

EXERCISE 2C (P. 49)

(Level 1)

1. 8   **2.** 3   **3.** $\frac{4}{25}$
4. (a) 1   **(b)** 4
5. (a) 2 , $\frac{3}{2}$, $\frac{9}{8}$ **(b)** 40 , $\frac{40}{3}$, $\frac{40}{9}$

(Level 2)

6. (a) 2.21   **(b)** 0.15
7. (a) $\frac{1}{3}$ **(b)** $\frac{25}{3}$
8. (a) (i) 0.18 , 0.001 8 , 0.000 018
(ii) 0.01

(b) (i) $\frac{2}{11}$ **(ii)** $\frac{9}{110}$

9. (a) (i) 240   **(ii)** 180

     (b) 1 280

10. (a) 118.125 m   **(b)** 120 m   **(c)** 98.4%

11. (a) (i) $A_1B_1 = 16$ m , $A_2B_2 = 8$ m

     (ii) 64 m

     (b) (i) $AB_1 = 16\sqrt{3}$ m , $A_1B_2 = 8\sqrt{3}$ m ,

         $A_2B_3 = 4\sqrt{3}$ m

     (ii) $32\sqrt{3}$ m   **(c) (a)(ii)**

12. (a) 27 cm   **(b)** $\frac{27\pi}{2}$ cm   **(c)** yes

EXERCISE 2D   (P. 53)

(Level 1)

1. 62   **2.** 100   **3.** 93

4. $\sum_{r=1}^{n} (4r-3)$ **5.** $\sum_{r=1}^{n} r(r+3)$

(Level 2)

6. 864   **7.** 0

8. (a) (i) 40   **(ii)** 40

     (b) yes

9. (a) (i) k **(ii)** $k+1$

     (b) $\sum_{k=1}^{5} \frac{k}{k+1}$

10. (a) (i) 3^{n+1} **(ii)** $8(-1)^{n-1}$

     (b) $\sum_{n=1}^{4} \frac{3^{n+1}}{8(-1)^{n+1}}$

SUPPLEMENTARY EXERCISE 2   (P. 54)

1. (a) no. of terms = 11 , sum = 55

     (b) no. of terms = 16 , sum = $162\frac{2}{3}$

2. 1 210   **3.** 17 : 8

4. (a) 8   **(b)** 170°

5. (a) (i) 248   **(ii)** 306   **(iii)** 58

     (b) (i) 10   **(ii)** 6

6. (c) 2 , 12 , 22   **7.** 510

8. (a) $\frac{a^{10}-b^{10}}{a^8 b(a+b)}$ **(b)** 0.88

9. (a) 4 , −4   **(b)** $\frac{1}{30}$, $-\frac{1}{30}$

10. (a) (i) $2(2^n-1)$ **(ii)** $2(2^{2n}-1)$

     (b) (ii) 6

11. (b) 1.26 cm , 2.52 cm , 5.05 cm

12. (a) $-\frac{1}{3-\sqrt{2}}$ **(b)** yes   **(c)** $\frac{2(3-\sqrt{2})}{4-\sqrt{2}}$

13. (a) $15\frac{31}{32}$ **(b)** 16   **(c)** 0.20%

14. (a) 10 months

15. (a) 400   **(b)** (80 , 160)

16. (a) $\frac{71}{20}$ **(b)** 8

17. (a) $\sum_{n=1}^{10} (-1)^{n+1} n$ **(b)** $\sum_{n=1}^{7} (-1)^{n+1} \left(\frac{1}{n}\right)$

18. (a) $\log\frac{1}{2}$, $\log\frac{2}{3}$, $\log\frac{3}{4}$, $\log\frac{4}{5}$, $\log\frac{5}{6}$

     (b) −2

19. (a) $1-2^{-n}$ **(b)** 6   **(c)** no

20. (a) (i) 20 916   **(ii)** 13 860

     (iii) 6 804   **(b)** 27 972

21. (a) (i) $n(16-n)$ km   **(ii)** $\frac{n}{2}(25+3n)$ km

     (b) 7 days

22. (a) $\frac{n}{2}(1+n)$ **(b)** $\frac{n(n+1)}{8}(3n^2+3n+2)$

     (c) 17th

23. (a) $216\sqrt{3}$ cm^2 **(b)** $162\sqrt{3}$ cm^2

     (c) $864\sqrt{3}$ cm^2

24. (a) $\frac{2}{9}(10^n-1)$ **(b)** $\frac{2}{9}\left[\frac{10(10^n-1)}{9}-n\right]$

25. (a) 4   **(b)** $a = 4$, $b = 1$

     (c) (i) $\frac{8}{3}$ **(ii)** $\frac{16}{3}$

26. (a) (i) $5-3n$ **(ii)** $\frac{n}{2}(7-3n)$

     (iii) −715   **(b)** 28

27. (a) smallest: 105 , largest: 994

     (b) no. of multiples of 7 = 128 , sum = 70 336

     (c) 424 214

28. (a) (i) 16 , 17 , 18 , 19 , 20 , 21   **(ii)** 21

     (b) (i) $u_{k-1} = \frac{k(k-1)}{2}$, $v_1 = \frac{k^2-k+2}{2}$

     (ii) $\frac{k(k^2+1)}{2}$

29. (a) common ratio = $\frac{b}{a}$, sum = $\frac{a(a^n-b^n)}{a-b}$

     (b) (i) (1) \$1.08P

         (2) \$($1.08^2 P + 1.1 \times 1.08P$)

         (3) \$($1.08^3 P + 1.1 \times 1.08^2 P + 1.1^2 \times 1.08P$)

30. (a) (i) 71 400   **(ii)** 70 000$(1.02)^n$
   (b) 2007   **(c)** 6 280 000
   (d) (i) 12   **(ii)** 1 520 000

(MC)

31. E   **32.** A   **33.** C

EXERCISE 3A (P. 72)

(Level 1)

1. a straight line at a distance 10 m from the shore

2. (a) AC   **(b)** BD   **(c)** E

4. a circle concentric with the smaller coin and of radius equal to the sum of the two radii

(Level 2)

5. (a) a straight line parallel to the inclined plane
   (b) the radius of the balloon

6. the angle bisector of $\angle POQ$

8. a circle of radius 1 cm, centre O

9. a circle concentric with the given circle and of radius 6 cm

EXERCISE 3B (P. 82)

(Level 1)

1. (a) $(0,0)$, 4   **(b)** $(2,-4)$, 3   **(c)** $\left(-\frac{1}{2},\frac{3}{2}\right)$, 2

2. (a) $(-4,1)$, 5   **(b)** $(-3,0)$, 4   **(c)** $(0,3)$, $\sqrt{10}$

3. (a) $x^2+y^2=16$
   (b) $(x+5)^2+(y-5)^2=25$
   (c) $(x-6)^2+(y-5)^2=9$

4. (a) $x^2+y^2-8x+2y+8=0$
   (b) $x^2+y^2-10x+9=0$

5. (a) $x^2+y^2+4x-10y-29=0$
   (b) $x^2+y^2-8x+6y-16=0$

6. (a) $(3,-5)$ **(b)** $2\sqrt{2}$
   (c) $x^2+y^2-6x+10y+26=0$

7. $x^2+y^2-5x+3y=0$

(Level 2)

8. (a) $(1,3)$, 3   **(b)** $(0,2)$, 10

9. (a) $x^2+y^2-2x-12y+32=0$
   (b) $x^2+y^2-4x=0$, $x^2+y^2-12x+32=0$

10. (b) $\left(\frac{1}{4},-3\right)$, $\sqrt{5}$

11. (a) A: $(-3,0)$, B: $(5,0)$
   (b) $x^2+y^2-2x-15=0$ **(c)** no

12. (b) $x^2+y^2-12y+11=0$ **(c)** $\sqrt{5}$

13. (a) $(1,0)$ **(b)** $\sqrt{5}$
   (c) $x^2+y^2-2x-4=0$ **(d)** outside

14. (a) $x-3y-11=0$ **(b)** $(2,-3)$
   (c) $x^2+y^2-4x+6y+8=0$

EXERCISE 3C (P. 90)

(Level 1)

1. (a) 1   **(b)** 0

2. (a) $(-5,-5)$, $(7,1)$ **(b)** $(1,-1)$

3. (a) $2x-5y+29=0$ **(b)** $3x+2y+7=0$

4. (a) A: $(4,4)$, B: $(8,0)$ **(b)** $4\sqrt{2}$

5. A: $(-4,-3)$, B: $(4,-3)$

(Level 2)

6. (a) 2   **(b)** $(0,0)$

7. (a) $y=mx-2m$ **(b)** $\pm\frac{4}{3}$
   (c) $4x-3y-8=0$, $4x+3y-8=0$

8. (a) $x^2+y^2-4x+2y=0$
   (b) (ii) $\frac{1}{2}$, $-\frac{9}{2}$; $x-2y+1=0$, $x-2y-9=0$
   (c) $(1,1)$

9. (a) (ii) 1
   (b) (i) -1
   (ii) $x+y-14=0$, $x+y-6=0$

10. (b) $(3,-2)$
   (c) (i) $x+3y+3=0$ **(ii)** $(-9,2)$

11. (a) 3   **(b) (i)** 5   **(ii)** $\frac{5\sqrt{3}}{2}$

12. (a) $(4,2)$ **(b) (i)** $(0,6)$ **(ii)** $x-y+6=0$

1. two straight lines parallel to AB , each being 6 cm from AB

2. (a) yes

(b) a quarter of circle with centre at O and radius 1 m

3. (a) $\sqrt{30}$, $(3,-3)$ **(b)** $\frac{\sqrt{3}}{2}$, $\left(3,-\frac{1}{2}\right)$

4. (a) $x^2+y^2+8x-6y = 0$

(b) $x^2+y^2+6x+4y+4 = 0$

5. (a) $x^2+y^2-2x-4y-29 = 0$ **(b)** $\mathcal{C}_1$

6. (a) $x^2+y^2-8x+10y+21 = 0$

(b) $x^2+y^2-8x+2y+13 = 0$ **(c)** no

7. (b) $\left(\frac{7}{2},-2\right)$

(c) $x^2+y^2-7x+4y-15 = 0$ **(e)** $90°$

8. (a) 3   **(b)** A: $(-3,4)$, B: $(-3,-2)$

(c) $\mathcal{C}_1 : x^2+y^2+6x-8y+16 = 0$,

$\mathcal{C}_2 : x^2+y^2+6x+4y+4 = 0$

(d) $x^2+y^2-2y-17 = 0$

9. (a) A: $(2,0)$, B: $(0,2)$ *or* A: $(10,0)$, B: $(0,10)$

(b) $x^2+y^2-4x-4y+4 = 0$,

$x^2+y^2-20x-20y+100 = 0$

(c) $x^2+y^2-4x-4y+4 = 0$ **(d)** 4

10. (a) $x^2+y^2-8x+10y+37 = 0$

(b) $x^2+y^2-8x+10y+\frac{139}{4} = 0$

11. (a) $x+y-4 = 0$ **(b)** $9x-y+28 = 0$

12. (a) A: $(-9,0)$, B: $(-1,0)$, C: $(0,3)$

(b) (i) $3x-y+27 = 0$ **(ii)** $(-6.4,7.8)$

13. (a) $(5,-3)$ **(b)** $\sqrt{2}$

14. (a) $(-3,5)$ **(c)** $x-y+10 = 0$

(d) P: $(-6,4)$, Q: $(-2,8)$ *or*

P: $(-2,8)$, Q: $(-6,4)$

(e) $(-8,10)$ **(f)** 20

15. (b) $(8,9)$ **(c)** $x^2+y^2-25x-5y+100 = 0$

16. (a) $x^2+y^2-6x+2y-16 = 0$

(b) $\sqrt{26}$, $(3,-1)$

17. (a) $\left(2,\frac{2\sqrt{3}}{3}\right)$ **(b)** $\frac{4}{\sqrt{3}}$

(c) $(x-2)^2+\left(y-\frac{2\sqrt{3}}{3}\right)^2 = \frac{16}{3}$

18. (a) A: $(0,3)$, B: $(-2,1)$

(b) $x^2+y^2+2x-4y+3 = 0$

19. (a) A: $(1,-2)$, B: $(3,-2)$

(b) AB $= 2$, BP $= 3$, AP $= 5$ **(c)** yes

20. (a) 4   **(b)** $(8,8)$

(c) $x^2+y^2-5x-18y+56 = 0$

21. (b) (ii) $D = 0$, $E = -6$, $F = -16$ *or*

$D = 2$, $E = -8$, $F = -8$

(iii) $x^2+y^2-6y-16 = 0$

22. (a) $(-2,3)$, $\sqrt{10}$ **(c)** $\left(\frac{-k-14}{5},\frac{7-2k}{5}\right)$

(d) $-9,1$

23. (a) $(2,-5)$ **(b)** radius $= 2$, $k = 25$

24. (a) $2x+y-25 = 0$ **(b)** $(9,7)$

25. (a) $\pm2\sqrt{2}$

(b) (i) $2,(0,2)$ **(ii)** $x^2+y^2-2x-2y = 0$

26. (a) B: $(3,9)$, C: $(-2,4)$

(b) A: $(6,0)$, D: $(0,8)$

(c) $\angle$ABO $= \angle$ACO $= \angle$ADO $= 37°$

(d) 12

27. (a) $(1,-3)$, 3   **(b)** 5 , A lies outside $(\mathcal{C}_1)$

(c) (i) 2

(ii) $x^2+y^2-10x+21 = 0$

(d) $2\sqrt{6}$

28. (a) $(9,7)$, 5

(c) OA $= (\sqrt{1+m^2})x_1$, OB $= (\sqrt{1+m^2})x_2$,

OA$\times$OB $= 105$

(d) AB $= 8$, OA $= 7$

29. (a) A: $(10,0)$, 7   **(b)** $-\frac{5}{3}$

(c) $\frac{3}{4}$ **(d)** $3x-4y+5 = 0$

(e) $3x+4y+5 = 0$

(MC)

30. A	**31.** D	**32.** B
33. A	**34.** E	**35.** B
36. A	**37.** C	**38.** E

EXERCISE 4A (P. 109)

(*Level 1*)

1. $x \geqslant 9$ **2.** $x > -4$ **3.** $x \leqslant 4$

4. $x < 1$ **5.** $-5 < x < 3$ **6.** $x \geqslant 12$

7. $\frac{9}{2} < x < 6$ **8.** $x > 5 \ \ or \ \ x < 2$

(*Level 2*)

9. $x \leqslant -\frac{14}{3}$ **10. (a)** $x < 12$ **(b)** $y < \frac{9}{2}$

11. $x \geqslant 11$ **12.** -6 **13.** no solution

14. all values **15.** $x \leqslant -21$ **16.** $x \geqslant -\frac{3}{2}$

17. (a) $-3 < x \leqslant 2$ **(b)** $1 , 2$

18. (a) $-6 < x \leqslant -\frac{2}{5}$ **(b)** greatest : -1 , least : -5

EXERCISE 4B (P. 118)

(*Level 1*)

1. $x < \frac{1}{3} \ \ or \ \ x > \frac{1}{2}$ **2.** $-3 < x < 4$

3. $-3 < x < 1$ **4.** $-3 \leqslant x \leqslant 3$

5. $x \leqslant 0 \ \ or \ \ x \geqslant 2$ **6.** no solution

(*Level 2*)

7. $x \leqslant -2 \ \ or \ \ x \geqslant \frac{1}{2}$ **8.** $-7 < x < 5$

9. $1 - \sqrt{2} \leqslant x \leqslant 1 + \sqrt{2}$

10. all values except $\frac{3}{2}$ **11.** no solution

12. $x \leqslant -3 \ \ or \ \ x \geqslant \frac{2}{3}$ **13.** 2

EXERCISE 4C (P. 122)

(*Level 1*)

1. $-8 < x < -1\frac{1}{3}$ **2.** $x \leqslant -0.3 \ \ or \ \ x \geqslant 8$

3. $x < 3 \ \ or \ \ x > 11$ **4.** $-4 \leqslant x \leqslant 4$

5. $x < 0 \ \ or \ \ x > \frac{1}{4}$ **6.** $-2 < x < 6$

7. $-2 \leqslant x \leqslant 3$ **8.** $x \leqslant 2 \ \ or \ \ x \geqslant 3$

(*Level 2*)

9. $x < -\frac{1}{2} \ \ or \ \ x > \frac{4}{3}$ **10.** $-\frac{1}{3} < x < \frac{1}{2}$

11. $\frac{1}{2} \leqslant x \leqslant \frac{2}{3}$ **12.** $x \leqslant -\frac{2}{3} \ \ or \ \ x \geqslant 4$

13. $x < 2 - \sqrt{7} \ \ or \ \ x > 2 + \sqrt{7}$

14. no solution **15.** 2

16. $-\frac{1}{3} < x < 2$ **17.** all values

18. $x \leqslant 0 \ \ or \ \ x \geqslant 4$ **19.** $-10.5 \leqslant x \leqslant -2.3$

20. (a) $-1 \leqslant x < \frac{1}{2}$ **(b)** 0

EXERCISE 4D (P. 124)

(*Level 1*)

1. (a) $k \leqslant -36 \ \ or \ \ k > 0$ **(b)** $k < -36 \ \ or \ \ k > 0$

(c) $-36 < k < 0$ **2.** $1 < k < 3\frac{1}{2}$

3. $1 < t < 2$ **4.** $5.64 \leqslant r \leqslant 5.78$

5. $1 , 2 , 3$

(*Level 2*)

6. (a) $1 , 2 , 3 , 4 , 5 , 6 , 7 , 8 , 9 , 10$

(b) 20 **7.** $(3 , 5) , (5 , 7) , (11 , 13)$

8. 80 m **9.** 2 cm **10.** $x > 40$

11. (a) $\$(0.015x^2 + 4.8x)$ **(b)** $19.6 \leqslant x \leqslant 28.7$

SUPPLEMENTARY EXERCISE 4 (P. 126)

1. $x < \frac{5}{3}$ **2.** $\frac{3}{2} < x < \frac{11}{2}$ **3.** no solution

4. (a) $120x$ **(b)** $x \leqslant 1$

5. (a) $26 , 27 , 28 , 29$ **(b)** $21 , 24$

6. $-2 < x < 3$ **7.** $x < \frac{3 - \sqrt{15}}{2} \ \ or \ \ x > \frac{3 + \sqrt{15}}{2}$

8. $2 - 2\sqrt{7} \leqslant x \leqslant 2 + 2\sqrt{7}$ **9.** $0 , 1$

10. $x < 1 \ \ or \ \ x > 3$ **11.** $x \leqslant -7 \ \ or \ \ x \geqslant -\frac{2}{5}$

12. $1 \leqslant x \leqslant 3$

13. (a) $-2 \leqslant y \leqslant 3$

(b) $-1 \leqslant x \leqslant 0 \ \ or \ \ 4 \leqslant x \leqslant 5$

14. 99 **15. (a)** 2 **(b)** 4

16. 30.53 cm

17. area = $1\,500$ cm^2, dimensions = 30 cm $\times 50$ cm

18. $k < -8 \ \ or \ \ 0 < k < 1$

19. (a) $0 \leqslant x \leqslant 2$ **(b)** $6 - 2\sqrt{5} < x < 2$

20. $x \geqslant -\frac{1}{40}$ **21. (a)** $a^2 - 2ab + b^2$

22. $10 < x < 20$ **23.** $2 < r < 4$

24. $-1 \leqslant x \leqslant 0$

25. 14 cm < slant height < 21 cm

26. (b) $0° < A < 49°$

27. (a) $0 < x < 4$ **(b)** $x < -2 \ or \ x > 1$

28. $x \leqslant 0 \ or \ x \geqslant \dfrac{5}{2}$

29. (a) (i) $x \geqslant -1$ **(ii)** $-3 < x < 2$

     (b) $-1 \leqslant x < 2$

(MC)

30. D   **31.** E

32. E   **33.** E

Recreational Maths.	
Something More (P. 105)	*What is Wrong?* (P. 108)
e.g. $3 > 2$, $x + 1 > x$, etc.	no

EXERCISE 5A (P. 137)

(Level 2)

19. $(4,3)$, $(4,4)$, $(5,3)$

20. $(1,3)$, $(-1.4,0.6)$, $(10.7,-4.3)$

EXERCISE 5B (P. 144)

(Level 1)

1. max.: 10 , min.: -4 **2.** max.: 9.5 , min.: -7

3. 4.8   **4.** 28

(Level 2)

5. $x = 1$, $y = 5$

6. (b) 5.25

7. (b) max.: 13 , min.: 0

8. (b) smallest: -3 , greatest: 5

9. (b) $(1,6)$, $(2,5)$, $(2,-2)$, $(-3,-2)$

     (c) max.: 10 , min.: -9

10. (b) smallest: -25.4 , greatest: 2.6

EXERCISE 5C (P. 152)

(Level 1)

1. (a) $0 \leqslant x \leqslant 5$, $0 \leqslant y \leqslant 10$

     (b) $35x + 80y \leqslant 450$

2. x and y are non-negative integers ,
$10x + 9y \leqslant 1\ 000$, $150x + 240y \leqslant 24\ 000$

3. (a) x and y are non-negative integers ,
$6x + 24y \leqslant 720$, $x + y \leqslant 60$

     (c) car: 40 , truck: 20 , income: \$1 800

4. (a) $x \geqslant 0$, $y \geqslant 0$, $y \geqslant 6x$, $15x + 12.5y \leqslant 4\ 500$

     (c) carrot: 50 kg , lettuce: 300 kg

5. (a) $x \geqslant 0$, $y \geqslant 0$, $10x + 6y \geqslant 60$, $4x + 4y \geqslant 32$

     (c) man: 3 h , boy: 5 h

(Level 2)

6. (a) x and y are non-negative integers , $y \geqslant x$,
$100x + 40y \geqslant 500$

     (c) lorry: 3 , van: 5 , min. cost = \$1 710

     (d) lorry: 1 , van: 10 , min. cost = \$1 520

7. (a) x and y are non-negative integers ,
$200x + 80y \leqslant 1\ 000$, $100x + 250y \leqslant 1\ 000$

     (c) pullover: 4 , jersey: 2

8. (a) x and y are non-negative integers , $3x \geqslant 5y$,
$x + y \leqslant 12\ 000$

     (c) print film: 7 600 , slide film: 4 400

9. (a) (i) $y \geqslant 5$ **(ii)** $2 \leqslant x \leqslant 7$ **(iii)** $y \geqslant x + 2$

     (c) soft drink: 16 , boy: 2 , girl: 5

10. (a) $x \geqslant 0$, $y \geqslant 0$, $2x + 3y \geqslant 18$, $x + 3y \geqslant 12$,
$4x + 3y \geqslant 24$

     (c) A: 3 g , B: 4 g

11. (a) x and y are non-negative integers , $x \leqslant 10$,
$y \leqslant 10$, $x + y \geqslant 9$, $8x + 10y \leqslant 80$

     (c) A: 5 , B: 4 , max. score = 83

12. (a) $x \geqslant 0$, $y \geqslant 0$, $x + y \geqslant 10$, $\dfrac{0.7x + 0.4y}{x + y} \geqslant 0.5$,
$\dfrac{0.3x + 0.6y}{x + y} \geqslant 0.35$

     (c) Tasty: 8.3 kg , Chewy: 1.7 kg

13. (a) x and y are non-negative integers ,
$2x + 3y \leqslant 35.5$, $1\ 000x + 6\ 000y \leqslant 47\ 000$,
$x \leqslant 2y$

     (c) 15

     (d) A: 5 , B: 7

SUPPLEMENTARY EXERCISE **5** (P. 157)

1. (b) 5

2. (b) $(1,2)$, $(2,1)$, $(2,2)$, $(3,1)$, $(3,2)$

3. (a) $x \geqslant 0$, $0 \leqslant y \leqslant 2$, $x+y \leqslant 6$
   (b) $x \geqslant 2$, $y \geqslant 0$, $2x-y \geqslant 0$

4. $x \leqslant 1$ *or* $x \geqslant 3$ *or* $y \geqslant 3$ *or* $y \leqslant 1$

5. max.: 20 , min.: 2.8

6. max.: 36 , min.: 1

7. (b) max.: 294 , min.: 279

8. (b) (i) $x = 3$, $y = 3$ **(ii)** 8

9. (a) $2x+11y \geqslant -17$, $8x+7y \leqslant 43$, $3x-2y \geqslant -7$
   (b) max.: 24 , min.: -14
   (c) max.: $\dfrac{12}{11}$, min.: -9

10. (b) 6 , 8 , 10

11. (a) A: 7 kg , B: 8 kg   **(b)** min. cost = \$326.4

12. (a) x and y are non-negative integers , $x+y \geqslant 9$,
   $x+7 \geqslant y$, $60x+30y \leqslant 480$
   (b) $x = 3$, $y = 10$

13. (a) y is a non-negative integer ,
   $2\,400x+3\,000y \leqslant 84\,000$, $x \geqslant 15$, $y \geqslant 6$,
   $3\,000y \leqslant 2\,400x$
   (b) min.: 2 940 , max.: 5 110

14. (a) x and y are non-negative integers , $x \geqslant 10$,
   $9x+13y \geqslant 300$
   (c) A: 34 , B: 0 ; A: 32 , B: 1

15. (b) $(0,0)$, $(1,0)$, $(0,1)$, $(0,2)$

16. (a) $x \geqslant 0$, $y \geqslant 0$, $3y+4x \geqslant 15$, $x+3y \geqslant 6$
   (b) 109

17. (a) $x \geqslant 0$, $y \geqslant 0$, $x \geqslant y$, $6 \leqslant x+y \leqslant 9$
   (b) gardening: 4.6 h , woodcarving: 4.4 h
   (c) gardening: 4 h , woodcarving: 4 h

18. (c) $(105,40)$ **19.** greatest: 22 , least: -11

20. (a) $y \geqslant \dfrac{1}{2}$, $2x-y \geqslant 2$, $3x+5y \leqslant 30$
   (b) 16

21. (a) $x+y = 10$
   (b) A: $\left(1,\dfrac{3}{2}\right)$, B: $(4,6)$, C: $\left(\dfrac{17}{2},\dfrac{3}{2}\right)$
   (c) $2y \geqslant 3$, $3x-2y \geqslant 0$, $x+y \leqslant 10$
   (d) max.: 11 , min.: -1

22. (b) $x = 30$, $y = 10$

23. (a) $4x+3y = 12$
   (b) $y \leqslant 4$, $x \leqslant 3$, $4x+3y \geqslant 12$
   (c) greatest: 19 , least: 3   **(d)** $\dfrac{19}{2}$

24. (b) (i) $2x+2y \geqslant 20$, $2x \geqslant 3y$, $x+2y \geqslant 12$,
   $y > 0$
   (ii) length = 6 m , width = 4 m ;
   min. total payment = \$7 200

(MC)

25. D

EXERCISE **6A** (P. 187)

(Level 1)

1. (a)

x	0	1	2	3
$f(x)$	-3	-1	7	27

   (b) 1.2

2. (b) -0.7 **3. (a)** -2.8 **(b)** -2.78

4. (a) 2.5   **(b)** 2.51

(Level 2)

5. (b) 2.37   **6. (a)** $2 < x < 3$ **(b)** 2.22

7. (b) 3.73

8. (a) (i) $\dfrac{2k}{1+k^2}$ **(ii)** $\dfrac{2k(4k^2+3)}{1+k^2}$
   (b) (iii) 1.6

SUPPLEMENTARY EXERCISE **6** (P. 190)

1. (b) -0.8

2. (a)

x	-2	-1.5	-1	-0.5
$f(x)$	-2.65	-2.49	-1.42	0.04

   (b) $-1 < x < -0.5$ **(c)** -0.5

3. (c) 6.64

4. (a) $r^2 x$ **(b)** $\dfrac{1}{2}r^2 \sin 2x$ **(e)** 0.42

5. (a) 1.4   **(b)** 1.42   **(c)** 1.2

6. (c) 1   **(d)** -1.45 , 0.74   **(e)** 7.7

7. (a) (i) 1.1 *or* 1.2   **(ii)** 1.15
   (b) (ii) 15

8. (a) 1.2   **(b)** 1.22   **(c)** 2.22

9. (a) (i) $2.0 < r < 2.1$
     (ii) 2.06   **(b)** 1.06

10. (a) (i) $S = 2\pi r^2 + 2\pi rh$
   (b) 1   **(c)** 1.8

11. (a) (i) $2a^3 - 4a^2 + 3a$ **(ii)** $\frac{3}{2}$, 1
   (b) (ii) 1.29

12. (a) 6π m^3 **(b)** 0.072   **(c) (ii)** 0.85

(MC)

13. C   **14.** E   **15.** C

EXERCISE 7A (P. 205)

(*Level 1*)

1. (a) $\frac{1}{8}$ **(b)** $\frac{3}{8}$

2. (a) $\frac{2}{11}$ **(b)** $\frac{4}{11}$

3. (a) $\frac{1}{52}$ **(b)** $\frac{1}{13}$

(*Level 2*)

4. $\frac{3}{5}$

5. (a) $\frac{1}{3}$ **(b)** $\frac{2}{3}$
   (c) 0   **(d)** 1

6. (a) $\frac{1}{5}$ **(b)** $\frac{1}{10}$ **(c)** $\frac{3}{10}$

7. (a) 0.485   **(b)** 0.353   **(c)** 0.515

8. 21   **9.** ducks: 66 , geese: 54

10. (a) $3n - 5x = 0$
   (b) (i) $2n - 3x - 8 = 0$; $x = 24$, $n = 40$
     (ii) 5

EXERCISE 7B (P. 210)

(*Level 1*)

1. $\frac{27}{52}$ **2.** $\frac{7}{20}$

---

3. (a) $\frac{7}{12}$ **(b)** $\frac{5}{12}$

4. 0.022

(*Level 2*)

5. (a) $\frac{3}{11}$ **(b)** $\frac{6}{11}$

6. (a) $\frac{9}{25}$ **(b)** $\frac{66}{125}$

7. (a) $\frac{1}{6}$ **(b)** $\frac{5}{6}$

8. (a) (i) $\frac{3}{500}$ **(ii)** $\frac{497}{500}$ **(b)** 72

9. (a) $\frac{1}{8}$ **(b)** $\frac{23}{100}$
   (c) $\frac{83}{500}$ **(d)** $\frac{141}{200}$

EXERCISE 7C (P. 217)

(*Level 1*)

1. (a) $\frac{1}{36}$ **(b)** $\frac{1}{4}$

2. (a) $\frac{1}{169}$ **(b)** $\frac{9}{16}$

3. (a) $\frac{15}{92}$ **(b)** $\frac{35}{138}$

4. (a) $\frac{1}{66}$ **(b)** $\frac{15}{22}$

5. (a) $\frac{1}{110}$ **(b)** $\frac{19}{110}$

6. $\frac{25}{52}$

(*Level 2*)

7. (a) $\frac{3}{5}$ **(b)** $\frac{1}{5}$

8. (a) $\frac{1}{9}$ **(b)** $\frac{2}{9}$

9. (a) 0.44   **(b)** 0.193 6

10. (a) $\frac{1}{24}$ **(b)** $\frac{1}{8}$ **(c)** $\frac{1}{2}$

11. (a) $\frac{1}{13}$ **(b)** $\frac{57}{65}$

12. $\frac{1}{6}$ **13. (a)** $\frac{3}{4}$ **(b)** $\frac{1}{3}$

14. (a) $\frac{1}{4}$ **(b)** even
   (c) $\frac{7}{192}$

15. (a) 0.414   **(b)** 0.468

16. (a) $\frac{7}{288}$ **(b)** $\frac{281}{288}$

17. (a) $\frac{4}{27}$ **(b)** $\frac{5}{27}$

18. $\frac{38}{49}$

EXERCISE **7D** (P. 222)

(*Level 1*)

1. $\frac{3}{8}$ **2.** 1   **3.** $\frac{3}{8}$

(*Level 2*)

4. 0.441   **5.** $\frac{1}{3}$

6. (a) $\frac{1}{8}$ **(b)** $\frac{27}{125}$

   (c) $\frac{1}{50}$ **(d)** $\frac{19}{100}$

7. (a) $\frac{1}{286}$ **(b)** $\frac{135}{286}$ **(c)** $\frac{31}{286}$

SUPPLEMENTARY EXERCISE **7** (P. 223)

1. (a) $\frac{1}{23}$ **(b)** $\frac{1}{23}$ **(c)** $\frac{5}{23}$

2. (a) $\frac{1}{5}$ **(b)** $\frac{1}{2}$

3. (a) (i) $\frac{71}{150}$ **(ii)** $\frac{79}{150}$

   (b) 568

4. $\frac{5}{11}$ **5.** $\frac{12}{23}$ **6.** $\frac{9}{14}$

7. (a) $\frac{9}{50}$ **(b)** $\frac{1}{5}$ **(c)** $\frac{18}{25}$

8. $\frac{1}{5}$ **9. (a)** $\frac{1}{60}$ **(b)** $\frac{2}{5}$

10. (a) $\frac{7}{69}$ **(b)** $\frac{5}{23}$

11. (a) $\frac{1}{48}$ **(b)** $\frac{1}{12}$

12. (a) 5   **(b) (i)** 0.001 01
   (ii) 0.296   **(iii)** 0.662

13. (a) $\frac{25}{102}$ **(b)** $\frac{1}{221}$

   (c) $\frac{8}{663}$ **(d)** $\frac{4}{17}$

14. (a) $\frac{5}{12}$ **(b)** $\frac{31}{72}$

15. (a) $\frac{1}{376}$ **(b)** $\frac{1}{188}$ **(c)** 0

16. (a) $\frac{1}{8}$ **(b)** $\frac{1}{8}$

17. (a) $\frac{3}{5}$ **(b)** $\frac{3}{5}$

   (c) $\frac{3}{10}$ **(d)** $\frac{9}{200}$

18. (a) $\frac{1}{6}$ **(b)** $\frac{7}{8}$ **(c)** $\frac{5}{8}$

19. (a) (i) $\frac{10}{21}$ **(ii)** $\frac{9}{14}$ **(iii)** $\frac{5}{6}$

   (b) $\frac{2}{17}$

20. blue: 8 , pink: 6

21. (a) $\frac{13}{25}$ **(b)** $\frac{7}{25}$ **(c)** $\frac{17}{25}$

22. (a) $\frac{2}{3}$ **(b)** $\frac{1}{3}$ **(c)** $\frac{1}{6}$

   (d) $\frac{59}{126}$ **(e)** $\frac{40}{63}$

23. (a) $\frac{2}{5}$ **(b)** $\frac{3}{5}$ **(c)** $\frac{11}{20}$

24. (a) $\frac{4}{9}$ **(b)** $\frac{8}{81}$

   (c) $\frac{32}{729}$ **(d)** $\frac{4}{9}$

25. (a) (i) 50   **(ii)** 36   **(iii)** 40
   (b) (i) 0.035 6   **(ii)** 0.421

26. (a) (i) $\frac{1}{9}$ **(ii)** $\frac{1}{3}$ **(iii)** $\frac{2}{3}$
   (b) (i) $\frac{4}{49}$ **(ii)** $\frac{17}{49}$ **(iii)** $\frac{32}{49}$

27. (a) (i) $\frac{1}{5}$ **(ii)** $\frac{1}{25}$ **(iii)** $\frac{8}{75}$
   (b) (i) $\frac{1}{9}$ **(ii)** $\frac{2}{9}$ **(iii)** $\frac{2}{3}$

28. (a) (i) $\frac{2}{9}$ **(ii)** $\frac{4}{9}$
   (b) (i) $\frac{4}{81}$ **(ii)** $\frac{10}{81}$

29. (a) (i) $\frac{3}{5}$ **(ii)** $\frac{3}{7}$
   (iii) $\frac{3}{35}$ **(iv)** $\frac{12}{35}$
   (b) (i) $\frac{4}{49}$ **(ii)** $\frac{48}{1\,225}$

30. (a) (i) $\frac{1}{343}$ **(ii)** $\frac{216}{343}$
   (b) (i) $\frac{9}{1\,000}$ **(ii)** $\frac{27}{1\,000}$
   (c) $\frac{17}{140}$

(MC)

31. E   **32.** E   **33.** B

Recreational Maths.	
Just for Fun (P. 205)	*Try This* (P. 213)
from experiment	$\frac{1}{4}$

EXERCISE 8A (P. 239)

(*Level 1*)

1. 72   **2.** 62   **3.** 165.03 cm

(*Level 2*)

4. 303   **5.** $a = 80$, $b = 3$

6. (a) 57.5   **(b)** 47.5   **(c)** no

7. John: 60, Joan: 77.5, Joyce: 58.75 ; Joan

EXERCISE 8B (P. 248)

(*Level 1*)

1. (a) 7   **(b)** 4

2. (a) 44 kg   **(b)** 12 kg

3. (a) 34   **(b)** 5.5   **4.** 27 s

(*Level 2*)

5. (a) 36°C   **(b)** 12°C

6. (a) 3.4   **(b)** 0.55

7. (a) $\frac{5}{6}$ **(b)** $\frac{11}{24}$

8. (a) 4.6 s   **(b)** 2 s

9. (a) range = $80 + 3x$,
    inter-quartile range = $44 + x$

  (b) 8

10. (c) 6.2 cm

11. (a)

Time less than (min)	3.5	6.5	9.5	12.5
Cumulative frequency	42	65	84	100

  (c) 5.7 min

EXERCISE 8C (P. 254)

(*Level 1*)

1. 2   **2.** 4   **3.** 2.73

4. (a) 26.2   **(b)** 5.0

(*Level 2*)

5. 2.4   **6.** $\frac{6}{5}(p + 2q)$

7. (a) Set A: 10.20 , Set B: 9.35   **(b)** Set A

8. (a) 1.89 min   **(b)** 0.51 min

EXERCISE 8D (P. 259)

(*Level 1*)

1. (a) 3.69   **(b)** 1.92

2. (a) 16   **(b)** 4

3. (a) 11.2°C   **(b)** 5.6°C

4. 9.50   **5.** $4a$

6. 0.63 cm   **7.** $1 060

8. (a) s **(b)** $2s$

EXERCISE 8E (P. 266)

(*Level 1*)

1. (a) 1.08   **(b)** −0.33   **(c)** 1.19

2. 55   **3.** English

(*Level 2*)

4. mean = 100 , standard deviation = 10

5. (a)

Pupil	A	B	C	D	E	F
Marks	68	72	56	60	80	76
Standard score	0.5	1	−1	−0.5	2	1.5

  (b)

Pupil	A	B	C	D	E	F
Marks	58	52	43	49	64	52
Standard score	1.5	0.5	−1	0	2.5	0.5

  (c) (i) A **(ii)** F
  (iii) C

6. (a) (i) Biology   **(ii)** Chemistry
  (b) 85

EXERCISE 8F (P. 270)

(*Level 1*)

1. 16%

2. (a) 50%   **(b)** 16%   **(c)** 81.5%

3. min.: 24.8 cm , max.: 25.2 cm

4. (a) 35 w.p.m.   **(b)** 59 w.p.m.

(*Level 2*)

5. (a) 2.5%　　　　　**(b)** 84%

6. A: 25 , B: 135 , C: 340 , D: 340 , E: 135 , F: 25

7. (a) 47　　　　　　**(b)** 27

8. (a) 164 cm　　　　**(b)** 6 cm

　(c) 81.5%　　　　　**(d)** 25

SUPPLEMENTARY EXERCISE　8　(P. 272)

1. 64

2. (a) 60　　　**(b)** 59　　　**(c)** no

3. (b) 5　　　　　　　　**(c)** 9

4. (a) Set A: range = 10 , inter-quartile range = 6.5 ;
　　　Set B: range = 23 , inter-quartile range = 19

　(b) Set B

5. (a) (i) 38　　　　　　**(ii)** 17

　(b) (i) 38　　　　　　**(ii)** 17

　(c) (i) 19　　　　　　**(ii)** 8.5

6. (a) 10　　　　　　　**(b)** 6

7. (a) 17.45 mm　**(b)** 17.7 mm　**(c)** 17.9 mm

　(d) 2.5 mm　　**(e)** 0.45 mm

8. (a) group A: 50 kg , group B: 60 kg

　(b) (i) group A: 45.5 kg , group B: 45.5 kg

　　　(ii) group A: 4 kg , group B: 16.5 kg

　(c) (ii) range = 60 kg , inter-quartile range = 9 kg

9. (a) Group A: $\frac{8}{9}$, Group B: $\frac{4}{9}$　　**(b)** Group A

10. Set A: 4 , Set B: 4 ; equal dispersion

11. (a) 22 cm　　　　　**(b)** 5.4 cm

12. (b) $x = 11 , y = 29$

13. (a) variance = 1.01 , standard deviation = 1.00

　(b) variance = 2.5 , standard deviation = 1.58

14. 40　　　**15. (a)** 7　　　　**(b)** $\sqrt{5}$

16. (b) $x = 75$, mean = 76.8

17. (a) 779.5 h　**(b)** 9 100 h^2　**(c)** 95.4 h

18. (a) class A: 12.9 cm , class B: 9.3 cm

　(b) class A

19. (a) 78　　　　　　**(b)** 15.03

　(c) 60: −1.20 , 60: −1.20 , 85: 0.47 , 90: 0.80 ,
　　　95: 1.13

20. Mathematics

21. (a) 2.5%　　　　　**(b)** 97.5%

22. (a) (i) 83.75%　　　**(ii)** 84%

　(b) (i) 7 960　　　　**(ii)** 7 800

　(iii) 7 800

23. (a) (i) 81.5%　　　　**(ii)** 5%

　(b) 16.25%

24. (a) 2.5%　　**(b)** 80 000　　**(c)** 42

25. (b) Group A: $\frac{22}{13}$, Group B: $\frac{328}{169}$

26. Miss Yeung: 22 , Mr. Lau: 34　**27. (c)** 4.5 cm

29. $x = 45$, mean = 46.8

30. (b) 1: 10 , 2: 8 , 4: 4 , 5: 2

31. (a) Biology: 1 , Mathematics: $\frac{10}{7}$

　(b) Mathematics

32. (a) 107　　　**(b)** 11　　　**(c)** 3

33. 5　　　　　　　　　**34.** 31

35. (a) $70(m+n)$　**(b)** 8 : 5　　**(c)** 24

36. (a) 50　　　**(b)** 65　　　**(c)** 60

37. (a) (i) 70　　　　　　**(ii)** 36

　(b) (i) 60　　　　　　**(ii)** $\frac{1}{10}$

　(iii)(1) 0.01　　　　**(2)** 0.19

38. (a) (i) modal class = $6 000 – $7 000 ,
　　　median = $6 500 , mean = $6 500 ,
　　　inter-quartile range = $3 000 ,
　　　mean deviation = $1 740

　(ii) smaller

　(b) 2

(*MC*)

39. A　　　　**40.** A　　　　**41.** D

42. C　　　　**43.** B　　　　**44.** C

Preparatory Ex. for HKCEE
(Strand : *Algebra*)   (P. 285)

1. $x \geqslant 3$ **2.** $-4 < x < \frac{3}{2}$ **3.** $-\frac{7}{3} < x < \frac{2}{5}$

4. $x \leqslant -3$ *or* $x \geqslant 0$ **5.** $x > -3$

6. $-2 < x < 3$, $198 < y < 203$

7. max.: 46 , $(2,6)$; min.: -21 , $(-7,-1)$

8. (a) $x = \sqrt{ab}$ **(b)** $x = \frac{b^2}{c}$

9. (a) $x > -\frac{3}{4}$ **(b)** $-\frac{3}{4} < x \leqslant 1$

10. (a) -210 **(b)** $\frac{2}{3}$ **11.** 2.56

12. $b^2 = ac$ **13.** $\frac{5}{4}$ **14.** 54

15. 4 **16.** $-\frac{1}{5}$ **17.** 2^{2n-4}

18. $\frac{p^2}{p-q}$ **19.** $-\frac{1}{2}$ **20.** I , III

21. I , II   **22.** $x < -2$ *or* $x > 3$

23. $x < -3$ **24.** $p = 7$, $q = 3$

25. 18 **26.** -9 **28.** $0 < x < 0.1$

29. (b) (i) $\log 5x^{n-1}$ **(ii)** $\frac{n \log 5^2 x^{n-1}}{2}$

    (iii) $2^{\frac{1}{10}}$

30. (a) (i) 3^{n-2} **(ii)** $\frac{3^n-1}{6}$

    (iii) $9\,801$ **(b)** 8

31. (b) max.: 0 , min.: -5

    (c) max.: -0.5 , min.: -5

32. (a) A: $(1,-3)$, B: $\left(\frac{4}{1-k}, \frac{4k}{1-k}\right)$,

    C: $\left(-\frac{3}{3+2k}, -\frac{3k}{3+2k}\right)$

    (b) $y - kx \leqslant 0$, $3x + 2y + 3 \geqslant 0$, $x - y - 4 \leqslant 0$

    (c) -1

33. (a) 22 **(b)** 21.8

34. (a) $a = 5$, $b = -12$ **(b)** 2

    (c) 1.96

Preparatory Ex. for HKCEE
(Strand : *Geometry*)   (P. 290)

1. $x + 2y - 3 = 0$ **2.** $2x - y + 5 = 0$

3. (a) $L_1 : \frac{5}{2}$, $L_2 : -\frac{2}{5}$, $L_3 : -\frac{5}{2}$ **(b)** L_1 and L_2

4. (a) $(3,-1)$ **(b)** $7x + y - 20 = 0$

5. (a) L_1 and L_2 : $(-5,4)$, L_1 and L_3 : $(5,4)$,

    L_2 and L_3 : $(3,8)$

    (b) 20

6. (a) $(-2,3)$, 2 **(b)** -4

7. (a) $x^2 + y^2 = 144$ **(b)** 15

8. I   **9.** II

10. $a = -7$, $b = 3$

11. $x^2 + y^2 - 6x - 4y + 5 = 0$ **12.** 5

13. $3x - 2y - 1 = 0$ **14.** 25π

15. (a) $m \geqslant 2$ *or* $m \leqslant -2$

    (b) $y = 2x + 10$, $y = -2x + 10$ **(c)** yes

16. (a) $p = -4$, $k = 4$ **(b)** $(2,-2)$

    (c) $(0,-4)$ **(d)** $x^2 + y^2 - 6x + 6y + 8 = 0$

    (e) $3x + y + 4 = 0$

17. (b) (i) $x + y - 2 = 0$

    (ii) P: $(2,0)$, Q: $(0,2)$

    (c) $7x - y + 2 = 0$

    (d) $x^2 + y^2 - \frac{6}{5}x - \frac{22}{5}y + \frac{18}{5} = 0$

Preparatory Ex. for HKCEE
(Strand : *Statistics*)   (P. 294)

1. $\frac{1}{496}$ **2.** $\frac{473}{663}$ **3.** 2

4. (a) $\frac{1}{36}$ **(b)** $\frac{5}{18}$

5. (a) $\$449.5$ **(b)** $\$379.5$

6. (a) $r + 1$ **(b)** 2

7. (a) 780 **(b)** 652

8. (a) $\frac{1}{12}$ **(b)** $\frac{1}{12}$ **(c)** $\frac{5}{6}$

9. (a) $\frac{1}{8}$ **(b)** $\frac{3}{8}$ **(c)** $\frac{1}{2}$

10. (a) 59.5

(b) (i)

Marks	Number of students
0 – 19	<u>0</u>
20 – 39	<u>30</u>
40 – 59	<u>50</u>
60 – 79	<u>70</u>
80 – 99	<u>10</u>

    (ii) 57

11. (a) 54   **(b)** 64   **(c)** 22

12. $\frac{1}{8}$ **13.** $\frac{1}{3}$ **14.** $\frac{1}{5}$

15. $\frac{5}{12}$ **16.** $\frac{7}{36}$ **17.** $\frac{5}{72}$

18. $\frac{4}{7}$ **19.** $\frac{1}{56}$

20. $\frac{11}{18}$ **21.** 0.936

22. mean = 1.2 m , standard deviation = $1.2s$

23. mean = $m - 5$, standard deviation = s , inter-quartile range = q

24. I , II   **25.** III , I , II

26. II , III , I   **27.** III   **28.** II , III

29. (a) $\frac{1}{12}$ **(b)** $\frac{1}{16}$ **(c)** $\frac{1}{30}$

30. (a) $108.7   **(b)** $31   **(c)** 66%

   (d) (i) $170   **(ii)** 4%

31. (a) (i) 18 min   **(ii)** 9 min

(b) (i)

Travelling time (min)	Frequency
6 – 10	<u>3</u>
11 – 15	<u>10</u>
16 – 20	<u>14</u>
21 – 25	<u>6</u>
26 – 30	<u>6</u>
31 – 35	<u>1</u>

    (ii) 18.625 min   **(iii)** 6.14 min

(c) (i) $\frac{7}{195}$ **(ii)** $\frac{71}{195}$

INDEX